Discovering Algebra
An Investigative Approach

Assessment Resources

DISCOVERING

MATHEMATICS™

Key Curriculum Press
Innovators in Mathematics Education

Teacher's Materials Project Editor: Elizabeth DeCarli

Project Administrator: Aaron Madrigal

Coordinating Writer: David Rasmussen

Contributors: Crystal Mills, Jerald Murdock, Wayne Nirode

Accuracy Checker: Dudley Brooks

Project Manager: Rozi Harris, Interactive Composition Corporation

Copyeditor: Bob Cooper

Editorial Production Supervisor: Christine Osborne

Production Director: McKinley Williams

Production Coordinator: Ann Rothenbuhler

Text Designer: Jenny Somerville

Composition, Technical Art, Prepress: Interactive Composition Corporation

Cover Designers: Jill Kongabel, Marilyn Perry

Printer: Alonzo Printing

Textbook Product Manager: James Ryan

Executive Editor: Casey FitzSimons

Publisher: Steven Rasmussen

Key Curriculum Press
1150 65th Street
Emeryville, CA 94608
(510) 595-7000
editorial@keypress.com
www.keypress.com

Printed in the United States of America

10 9 8 7 6 5 4 3 2   11 10 09 08 07 06   ISBN-13: 978-1-55953-765-0
                                                 ISBN-10: 1-55953-765-5

Contents

Chapter 4

Chapter 5

Chapter 6

Chapter 7

Chapter 8

Chapter 9

Chapter 10

Chapter 11

Introduction

Assessment Resources includes quizzes, chapter tests, cumulative exams, constructive assessment options, answers, and rubrics for use with *Discovering Algebra: An Investigative Approach*. These written assessments are not the only way for you to evaluate your students, but they are one way to let you and your students know what they have learned.

Quizzes and Tests

This volume includes one test and as many as three quizzes for each chapter. Each quiz covers material from two or three lessons, and the test covers material from the entire chapter. Three cumulative tests are also provided, covering Chapters 1–3, Chapters 4–7, and Chapters 8–11. A final exam covers Chapters 1–11. Two versions, Form A and Form B, are provided for each quiz, test, and exam.

The quizzes and tests are written assignments that pose specific, often closed-ended problems and questions designed to test a student's mastery of particular subject matter and skills. Typically, students work on quizzes and tests individually and are expected to complete them during a limited amount of class time.

The advantage of a traditional quiz or test is that it provides a simple tool for rating a student's understanding of the material. You can usually translate a test result into a numerical grade fairly easily. This gives you, students, and parents objective feedback on how well the students are doing.

Traditional timed tests are stressful for many students. Some students suffer from so much test anxiety that they simply cannot complete their tests. (Of course, there are also those students who perform at their best in these situations.) You may want to try some ideas for making traditional testing less stressful. One strategy is to allow students to create and bring a "cheat sheet"—a collection of notes on a notecard or sheet of paper that they can refer to during a test. Teachers find students do some useful review as they put their notes together. Discourage students from sharing notecards and guard against opportunities for copying information from students who took the same test earlier, perhaps by collecting cards at the end of the test day. Also, you might want to require that each notecard be in the student's own handwriting so students don't borrow or duplicate those of other students. Some teachers collect the notecards and count them as part of the test grade. Students often find that they hardly ever look at their notecards during the test, but they feel less pressure by having them handy.

Some teachers allow students to use their notebooks during tests and quizzes. This encourages students to keep their notebooks organized. Sometimes teachers even allow students to use their books. This encourages them to read and learn to navigate through their mathematics textbook. Remind students that good problem solving involves knowing how to use the proper resources.

You can also alleviate test anxiety by allowing students to retake tests. The disadvantage to this strategy is that it requires extra time for you to make and correct a second set of tests. Some teachers require students to correct their first test completely before they are allowed a retake. Some teachers permit students to keep the highest grade from the two tests, but many prefer to average the grades or require that the second grade count as the only grade (this last technique cuts down on the number of students who opt for the retake test).

It is not always a good idea to test students on how quickly they can work mathematics problems. Good mathematical reasoning is a systematic and thoughtful process. For this reason, it is fair to allow students extra time to finish a test if they need it. This is especially accommodating for students who may have linguistic, physical, emotional, or psychological needs that slow them down. It can be hard to find the extra time to allow students to finish. Sometimes it is worth having students come in after school or at lunchtime to allow them the few extra minutes they need. Be alert to students who misuse this privilege and discuss test questions outside of class before they return to finish.

Constructive Assessment Options

This volume also includes constructive assessment items for each chapter. These items are deeper and richer than items on the tests and quizzes. While the quiz and test items tend to call for definitive answers, most constructive assessment items are open-ended, with many possible correct answers. And, while quiz and test items assess particular skills, constructive assessment items assess a student's ability to explain, apply, connect, and extend the important concepts of the lessons.

Here are some suggestions for how you might use these items.

- Use three or four constructive assessment items in place of a traditional chapter test.
- Give several constructive assessment items as a group quiz. Allow plenty of time for students to discuss and explore the problems. Grade one item from each group member's paper to determine the group score.
- Create a chapter test by combining one or two constructive assessment items with items from the chapter test.
- Include one constructive assessment item as an extra-credit problem on the chapter test.
- Use the constructive assessment items on take-home tests.
- Assign the items as additional homework questions for extra credit.

Because of their open-ended nature, constructive assessment items can be more difficult to score than traditional test items. The answer section of this book provides a rubric for each item, giving criteria for 5-point, 3-point, and 1-point answers. For example, consider this item, with its scoring rubric, from Chapter 5 Constructive Assessment Options.

> **3.** *(Lesson 5.5)*
> Sam was absent when his class worked with linear inequalities in one variable. Sarah told him, "If you can solve equations, then you can solve inequalities. There are only a couple of new things you need to know." Write a note to Sam explaining how to solve linear inequalities. (Assume he knows how to solve equations.) Also explain how to graph an inequality on a number line.

SCORING RUBRIC

3. 5 points

The answer is clear and includes the following points:

- When you add a number to or subtract a number from both sides of an inequality, the direction of the inequality symbol stays the same.
- When you multiply or divide both sides of an inequality by a positive number, the direction of the inequality symbol stays the same.
- When you multiply or divide both sides of an inequality by a negative number, the direction of the inequality symbol is reversed.
- If an inequality is of the form $x < a$ or $x > a$, graph it by first making an open circle at a. For $x < a$, draw an arrow through all the values to the left of a. For $x > a$, draw an arrow through all the values to the right of a.
- If an inequality is of the form $x \leq a$ or $x \geq a$, graph it by first making a solid circle at a. For $x \leq a$, draw an arrow through all the values to the left of a. For $x \geq a$, draw an arrow through all the values to the right of a.
- For a compound inequality, such as $-2 \leq x < 4$, make open or solid circles at the numbers (depending on the signs of the inequalities) and draw a line segment through all the values in between.

3 points

The answer mentions that the inequality symbol is reversed when both sides are multiplied or divided by a negative number. Two of the other points from the list are missing. Other minor details may also be missing.

1 point

Four major concepts from the list are missing.

Notice that although the rubric mentions only 5-point, 3-point, and 1-point answers, you can also determine criteria for 4-point and 2-point answers. For example, a solution that mentions reversing the inequality symbol when both sides are multiplied or divided by a negative number, but that is missing *one* other major concept, would get 4 points. A solution that is missing *three* major concepts would get 2 points.

For some multi-part items, you may find it easiest to score each part separately, on a scale from 1 to 5, and then use the average as the score for the problem. For example, consider this item, with its scoring rubric, from Chapter 4 Constructive Assessment Options.

7. *(Lessons 4.2 and 4.5–4.7)*
The table shows the percentage of U.S. households that had cable television in the even-numbered years 1978 through 2002.

a. Find a linear equation that fits the data. Describe the method you used and explain why you think your equation is a good fit.

b. Predict how the percentage of U.S. households with cable television will change over the next 10 to 15 years. Use your equation and the data to support your prediction.

Year	Percent	Year	Percent
1978	17.9	1992	61.5
1980	22.6	1994	63.4
1982	35.0	1996	66.7
1984	43.7	1998	67.4
1986	48.1	2000	67.8
1988	53.8	2002	68.9
1990	59.0		

(Nielsen Media Research, *World Almanac and Book of Facts 2005*, p. 310)

7. 5 points

  a. The equation of the line and the data are correctly shown. The description of the method for finding the line is clear and correct. The explanation of how well the equation fits is clearly presented. Sample answer: I found the Q-line. I first found the Q-points. The quartiles of the *year* data are 1983 and 1997, and the quartiles of the *percentage* data are 39.35 and 67.05. Because the data values are increasing, the line of fit passes through the Q-points (1983, 39.35) and (1997, 67.05). The slope of the line through these points is $\frac{67.05 - 39.35}{1997 - 1983} = \frac{27.7}{14} \approx 1.98$. This slope and the point (1983, 39.35) give the equation $y = 39.35 + 1.98(x - 1983)$. I graphed the points and the equation.

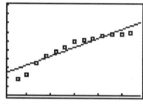

[1976, 2004, 5, 0, 100, 10]

    The line is a pretty good fit for most of the data, particularly from about 1982 to 1998. It shows the general direction of the data until about 2000. There are about the same number of points above as below the line.

  b. The answer is clear and convincing and is based on the data and the graph. Sample answer: The equation indicates that the average percentage increase is about 1.98% each year. However, the data show that the rate of increase in the early years (from 1978 to 1982) was greater than 1.98%, and in the later years (since the mid-'90s) has been less. So I would predict that the model will not accurately predict the percentage of households using cable over the next 10 to 15 years. Over that period of time the percentage may go up, but I predict it will be by less than 1% a year, and in some years there may be a decrease.

3 Points

a. The equation fits the data reasonably well. The description of the method and explanation of why the line is a good fit are missing minor details. Sample answer: I got the equation $y = 67.4 + 2.025(x - 1998)$ by plotting the data and finding a line through two of the points. I graphed the points and the line on my calculator and could see that the line fits very well.

b. The prediction is reasonable, but it is not strongly tied to the data or the equation. Possible answer: I think the percentage will keep increasing because many people are getting digital cable and cable modems for their computers.

1 Point

a. A reasonable equation is given, but both the description of the method and the explanation of why the line fits are missing, or the equation, description, and explanation are given, but the line is not a good fit and the explanation of why it fits is not convincing. Sample answer: I got the equation $y = 43.7 + 1.7(x - 1984)$ by plotting the data and finding a line through two of the points. The line fits because it goes in the same direction as the points and contains two of the points.

b. The prediction is unreasonable and is not tied to the data or the equation. Possible answer: I think the percentage will start going down by a lot because more people are getting satellite dishes instead of cable.

In part a, a student may find a good line of fit, provide a clear description of the method used, and give a convincing explanation for why the line fits. However, in part b, the student may give an unreasonable prediction that is not tied to the data. This student would score 5 points on part a and 1 point on part b. Averaging these scores gives a score of 3 points for the problem.

Creating Individual Assessment

Items from both forms of the tests and constructive assessments are on the *TestCheck™: Test Generator and Worksheet Builder™* CD. These items can be part of any test you create with the test generator. Using the worksheet building software, you can combine items from this book with any of the dozens of other items for each chapter.

If you do not want to change the chapter tests, copy them from this book or print them directly from the *TestCheck* CD, where they exist as saved worksheets. The constructive assessment items for each chapter are also on the CD as saved worksheets, but those worksheets should not be printed out as tests because each contains many more items than would be reasonable for a timed test. These harder items have been included as saved worksheets only so that the items (and their scoring rubrics) will be available for tests you create, which might have one or two constructive assessment items and a few shorter questions. Instructions for using *TestCheck* are included on the CD.

Other Opportunities for Assessment

These materials are only some of the assessment opportunities available. Because *Discovering Algebra* engages students as active learners, it provides ample opportunities to assess student learning throughout the course. Investigations provide opportunities for performance assessment (assessment that focuses on the student's thought process). Journal-writing prompts are included in exercise sets. Exercises and other features can stimulate portfolio entries and presentations. Projects in the student text give students opportunities to demonstrate their learning in new contexts. Each chapter ends with Assessing What You Have Learned, a chance for students to write in their journals, organize their notebooks, update their portfolios, give a presentation, or do a performance assessment.

It is always best to mix traditional testing with other types of assessment. A good mix helps accommodate the various learning styles and needs of your students, and it allows you to stress that there are many different ways of doing and learning mathematics.

Name _____ Period _____ Date _____

Answer each question and show all work clearly on a separate piece of paper.

1. Look at the beginning stages of this fractal design.

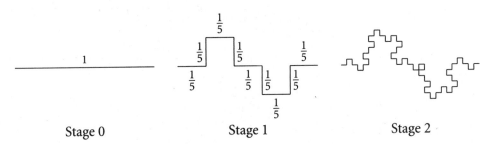

Stage 0   Stage 1   Stage 2

  a. Complete the table by calculating the total length of the Stage 2 and
  Stage 3 figures.

Stage number	Total length		
	Multiplication form	**Exponent form**	**Decimal form (rounded to the nearest hundredth)**
0	1	$9^0 \cdot \left(\dfrac{1}{5}\right)^0 = \left(\dfrac{9}{5}\right)^0$	1
1	$9 \cdot \dfrac{1}{5}$	$9^1 \cdot \left(\dfrac{1}{5}\right)^1 = \left(\dfrac{9}{5}\right)^1$	1.80
2			
3			

  b. What is the length of the Stage 7 figure? Give your answer in exponent
  and decimal form (rounded to the nearest hundredth).

  c. At what stage does the figure have length $\dfrac{6561}{625}$?

  d. At what stage is the length of the figure closest to 100?

2. Investigate the expression $0.2 \cdot \square - 4$.

  a. Recursively evaluate the expression for different
  starting values, and record your results in a table like
  the one shown here.

  b. Based on the table, do you think this expression
  reaches an attractor value in the long run? If so, what
  is it? If not, why not?

Starting value	2	−1	10
First recursion			
Second recursion			
Third recursion			
Fourth recursion			
Fifth recursion			

(continued)

Name _____   **Period** _____   **Date** _____

3. Stages 0 to 3 of a fractal design are shown here.

   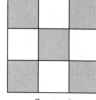   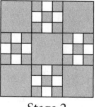   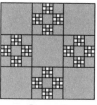

  Stage 0   Stage 1   Stage 2   Stage 3

  a. Write a recursive rule that could be used to generate this design.

  b. If the area of the Stage 0 square is 1, what is the area of each small square at Stage 1?

  c. What is the area of each smallest square at Stage 2? What is the area of each smallest square at Stage 3?

  d. What is the combined area of one smallest Stage 1 square, two smallest Stage 2 squares, and three smallest Stage 3 squares?

4. Refer to the pattern in Problem 3.

  a. Stage 1 has four white squares. How many white squares are there at Stage 2?

  b. How many white squares are there at Stage 3?

  c. How many white squares are there at Stage 6? Write your answer in exponent form.

Discovering Algebra Assessment Resources
©2007 Key Curriculum Press

Chapter 0 • Constructive Assessment Options

Choose one or more of these items to replace all or part of the chapter test. Let students know that they will receive from 0 to 5 points for each item depending on the correctness and completeness of their answer.

1. *(Lessons 0.1–0.3)*
The Koch curve and tree fractals start with a line segment at Stage 0.

  a. Create your own fractal pattern that starts with a line segment at Stage 0. Draw Stages 0 through 3 of your pattern and describe its recursive rule.

  b. Write and answer two questions about your fractal pattern. One of your questions should require working with fractions, and the other should require working with exponents.

2. *(Lessons 0.1–0.3)*
Here are the first two stages of a fractal pattern.

  a. Give the rule for creating this fractal pattern. Then carefully draw the next two stages.

  b. Write and answer two questions about this fractal pattern. One question should be about the white squares, and the other should be about the gray squares. Use fractions or exponents in your answers.

Stage 0   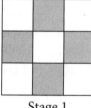
Stage 1

3. *(Lesson 0.3)*

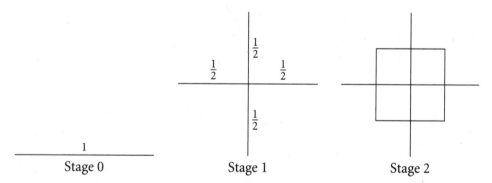
Stage 0   Stage 1   Stage 2

The fractal pattern above is a cross design in which the vertical segment goes through the midpoint of the horizontal segment. The Stage 0 figure has a length of 1.

  a. Draw Stage 3 and Stage 4.

  b. What is the total length of all segments in Stages 1, 2, 3, and 4?

  c. Express the answers to part b (including Stage 0) in exponent form. Each answer should have the same base. What is the total segment length of a Stage 8 fractal?

(continued)

   d. The Stage 2 fractal encloses an area. What is the total area enclosed in Stage 2? In Stage 3? In Stage 4?

   e. What happens to the enclosed area in higher stages of the fractal? Explain.

4. *(Lesson 0.4)*
Consider this expression.

$$N \cdot \square + 2$$

   a. Substitute 0.2 for N and find the attractor value for the resulting expression. Repeat this process for $N = 0.5$, $N = 0.75$, $N = 0.9$, and at least two other N-values between 0 and 1. Make a table that shows each N-value and the attractor value for the resulting expression.

   b. Give a rule that can be used to find the attractor value for any expression of the form $N \cdot \square + 2$.

5. *(Lesson 0.4)*
Each of these expressions has an attractor value of 2.

$$0.25 \cdot \square + 1.5 \qquad 0.5 \cdot \square + 1 \qquad 0.8 \cdot \square + 0.4$$

   a. Find at least four more expressions that have an attractor value of 2. To help find your expressions, think about how the numbers in the given expressions are related to the attractor value 2.

   b. Describe a rule that can be used to write expressions with an attractor value of 2.

Discovering Algebra Assessment Resources
©2007 Key Curriculum Press

Name _____   Period _____   Date _____

Nutritional Data for Selected Breakfast Cereals

ID number	Brand name	Serving size (g)	Calories per serving	Fat per serving (g)	Carbohydrates per serving (g)	Protein per serving (g)
1	Quaker Oats	40	150	3	27	5
2	Quaker Instant Apple and Cinnamon Oatmeal	35	130	1.5	26	3
3	General Mills Cheerios	30	110	2	22	3
4	Kellogg's Special K	31	110	0	22	7
5	Kellogg's Raisin Bran	59	190	1.5	45	5
6	Quaker 100% Natural Granola	48	210	7	35	5
7	Kellogg's Corn Flakes	28	100	0	24	2
8	General Mills Lucky Charms	30	120	1	25	2
9	Post Shredded Wheat	47	160	1	37	5
10	General Mills Cinnamon Toast Crunch	30	130	3.5	24	1
11	Kellogg's Fruit Loops	32	120	1	28	1
12	Kellogg's Apple Jacks	33	130	0.5	30	1

(Obtained from cereal boxes, October 2004)

1. Make a bar graph to compare the calories per serving for the 12 cereals listed. Label the horizontal axis with ID numbers rather than cereal names.

2. Make a dot plot to show the calories per serving for the 12 cereals.

3. Find the mean, median, and mode of the calories per serving for the cereals.

Name _____ Period _____ Date _____

Nutritional Data for Selected Breakfast Cereals

ID number	Brand name	Serving size (g)	Calories per serving	Fat per serving (g)	Carbohydrates per serving (g)	Protein per serving (g)
1	Quaker Oats	40	150	3	27	5
2	Quaker Instant Apple and Cinnamon Oatmeal	35	130	1.5	26	3
3	General Mills Cheerios	30	110	2	22	3
4	Kellogg's Special K	31	110	0	22	7
5	Kellogg's Raisin Bran	59	190	1.5	45	5
6	Quaker 100% Natural Granola	48	210	7	35	5
7	Kellogg's Corn Flakes	28	100	0	24	2
8	General Mills Lucky Charms	30	120	1	25	2
9	Post Shredded Wheat	47	160	1	37	5
10	General Mills Cinnamon Toast Crunch	30	130	3.5	24	1
11	Kellogg's Fruit Loops	32	120	1	28	1
12	Kellogg's Apple Jacks	33	130	0.5	30	1

(Obtained from cereal boxes, October 2004)

1. Make a bar graph to compare the carbohydrates per serving for the 12 cereals listed. Label the horizontal axis with ID numbers rather than cereal names.

2. Make a dot plot to show the carbohydrates per serving for the 12 cereals.

3. Find the mean, median, and mode of the carbohydrates per serving for the cereals.

Discovering Algebra Assessment Resources
©2007 Key Curriculum Press

Name _____ **Period** _____ **Date** _____

1. Explain how you would find the mean, median, and mode of the information pictured in this dot plot without using a calculator.

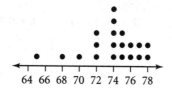

2. Enter the information from the dot plot into list L1 of your calculator. Use your calculator to find the mean, median, and five-number summary. Also find the mode.

3. Make a box plot of the information pictured in the dot plot. You may want to make the plot on the calculator and then copy the results.

Name _____   **Period** _____   **Date** _____

1. Explain how you would find the mean, median, and mode of the information pictured in this dot plot without using a calculator.

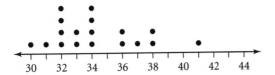

2. Enter the information from the dot plot into list L1 of your calculator. Use your calculator to find the mean, median, and five-number summary. Also find the mode.

3. Make a box plot of the information pictured in the dot plot. You may want to make the plot on the calculator and then copy the results.

Discovering Algebra Assessment Resources
©2007 Key Curriculum Press

Name _____   **Period** _____   **Date** _____

1. Select three of the numbers below so that the mode of the three numbers is 63 and the mean is 71.

   41 52 63 63 87

2. Six points are graphed.

   a. Give the coordinates of each point on the graph.

   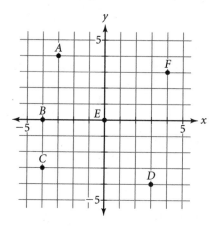

   b. Which points are in the third quadrant?

3. Mrs. Smythe gave her calculus class a 30-point quiz. The class results are listed below.

   15 28 23 30 3 12 29 22 24 28 25 29 30 21 24 28 29 23 23 19

   a. Make a histogram of these scores. Explain why you think the bin width you chose is the best one for this graph.

   b. Give the five-number summary for these scores.

   c. Use your answers to 3a and b to determine how you think letter grades should be assigned for this quiz. Explain your thinking.

4. Matrix [A] shows regular prices for different food items at the Buena Vista Taqueria. Leslie has a coupon for $\frac{1}{2}$ off any item. Do a matrix calculation to find the matrix that shows the sale prices.

Regular Food Prices ($)

Taco Burrito

$$[A] = \begin{bmatrix} 1.95 & 3.45 \\ 2.35 & 3.95 \\ 2.75 & 4.35 \end{bmatrix} \begin{matrix} \text{Regular} \\ \text{Special} \\ \text{Super} \end{matrix}$$

Name _____ Period _____ Date _____

1. Select three of the numbers below so that the mode of the three numbers is 42 and the mean is 47.

   42 52 42 57 65

2. Six points are graphed.

   a. Give the coordinates of each point.

   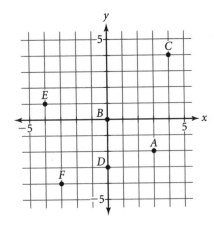

   b. Which points are in the second quadrant?

3. Mrs. Smythe gave her calculus class a 50-point quiz. The class results are listed below.

   47 37 12 40 25 18 48 42 30 30 36 42 30 15 35 38 35 30 34 38

   a. Make a histogram of these scores. Explain why you think the bin width you chose is the best one for this graph.

   b. Give the five-number summary for these scores.

   c. Use your answers to 3a and b to determine how you think letter grades should be assigned for this quiz. Explain your thinking.

4. Matrix [A] shows regular prices for yogurt shakes and fruit smoothies at FruitLand Juice Bar. To celebrate the first day of spring, the store is offering $\frac{1}{4}$ off any item. Do a matrix calculation to find the matrix that shows the sale prices.

Regular Drink Prices ($)

$$[A] = \begin{bmatrix} 2.25 & 2.70 \\ 2.85 & 3.30 \\ 3.45 & 3.90 \end{bmatrix} \begin{matrix} \text{Small} \\ \text{Medium} \\ \text{Large} \end{matrix}$$

with column headers Shake and Smoothie.

Discovering Algebra Assessment Resources
©2007 Key Curriculum Press

Chapter 1 • Test   Form A

Answer each question and show all work clearly on a separate piece of paper.

1. Fill in each blank with *always, sometimes,* or *never* to make a true statement.

   a. The median and the mode of a set of data are _____ the same.

   b. A scatter plot _____ involves two variables.

   c. Data sets _____ have outliers.

   d. A mean is _____ an outlier.

   e. A data set _____ has a mode.

2. The graph shows the length of red beans.

   a. Name the type of graph.

   b. Find the mean, median, and mode of the data in the graph.

   c. Give the five-number summary for the data and draw a box plot.

   d. What is the IQR (interquartile range) of the data?

   e. Is 8.5 an outlier? Explain why or why not.

   f. What is the range of the data?

   g. Describe the effect on the mean, median, mode, IQR, and range if each data value is increased by 1.

Red Beans

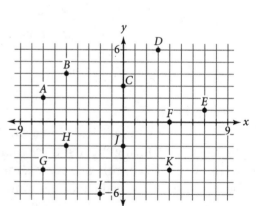

Length (mm)

3. Refer to the graph to answer each question.

   a. Name the points in Quadrant II.

   b. Name the points whose coordinates are both negative.

   c. Give the letter name and the coordinates of each point on an axis.

4. Listed below are the heights in inches of two groups of ten students.

   Group 1: 60, 62, 64, 64, 65, 66, 68, 70, 74, 75

   Group 2: 63, 64, 65, 66, 67, 67, 68, 69, 70, 72

   a. For each group, give the five-number summary, make a box plot, and find the mean height.

   b. Which group do you think is taller overall? Explain your reasoning.

(continued)

Name _____ Period _____ Date _____

5. Combine the height data for the two groups in Problem 4 and make a histogram of the 20 heights. Justify your choice of bin width.

6. The graph shows the speed of the car driven by a mother taking her children to school. Point *A* represents the driver's starting point (her home). The units for distance and time have been omitted deliberately.

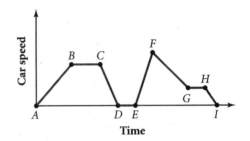

   a. Between which two points did the mother accelerate the most?

   b. What might the driver have been doing in the time interval between points *D* and *E* and in the time interval between points *F* and *G*?

   c. Write a brief story about the drive to school. Your story should account for each segment in the graph.

7. Matrix [*A*] shows the number of boys and girls in each grade level at East Side High. Matrix [*B*] shows the number of boys and girls in each grade level who will be attending a field trip to the marine lab. Do a matrix calculation to find the matrix that shows the number of boys and girls who will remain at school.

East Side High Student Body

$$[A] = \begin{bmatrix} 121 & 119 \\ 115 & 120 \\ 120 & 116 \\ 113 & 112 \end{bmatrix} \begin{matrix} \text{Freshmen} \\ \text{Sophomores} \\ \text{Juniors} \\ \text{Seniors} \end{matrix}$$

Boys Girls

Students Attending Field Trip

$$[B] = \begin{bmatrix} 45 & 50 \\ 7 & 5 \\ 12 & 11 \\ 22 & 24 \end{bmatrix} \begin{matrix} \text{Freshmen} \\ \text{Sophomores} \\ \text{Juniors} \\ \text{Seniors} \end{matrix}$$

Boys Girls

Challenge Problem

Aurora is saving money to attend a summer music festival with her school's choral group. During the first three months of the school year, she saved a mean of $53 per month. She saved a mean of $47 per month each of the next four months. What is the mean amount she must save each of the last three months to save a total of $500? Is it possible to calculate exactly how much she has saved during any given month? Explain.

Discovering Algebra Assessment Resources
©2007 Key Curriculum Press

Name _____ Period _____ Date _____

Answer each question and show all work clearly on a separate piece of paper.

1. Fill in each blank with *always, sometimes,* or *never* to make a true statement.

   a. The median of a data set is _____ a value in the data set.

   b. A scatter plot _____ involves only one variable.

   c. You can _____ tell how many values a data set has by looking at a box plot.

   d. A mode is _____ an outlier.

   e. The median of a data set that includes only whole numbers is _____ a whole number.

2. The graph shows the number of siblings.

   a. Name the type of graph.

   b. Find the mean, median, and mode of the data in the graph.

   c. Give the five-number summary for the data and draw a box plot.

   d. What is the IQR (interquartile range) of the data?

   e. Is 7 an outlier? Explain why or why not.

   f. What is the range of the data?

   g. Describe the effect on the mean, median, mode, IQR, and range if each data value is increased by 3.

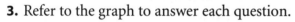

3. Refer to the graph to answer each question.

   a. Name the points in Quadrant IV.

   b. Name the points whose coordinates are both negative.

   c. Give the letter name and the coordinates of each point on an axis.

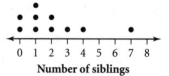

4. Listed below are the heights in inches of two groups of ten students.

   Group 1: 61, 61, 62, 64, 67, 67, 68, 68, 69, 69

   Group 2: 56, 58, 60, 61, 64, 64, 66, 72, 74, 75

   a. For each group, give the five-number summary, make a box plot, and find the mean height.

   b. Which group do you think is taller overall? Explain your reasoning.

(continued)

Name _____ Period _____ Date _____

5. Combine the height data for the two groups in Problem 4 and make a histogram of the 20 heights. Justify your choice of bin width.

6. The graph shows how Jamila's distance from home changed during her walk to school one day. Point *A* represents the start of her walk, and point *I* represents her arrival at school. The units for distance and time have been omitted deliberately.

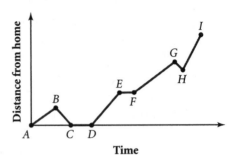

a. Between which two points is Jamila walking fastest?

b. What might Jamila have been doing in the time interval between points *B* and *C* and in the time interval between points *E* and *F*?

c. Write a brief story about Jamila's walk to school. Your story should account for each segment in the graph.

7. Matrix [*A*] shows the number of new players on the junior varsity and varsity teams at East Side High this year. Matrix [*B*] shows the number of players on the teams who were also on the teams last year. Do a matrix calculation to find the matrix that shows the total number of players on each junior varsity and varsity team.

	New Players			**Players Returning from Last Year**	
	J.V.	Varsity		J.V.	Varsity

$$[A] = \begin{bmatrix} 8 & 10 \\ 5 & 3 \\ 7 & 5 \\ 14 & 17 \end{bmatrix} \begin{matrix} \text{Soccer} \\ \text{Volleyball} \\ \text{Tennis} \\ \text{Field hockey} \end{matrix} \qquad [B] = \begin{bmatrix} 10 & 12 \\ 5 & 8 \\ 4 & 5 \\ 8 & 6 \end{bmatrix} \begin{matrix} \text{Soccer} \\ \text{Volleyball} \\ \text{Tennis} \\ \text{Field hockey} \end{matrix}$$

Challenge Problem

An art gallery is having a special Egyptian art exhibit. The gallery owner hopes to have a total of 2500 visitors during the ten-day exhibit. During the first four days, a mean of 224 visitors per day came to the exhibit. During the next two days, a mean of 328 visitors per day attended. What is the mean number of visitors per day that must come each of the last four days in order for the total number of visitors to be 2500? Is it possible to calculate exactly how many visitors attended the exhibit on any given day? Explain.

Discovering Algebra Assessment Resources
©2007 Key Curriculum Press

Chapter 1 • Constructive Assessment Options

Choose one or more of these items to replace part of the chapter test. Let students know that they will receive from 0 to 5 points for each item depending on the correctness and completeness of their answer.

1. *(Lessons 1.1–1.4)*
Dot plots, box plots, histograms, and stem plots are all used to display one-variable data. Use complete sentences to compare and contrast the types of information these four types of graphs reveal about a data set.

2. *(Lessons 1.1–1.3)*
For parts a–c, give a general description of a data set that has ten whole-number values less than or equal to 10 and fits the condition given. Give a specific example of such a data set, and make a box plot of your data.

 a. The mean is greater than the median.

 b. The median is greater than the mean.

 c. The median and the mean are equal.

3. *(Lessons 1.1–1.3)*
These box plots look a little strange, but all of them are possible. For each box plot, describe the relationships among the numbers in the five-number summary.

a. 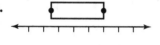   **b.**

c. 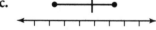   **d.**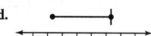

4. *(Lesson 1.3)*
This box plot shows the ages at the time of their missions of the ten youngest astronauts prior to January 1, 2004.

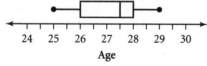

(*www.hoerstemeier.com/astroage.htm*)

 a. The second youngest astronaut was Valentina Tereshkova, who was the first woman to travel into space. Can you use the box plot to determine her age at the time of her mission? Explain.

 b. Explain what the box plot tells you about the spread of the data.

 c. From the box plot, you can find the age of the youngest astronaut. When possible, determine the age of each of the other astronauts at the time of their missions.

(continued)

5. *(Lesson 1.3)*

These box plots display mint years for samples of 20 pennies, 20 nickels, 20 dimes, and 20 quarters. Compare and contrast the four data sets using the vocabulary you have learned in the lesson (minimum, maximum, interquartile range, range, median, spread, and so on). Your answer should include at least five correct statements about the data.

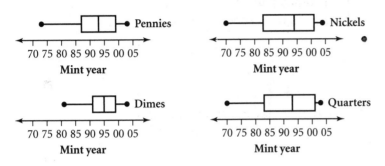

6. *(Lessons 1.3, 1.4)*

For each histogram, identify the matching box plot and justify your answer. The *x*-scale for the box plot and the bin width and *y*-scale for the histogram are all 1 unit.

a.

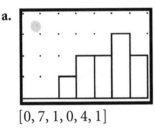

$[0, 7, 1, 0, 4, 1]$

b.

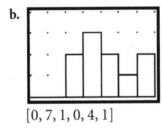

$[0, 7, 1, 0, 4, 1]$

c.

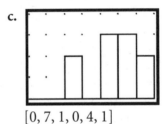

$[0, 7, 1, 0, 4, 1]$

i.

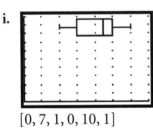

$[0, 7, 1, 0, 10, 1]$

ii.

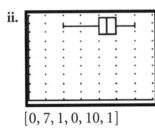

$[0, 7, 1, 0, 10, 1]$

iii.

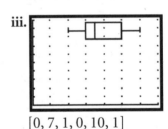

$[0, 7, 1, 0, 10, 1]$

(continued)

Discovering Algebra Assessment Resources
©2007 Key Curriculum Press

7. *(Lessons 1.1–1.7)*

Three graphs and the corresponding window settings are shown below. All three graphs show the same data—the gold-medal times (in seconds) for the Olympic men's 200-meter dash from 1900 through 2004. For each graph, list four observations you can make about the data using the graph. Also tell what type of information is easy to find from that graph, but difficult or impossible to find from the other graphs.

a.

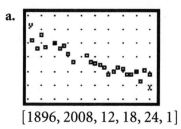

[1896, 2008, 12, 18, 24, 1]

b.

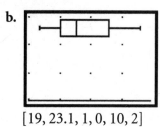

[19, 23.1, 1, 0, 10, 2]

c.

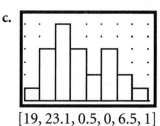

[19, 23.1, 0.5, 0, 6.5, 1]

8. *(Lessons 1.6, 1.7)*

The graph of $y = x$ includes all points for which the x-coordinate equals the y-coordinate. In parts a–c, list at least five points that meet the stated condition. Then describe the location of all the points that meet the condition, and illustrate your answer with a graph.

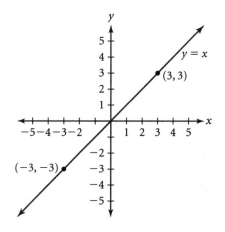

a. The y-coordinate is 2 more than the x-coordinate.

b. The y-coordinate is 2 times the x-coordinate.

c. The y-coordinate is 1 less than 3 times the x-coordinate.

1. Use the order of operations to evaluate each expression.

   a. $14 - 16 + 8 + 9 \cdot 5$

   b. $7 \cdot 9 - 21 + 7 + 4 \cdot 8$

   c. $3(8 - 6) + 49 + 7$

   d. $\dfrac{5 \cdot 4 + 2}{17 - 2 \cdot 3}$

   e. $\dfrac{24^2}{14.8 - 3 \cdot 9}$

2. Start with a number x and add 12, then divide by 4, next subtract 7, and finally multiply by 2.

   a. Convert the description to an algebraic expression.

   b. If $x = 5$, what is the value of the expression?

3. This expression describes a number trick.

   $$\frac{[(N + 9)3 + 6]}{3} - N$$

   a. Write in words the number trick that this expression describes.

   b. Test the number trick for two starting numbers. Do you get the same result for both numbers?

   c. Tell which operations undo each other to make this trick work.

4. Solve each equation by undoing the order of operations.

   a. $\dfrac{x}{7} + 9 = 17$

   b. $4(x - 8) + 14 = -24$

Name _____   Period _____   Date _____

1. Use the order of operations to evaluate each expression.

    a. $11 - 15 + 4 + (-3) \cdot 5$ **b.** $10 \cdot 5 - 35 + 5 + 7 \cdot (-8)$ **c.** $-5(-7 + 2) + 23 - 12$

    d. $\dfrac{8 + 7 \cdot (-5)}{-13 + 4^2}$ **e.** $\dfrac{\sqrt{0.22 + 0.14}}{3 \cdot 0.6 - 1.2}$

2. Start with a number x and subtract 8, then divide by -4, next add 11, and finally multiply by 3.

    a. Convert the description to an algebraic expression.

    b. If $x = 5$, what is the value of the expression?

3. This expression describes a number trick:

$$\frac{[5(N + 7) + 10]}{5} - N$$

    a. Write in words the number trick that this expression describes.

    b. Test the number trick for two starting numbers. Do you get the same result for both numbers?

    c. Tell which operations undo each other to make this trick work.

4. Solve each equation by undoing the order of operations.

    a. $\dfrac{x}{6} - 13 = -7$ **b.** $5(x + 9) - 8 = -19$

Chapter 2 • Constructive Assessment Options

Choose one or more of these items to replace part of the chapter test. Let students know that they will receive from 0 to 5 points for each item depending on the correctness and completeness of their answer.

1. *(Lessons 2.1–2.3)*
   Here are two of Jacki's homework problems, along with her answers.

   Q: In Ms. Collins's class, the ratio of boys to girls is 2 to 3. There are 12 girls in the class. How many boys are in the class?

   A: $\dfrac{2 \text{ boys}}{3 \text{ girls}} = \dfrac{x \text{ boys}}{12 \text{ girls}}$. There are 11 boys in the class.

   Q: Eight out of every 12 students are in the math club. If there are 112 students, how many students are in the math club?

   A: $\dfrac{8 \text{ math club}}{12 \text{ students}} = \dfrac{x \text{ math club}}{112 \text{ students}}$. There are 108 students in the math club.

   Explain what Jacki did wrong and why the reasoning she is using to solve proportions does not make sense. Then find the correct solution to each problem, showing all your work.

2. *(Lessons 2.1–2.3)*
   A drachma is an ancient unit of mass once used in Rome. This table shows the number of grams equivalent to various numbers of drachmas.

Drachmas	2.2	5.1	8.4	7.6	12	20.4
Grams	9.4	21.9	36.1	32.6	51.5	87.6

   Tell whether each of the following statements is true or false, and explain how you know.

   a. 1 drachma is heavier than 1 gram.

   b. 65 drachmas equal about 15 grams.

   c. The ratio of drachmas to grams is about 4.3 to 1.

   d. 100 grams equal about 23 drachmas.

3. *(Lesson 2.4)*
   You have looked at several relationships that are direct variations.

   a. If you are given a table of specific values for two variables that are directly proportional, how can you write an equation relating the two variables?

   b. Suppose you know the equation for a direct variation. Describe in detail three methods for finding the value of one variable if you know the value of the other variable.

(continued)

4. *(Lesson 2.4)*

Chen tried to make a graph showing the relationship between liquid ounces and cubic inches. She entered liquid-ounce values into list L1 and the corresponding cubic-inch values into list L2. The calculator screens illustrate the steps she followed to find the line. Unfortunately, her line did not go through the points in the scatter plot. Describe what Chen did wrong, and explain two ways she could fix her mistake.

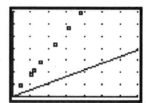

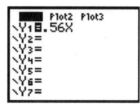

5. *(Lessons 2.4, 2.5)*

In this chapter you learned about direct and inverse variation.

a. If you are given data for two variables, how can you tell whether the relationship between the variables is a direct variation, an inverse variation, or neither?

b. How is the equation for a direct variation different from the equation for an inverse variation?

c. How is the graph of a direct variation different from the graph of an inverse variation?

6. *(Lessons 2.4, 2.5)*

Write two word problems, one involving direct variation and one involving inverse variation. Both problems should involve the numbers 2, 4, and 8 and should have the number 16 as their answer. Give a clear, complete solution for each problem.

7. *(Lesson 2.7)*

Use four 4s along with the symbols $+$, $-$, $\times$, and $\div$, and parentheses to create expressions equal to each whole number from 1 through 9. For example:

$$4 \div 4 + (4 - 4) = 1$$

Name _____ Period _____ Date _____

1. You can use the following recursive routine to keep track of the monthly savings account balances for the three people listed in the table:

   {0, 800, 1200, 2400} [ENTER]
   {Ans(1) + 1, Ans(2) + 25, Ans(3) − 42,
   Ans(4) − 85} [ENTER], [ENTER], . . .

   a. Complete the table for all three accounts.

   b. How many months elapse before Maria's balance is larger than Yolanda's balance?

   c. The recursive routine generates the list {5, 925, 990, 1975}. Explain the real-word meaning of each number in this list.

   d. How many months will elapse before Yolanda's balance is larger than Todd's balance?

Time elapsed (mo)	Maria	Yolanda	Todd
0	$800	$1,200	$2,400
1			
2			
3			
4			
5			
6			

2. Refer to Problem 1. Make a scatter plot that shows the balance in Maria's account over the 6-month period.

3. This graph shows Jon's distance from the 0 mark as he walks along a measuring tape. The horizontal axis goes from 0 to 6 seconds. The vertical axis goes from 0 to 4 meters. Describe Jon's walk, indicating the direction, walking speed, and time interval represented by each segment.

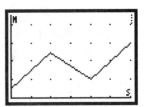

4. Match each recursive routine to a graph. Each square represents 1 unit.

   a. 3 [ENTER], Ans − 1 [ENTER], [ENTER], . . .   b. −1 [ENTER], Ans + 0.25 [ENTER], [ENTER], . . .

   c. −1.5 [ENTER], Ans + 1.5 [ENTER], [ENTER], . . .

   i.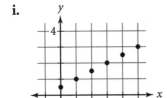

   ii.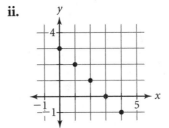

   iii.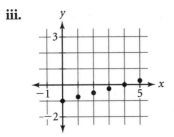

   iv.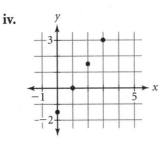

   d. Write a recursive routine for the graph that does not match any of the recursive routines in 4a–c.

Name _____   Period _____   Date _____

1. You can use the following recursive routine to keep track of the monthly savings account balances for the three people listed in the table:

{0, 1000, 1200, 2200} [ENTER]
{Ans(1) + 1, Ans(2) + 45, Ans(3) − 30, Ans(4) − 75} [ENTER], [ENTER], . . .

a. Complete the table for all three accounts.

b. How many months elapse before Maria's balance is larger than Yolanda's balance?

c. The recursive routine generates the list {4, 1180, 1080, 1900}. Explain the real-word meaning of each number in this list.

d. How many months will elapse before Yolanda's balance is larger than Todd's balance?

Time elapsed (mo)	Maria	Yolanda	Todd
0	$1000	$1,200	$2,200
1			
2			
3			
4			
5			
6			

2. Refer to Problem 1. Make a scatter plot that shows the balance in Maria's account over the 6-month period.

3. This graph shows Jon's distance from the 0 mark as he walks along a measuring tape. The horizontal axis goes from 0 to 6 seconds. The vertical axis goes from 0 to 4 meters. Describe Jon's walk, indicating the direction, speed, and time interval represented by each segment.

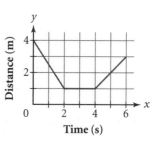

4. Match each recursive routine to a graph. Each square represents 1 unit.

a. 0.5 [ENTER], Ans + 0.5, [ENTER], [ENTER], . . .   b. 3 [ENTER], Ans − 0.75, [ENTER], [ENTER], . . .

c. −1 [ENTER], Ans + 1, [ENTER], [ENTER], . . .

i.
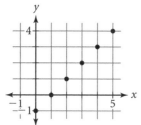

ii.
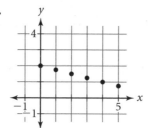

iii.
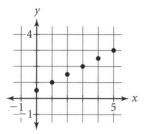

iv.
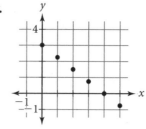

d. Write a recursive routine for the graph that does not match any of the recursive routines in 4a–c.

Name _____   **Period** _____   **Date** _____

1. Fun Times Amusement Park charges a $5 admission fee plus $1.25 per ride.

   a. Write an equation in intercept form for calculating the total cost, C, of going to the park and riding r rides.

   b. Graph your equation from 1a. How are the $5 admission fee and the $1.25 cost per ride shown in the graph?

   c. Jessie goes to the park with $13.75. How many rides can she go on?

   d. Ben has a coupon for free admission to the park. Write an equation for Ben's total cost, C, of going to the park and riding r rides. How is this equation similar to the equation you wrote in 1a? How is it different?

   e. Graph your equation from 1d on the same axes you used for 1b. How are the two graphs similar? How are they different?

2. The table at right shows an input-output relationship.

   a. Find the rate of change for this relationship.

   b. Find the output value that corresponds to an input value of 0.

   c. Use your results from 2a and b to write an equation in intercept form for the relationship.

Input, x	Output, y
-4	-18
-3	-15
2	0
5	9
10	24

3. Consider the following numbers:

   i. 12   **ii.** -7 **iii.** $-\dfrac{8}{3}$ **iv.** 5.1

   a. Give the additive inverse of each number.

   b. Give the multiplicative inverse of each number.

4. Use the method of your choice to solve each equation. Show each step.

   a. $-12 - 3.75x = 6.75$ **b.** $\dfrac{32 + 4(x - 8)}{3} = 10$

Name _____ Period _____ Date _____

1. Fun Times Amusement Park charges a $7 admission fee plus $1.50 per ride.

   a. Write an equation in intercept form for calculating the total cost, C, of going to the park and riding r rides.

   b. Graph your equation from 1a. How are the $7 admission fee and the $1.50 cost per ride shown in the graph?

   c. Jessie goes to the park with $23.50. How many rides can she go on?

   d. Ben has a coupon for free admission to the park. Write an equation for calculating Ben's total cost, C, of going to the park and riding r rides. How is this equation similar to the equation you wrote in 1a? How is it different?

   e. Graph your equation from 1d on the same axes you used for 1b. How are the two graphs similar? How are they different?

2. The table at right shows an input-output relationship.

   a. Find the rate of change for this relationship.

   b. Find the output value that corresponds to an input value of 0.

   c. Use your results from 2a and b to write an equation in intercept form for the relationship.

Input, x	Output, y
-4	21
-3	17
2	-3
5	-15
10	-35

3. Consider these numbers:

   i. 7   **ii.** -12 **iii.** $\dfrac{9}{2}$ **iv.** -3.8

   a. Give the additive inverse of each number.

   b. Give the multiplicative inverse of each number.

4. Use the method of your choice to solve each equation. Show each step.

   a. $-3.5 - 2.25x = 3.5$ **b.** $\dfrac{18 + 4(x + 6)}{3} = 20$

Discovering Algebra Assessment Resources
©2007 Key Curriculum Press

Name _____ **Period** _____ **Date** _____

Answer each question and show all work clearly on a separate piece of paper.

1. Leslie's sister gave Leslie her collection of glass animal figurines when she left for college. At that time the value of the collection was $120. Leslie then bought several new glass animal figurines for $4.75 each.

   a. Write a recursive routine to find the value of Leslie's collection after each new figurine is added. Assume each figurine does not increase or decrease in value.

   b. Write an equation in intercept form ($y = a + bx$) to describe the relationship between the value of the collection, y, and the number of new figurines, x.

   c. Explain the real-world meaning of the values of a and b in your equation.

   d. Show how you can use the equation you wrote in 1b to find the value of Leslie's collection if she buys 15 new figurines.

   e. If Leslie's collection is now worth $224.50, how many figurines has she acquired since her sister left for college?

2. Suppose an automobile cost $15,400 when it was new, and each year its value decreases by $935.

   a. Complete the table of values.

   b. Write an equation relating the value of the car, y, to the number of years elapsed, x.

   c. Use your calculator to graph your equation from 2b. Use window settings that allow you to see where the graph crosses both axes. Sketch the graph and indicate the window you used.

   d. What is the coefficient of x in your equation? What does this coefficient mean in the context of the problem?

   e. What is the y-intercept of the graph? What does this point mean in the context of the problem?

   f. Where does the graph cross the x-axis? What does this point mean in the context of the problem?

Time elapsed (yr)	Value ($)
0	15,400
1	
2	
3	
4	

3. Consider the sequence $-14.3, -13.5, -12.7, -11.9, \ldots$.

   a. Write a recursive routine that will keep track of the term number and the term for this sequence.

   b. Find the term number of the first positive term of the sequence.

(continued)

Name _____   Period _____   Date _____

4. For each table, write an equation for *y* in terms of *x*.

a.

x	*y*
0	4
1	5.5
2	7
3	8.5
4	10
5	11.5

b.

x	*y*
1	−3.5
2	−0.8
3	1.9
4	4.6
5	7.3
6	10

c.

x	*y*
−3	29.5
−1	15
0	7.75
2	−6.75
5	−28.5
7	−43

5. Solve each equation using the method of your choice. Give the action taken for each step.

a. $-6(1 - 2x) - 12 = 0$

b. $\dfrac{9 + 4x}{3} = -2$

6. Solve the formula for *h*.

$$V = \frac{\pi r^2 h}{3}$$

Challenge Problem

A line contains the points $(-10, -20)$ and $(0, 30)$, as shown on the graph.

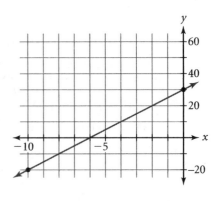

a. What is the rate of change for this line? How did you find it? What is the *y*-intercept for this line? How did you find it?

b. Write an equation in the form $y = a + bx$ for the line.

c. Name two other points on this line and show that their coordinates make your equation true.

Discovering Algebra Assessment Resources
©2007 Key Curriculum Press

Name _____ Period _____ Date _____

Answer each question and show all work clearly on a separate piece of paper.

1. Leslie's sister gave Leslie her collection of glass animal figurines when she left for college. At that time the value of the collection was $95. Leslie then bought several new glass animal figurines for $5.25 each.

   a. Write a recursive routine to find the value of Leslie's collection after each new figurine is added. Assume each figurine does not increase or decrease in value.

   b. Write an equation in intercept form ($y = a + bx$) to describe the relationship between the value of the collection, y, and the number of new figurines, x.

   c. Explain the real-world meaning of the values of a and b in your equation.

   d. Show how you can use the equation you wrote in 1b to find the value of Leslie's collection if she buys 10 new figurines.

   e. If Leslie's collection is now worth $189.50, how many figurines has she acquired since her sister left for college?

2. Suppose an automobile cost $16,500 when it was new and each year its value decreased by $1,250.

   a. Complete the table of values.

   b. Write an equation relating the value of the car, y, to the number of years elapsed, x.

   c. Use your calculator to graph your equation from 2b. Use window settings that allow you to see where the graph crosses both axes. Sketch the graph and indicate the window you used.

   d. What is the coefficient of x in your equation? What does this coefficient mean in the context of the problem?

   e. What is the y-intercept of the graph? What does this point mean in the context of the problem?

   f. Where does the graph cross the x-axis? What does this point mean in the context of the problem?

Time elapsed (yr)	Value ($)
0	16,500
1	
2	
3	
4	

3. Consider the sequence $-11.2, -8.6, -6, -3.4, \ldots$.

   a. Write a recursive routine that will keep track of the term number and the term for this sequence.

   b. Find the term number of the first term that is greater than 10.

(continued)

Name _____ Period _____ Date _____

4. For each table, write an equation for y in terms of x.

a.

x	y
0	3.5
1	6
2	8.5
3	11
4	13.5
5	16

b.

x	y
1	−9.6
2	−8.4
3	−7.2
4	−6
5	−4.8
6	−3.6

c.

x	y
−3	28.25
−1	18.75
0	14
2	4.5
5	−9.75
7	−19.25

5. Solve each equation using the method of your choice. Give the action taken for each step.

a. $36 - 3(2 - 4x) = 0$

b. $\dfrac{-7 + 5x}{5} = -3$

6. Solve the formula for w.

$$V = \frac{lwh}{3}$$

Challenge Problem

A line contains the points $(-10, -10)$ and $(0, 45)$, as shown on the graph.

a. What is the rate of change for this line? How did you find it? What is the y-intercept for this line? How did you find it?

b. Write an equation in the form $y = a + bx$ for the line.

c. Name two other points on this line and show that their coordinates make your equation true.

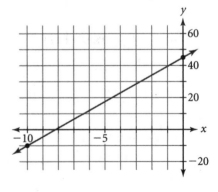

Discovering Algebra Assessment Resources
©2007 Key Curriculum Press

Chapter 3 • Constructive Assessment Options

Choose one or more of these items to replace part of the chapter test. Let students know that they will receive from 0 to 5 points for each item depending on the correctness and completeness of their answer.

1. *(Lessons 3.1, 3.2)*
Consider the following recursive routine:

$\{0, 213\}$ [ENTER]
$\{\text{Ans}(1) + 1, \text{Ans}(2) - 8\}$ [ENTER], [ENTER], ...

a. Describe a real-world situation that can be modeled with this routine. Explain how the starting values and recursive rules fit your situation.

b. Write two questions about your situation that can be answered using the recursive routine. Give the answer to each question.

2. *(Lessons 3.1, 3.2)*
Write a recursive routine that meets each set of conditions. Your routine should generate both the term number and the value of the term. The starting value should be the 0th term.

a. The starting value is 3, and the value of the 3rd term is 18.

b. The rule is "subtract 6," and the value of the 4th term is -26.

c. The starting value is positive, and the value of the 7th term is negative.

d. The starting value is negative, the value of the 3rd term is -5, and the value of the 4th term is positive.

3. *(Lesson 3.3)*
You can think of this graph as a time-distance graph. Choose a scale and unit for each axis, and then write a story that fits the graph. Your story should include specific times, rates, and distances.

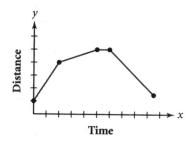

(continued)

4. *(Lessons 3.4, 3.5)*

In this problem, you'll look at graphs and equations representing trips to Chicago.

a. A car and a bus travel to Chicago. The car starts out farther from Chicago and drives at a greater speed than the bus. Each vehicle travels at a constant speed. On the same axes, sketch graphs showing how each vehicle's distance from Chicago changes over time. You do not need to include specific scale values. Indicate which graph represents which vehicle.

b. The equation $y = 540 - 65x$ can be used to find a minivan's distance from Chicago, y, after x hours.

   i. If the minivan had started closer to Chicago and had traveled more quickly, how would the numbers in the equation be different?

   ii. If the minivan had started the same distance from Chicago but had traveled more slowly, how would the numbers in the equation be different?

c. The graph shows how the distance of two cars from Chicago changed over time. Explain what the graph tells you about the two cars.

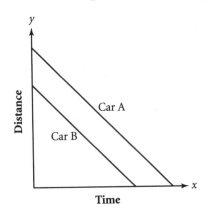

(continued)

Discovering Algebra Assessment Resources
©2007 Key Curriculum Press

5. *(Lessons 3.1–3.5)*

Divide these tables, recursive routines, equations, and graphs into groups so the items in each group represent the same relationship. Show all your work and explain how you found your answers.

a.

x	y
-3	7
-1	3
3	-5
5	-9
8	-15

b.

x	y
-5	-11
-4	-9
2	3
4	7
8	15

c.

x	y
-2	-3
1	-1.5
4	0
6	1
10	3

d. $\{0, 1\}$ ENTER
$\{Ans(1) + 1, Ans(2) - 2\}$ ENTER, ENTER, ...

e. $\{0, -2\}$ ENTER
$\{Ans(1) + 1, Ans(2) + 0\}$ ENTER, ENTER, ...

f. $\{0, -2\}$ ENTER
$\{Ans(1) + 1, Ans(2) + 0.5\}$ ENTER, ENTER, ...

g. $y = -2$ **h.** $y = -1 + 2x$ **i.** $y = 1 - 2x$

j.

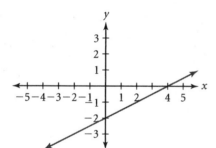

k.

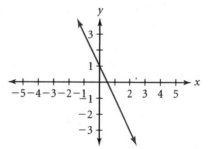

l.

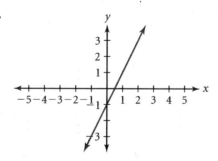

(continued)

6. *(Lessons 3.4–3.6)*

Rob runs a lemonade stand at the park. The table shows the profit he earns for different numbers of cups of lemonade sold.

Cups sold	Profit ($)
15	1.75
21	4.75
27	7.75
30	9.25
45	16.75

Tell whether each statement is true or false and explain how you know.

a. If Rob doesn't sell at least 12 cups of lemonade, he loses money.

b. Rob makes about $0.12 for each cup of lemonade he sells.

c. The equation $p = -5.75 + 0.5c$ can be used to model this situation.

d. For Rob to make over $100, he must sell at least 200 cups of lemonade.

7. *(Lessons 3.4–3.6)*

Samantha drives a transport truck between Flint and other cities in the Midwest. Her truck is equipped with a GPS (global positioning system) that allows her dispatcher to keep track of where she is. She has been driving all afternoon. The dispatcher noted her distance from Flint at three times: at 1:12 she was 140.4 mi from Flint, at 2:36 she was 213.2 mi away, and at 4:36 she was 317.2 mi away. She is a very steady driver and right on schedule.

a. Make a table showing the time, measured in hours from noon, and the distance from Flint. Plot the points on a graph. Sketch the line that shows Samantha's progress.

b. Write an equation modeling Samantha's trip.

c. What is Samantha's speed in miles per hour? Explain your thinking.

d. Where was Samantha at noon? How do you know?

e. At what time did Samantha leave Flint? Explain.

f. Samantha's destination is a truck depot 416 mi from Flint. At what time is she expected to arrive? Show your work.

Discovering Algebra Assessment Resources
©2007 Key Curriculum Press

Name _____ Period _____ Date _____

Answer each question and show all work clearly on a separate piece of paper.

1. The winner of a U.S. presidential election is the candidate who receives the most electoral votes. Each state is allotted a number of electoral votes based on its population. In 2004, the candidate who won the majority of the popular vote in a state received all that state's electoral votes. These histograms show the number of electoral votes for the states won by each major candidate in the 2004 election. (Note: For these graphs, Washington, D.C., is considered a state, so 51 states are represented.)

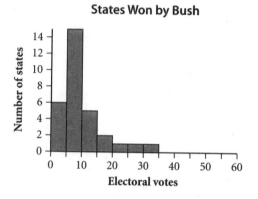

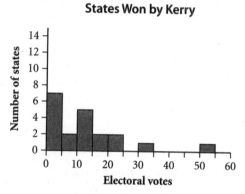

For each question, tell whether it is possible to answer the question based on the histograms. If it is possible, give the answer and explain how you found it. If it is not possible, explain why.

a. Bush won in Texas, the state with the second largest population. New York has the third largest population. Who won in New York?

b. How many states did Kerry win?

c. What is the total number of electoral votes that Bush won?

d. What percent of the states won by Bush had 10 or more electoral votes?

e. What is the greatest number of electoral votes any state had?

f. What percent of states with 15 or more electoral votes were won by Kerry?

2. Tasha put blue blocks and red blocks in a bag and then gave the bag to her friend Josh. Without looking, Josh drew a block from the bag, recorded the color, and returned the block to the bag. He repeated this 65 times, drawing a red block 22 times. Tasha told Josh that she had put 15 red blocks in the bag. Estimate the total number of blocks in the bag.

(continued)

Name _____ Period _____ Date _____

3. This table shows the total number of points scored by the players on the San Antonio Silver Stars who played at least ten games during the 2004 WNBA (Women's National Basketball Association) season. Find the five-number summary and make a box plot of these data.

Player	Total points scored
Thomas	440
Goodson	372
Johnson	287
Dydek	225
Ferdinand	199
Bibrzvcka	159
Randall	136
Hicks	127
T. Williams	55
Stevenson	38
Dillard	37
A. Williams	97

(*www.wnba.com/silverstars/stats/*)

4. At the Filler-Up gas station, Ji Young paid $11.90 for 5 gallons of gas. At Lou's Gas 'n' Stuff, Ted paid $19.28 for 8 gallons of the same type of gas.

   a. At which gas station is gas less expensive?

   b. How much would 12 gallons of gas cost at each station?

   c. If you had $10.00, how much gas could you buy at each station?

5. For each table of values, tell whether the relationship between x and y is a direct variation, an inverse variation, or neither, and explain how you decided. If the relationship is a direct or inverse variation, give its equation.

a.

x	y
2.5	1.6
5	0.8
0.16	25
100	0.04
1.25	3.2

b.

x	y
2	5
4	8
6	11
8	14
10	17

c.

x	y
1	2
2	4
3	8
4	16
5	32

d.

x	y
3	15
6	30
9	45
12	60
15	75

6. In October 2004, 1 U.S. dollar was equivalent to 1.23 Canadian dollars. 1 European euro was equivalent to 8.20 Norwegian kroner, and 1 Norwegian krone was equivalent to 0.15 U.S. dollars. How many European euros were equivalent to 1 Canadian dollar?

   (*www.currencyguide.com/exchange_body.html*)

(continued)

Name _____ Period _____ Date _____

7. Carmen is an avid baseball fan. For her birthday, on Monday, she was given a collection of 36 glossy, laminated baseball cards. Each card costs $0.75. She plans to add to her collection by buying 2 new cards every Monday.

   a. Write a recursive routine to generate a sequence showing the value of Carmen's collection for the six weeks following her birthday.

   b. Make a scatter plot showing (*number of Mondays since birthday, value of collection*).

   c. What is the rate of change of the value of her collection?

   d. Write an equation in intercept form describing the relationship between the number of Mondays since Carmen's birthday and the value of her collection.

   e. How long will it take for Carmen's collection to be worth more than $50?

8. Rashid filled his little brother's wading pool without realizing the pool had a leak. The table shows the amount of water in the pool at various times after it was filled.

Time since filling (min)	Volume of water (gal)
5	107.75
10	103.5
25	90.75
60	61
90	35.5
120	10

   a. Write a linear equation, in intercept form, for the relationship between the time since the pool was filled, x, and the volume of water in the pool, y.

   b. Explain what the slope and the y-intercept of your equation mean in this situation.

   c. If water continues to leak out of the pool at the same rate, when will the pool be empty?

9. Solve each equation.

   a. $4.5(5 - 2a) = 49.5$ **b.** $5\left(-6 + \dfrac{b}{3}\right) = -10$ **c.** $\dfrac{4(c + 7.3)}{2.5} - 3.6 = 8.4$

Name _____ Period _____ Date _____

Answer each question and show all work clearly on a separate piece of paper.

1. The winner of a U.S. presidential election is the candidate who receives the most electoral votes. Each state is allotted a number of electoral votes based on its population. In 2004, the candidate who won the majority of the popular vote in a state received all that state's electoral votes. These histograms show the number of electoral votes for the states won by each major candidate in the 2004 election. (Note: For these graphs, Washington, D.C., is considered a state, so 51 states are represented.)

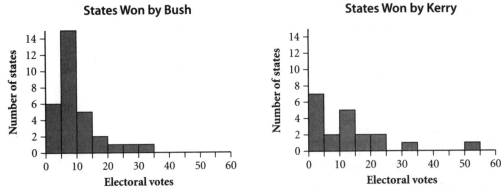

For each question, tell whether it is possible to answer the question based on the histograms. If it is possible, give the answer and explain how you found it. If it is not possible, explain why.

   a. Florida has 27 electoral votes. Which candidate won in Florida?

   b. How many states did Bush win?

   c. What is the total number of electoral votes that Kerry won?

   d. What percent of the states won by Kerry had 10 or more electoral votes?

   e. What is the least number of electoral votes any state has?

   f. What percent of states with fewer than 10 electoral votes were won by Bush?

2. Tasha put blue blocks and red blocks in a bag and then gave the bag to her friend Josh. Without looking, Josh drew a block from the bag, recorded the color, and returned the block to the bag. He repeated this 72 times, drawing a red block 45 times. Tasha told Josh that she had put 18 red blocks in the bag. Estimate the total number of blocks in the bag.

(continued)

Discovering Algebra Assessment Resources
©2007 Key Curriculum Press

Name _____ Period _____ Date _____

3. This table shows the total number of points scored by the players on the Detroit Shock who played at least ten games during the 2004 WNBA (Women's National Basketball Association) season. Find the five-number summary and make a box plot of these data.

Player	Total points scored
Cash	526
Nolan	464
Riley	378
Ford	329
M. Jones	180
Powell	133
Farris	118
C. Jones	107
Tillis	83
Sanchez	22
Walker	18

(*www.wnba.com/shock/stats/regular_season_2004.html*)

4. At the Filler-Up gas station, Ji Young paid $14.88 for 6 gallons of gas. At Lou's Gas 'n' Stuff, Ted paid $26.51 for 11 gallons of gas.

 a. At which gas station is gas less expensive?

 b. How much would 9 gallons of gas cost at each station?

 c. If you had $35.00, how much gas could you buy at each station?

5. For each table of values, tell whether the relationship between x and y is a direct variation, an inverse variation, or neither, and explain how you decided. If the relationship is a direct or inverse variation, give its equation.

a.

x	y
0.9	2.7
1.8	5.4
4.5	13.5
8.4	25.2
11.3	33.9

b.

x	y
1	64
2	32
3	16
4	8
5	4

c.

x	y
2	18
3	12
4	9
6	6
9	4

d.

x	y
1	1
2	6
3	11
4	16
5	21

6. In October 2004, 1 Japanese yen was equivalent to 0.64 Icelandic krona, 1 European euro was equivalent to 58 Indian rupees, and 1 Indian rupee was equivalent to 2.39 Japanese yen. How many European euros were equivalent to 1 Icelandic krona?

(continued)

Name _____ Period _____ Date _____

7. Carmen is an avid baseball fan. For her birthday, on Monday, she was given a collection of 32 glossy, laminated baseball cards. Each card costs $0.85. She plans to add to her collection by buying 2 new cards every Monday.

   a. Write a recursive routine to generate a sequence showing the value of Carmen's collection for the six weeks following her birthday.

   b. Make a scatter plot showing (*number of Mondays since birthday, value of collection*).

   c. What is the rate of change of the value of her collection?

   d. Write an equation in intercept form describing the relationship between the number of Mondays since Carmen's birthday and the value of her collection.

   e. How long will it take for Carmen's collection to be worth more than $50?

8. Rashid filled his little brother's wading pool without realizing the pool had a leak. The table shows the amount of water in the pool at various times after it was filled.

Time since filling (min)	Volume of water (gal)
5	120.25
10	116.5
25	105.25
60	79
90	56.5
120	34

   a. Write a linear equation, in intercept form, for the relationship between the time since the pool was filled, x, and the volume of water in the pool, y.

   b. Explain what the slope and the y-intercept of your equation mean in this situation.

   c. If water continues to leak out of the pool at the same rate, when will the pool be empty?

9. Solve each equation.

   a. $6.5(3 - 2a) = 71.5$

   b. $7\left(-4 + \dfrac{b}{3}\right) = 14$

   c. $\dfrac{3(c - 5.4)}{2.5} - 4.2 = 3$

Discovering Algebra Assessment Resources
©2007 Key Curriculum Press

Name _____ Period _____ Date _____

1. Find the slope and the equation of each line.

a. 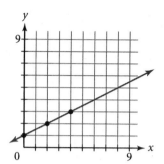   **b.** 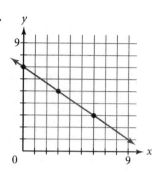   **c.**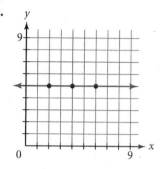

2. Find the slope of the line through each pair of points, then name another point on the same line.

a. $(2, 0)$ and $(5, 6)$ **b.** $(5, -2)$ and $(2, 3)$

3. Students in Carlos's class collected data comparing each student's height with the distance between his or her elbow and wrist. The table shows the results for Carlos's group.

a. Use your calculator to make a scatter plot of the (*elbow-to-wrist measurement, height*) data. Give the window values you used.

b. Find the slope of the line through the points $(66, 166)$ and $(73, 178)$. Explain the real-world meaning of the slope.

c. Use the slope you found in 3b to write an equation for the line in $y = bx$ form.

d. Graph your equation from 3c in the same window as the scatter plot. Explain why the line does not appear.

e. Change the equation to the form $y = a + bx$. Experiment with different values of a until you find a line that is a good fit for your data. Give the equation.

Elbow-to-wrist measurement (cm)	Height (cm)
61	160
66	166
70	172
73	178
77	183

4. Two lines are shown on the graph.

a. Which of the lines matches the equation $y = -1 + \frac{2}{3}x$?

b. What is the equation of the line that does not match the equation in 4a?

c. Describe the relationship between the two lines.

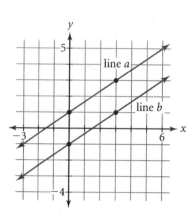

Name _____ Period _____ Date _____

1. Find the slope and equation of each line.

a.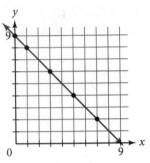

b.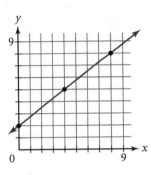

c.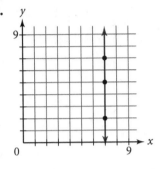

2. Find the slope of the line through each pair of points, then name another point on the same line.

   a. $(-2, 1)$ and $(5, -3)$ **b.** $(3, -5)$ and $(6, -5)$

3. Students in Carlos's class made a solar-powered cart as a class project. They tested the cart five times and made a table showing the time and distance traveled during each test run.

Time (s)	Distance (ft)
11.3	48
13.4	49
17.5	58
14.0	51
16.8	54

   a. Use your calculator to make a scatter plot of the (*time, distance*) data. Give the window values.

   b. Use the points $(13.4, 49)$ and $(16.8, 54)$ to calculate the slope of a line of fit. What is the real-world meaning of the slope?

   c. Use your answer from 3b to graph an equation in the form $y = bx$ over your scatter plot. Explain why the line does not match your data (it may not show on your screen at all).

   d. Change the equation to the form $y = a + bx$. Experiment with different values of a until you find a line that is a good fit for your data. Give the equation.

4. Two lines are shown on the graph.

   a. Which of the lines matches the equation $y = 2 - \frac{2}{3}x$?

   b. What is the equation of the line that does not match the equation in 4a?

   c. Describe the relationship between the two lines.

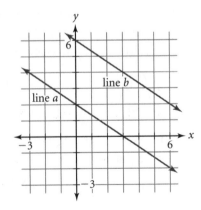

Discovering Algebra Assessment Resources
©2007 Key Curriculum Press

Name _____ **Period** _____ **Date** _____

1. Write an equation in point-slope form for a line, given its slope and one point that it passes through.

    a. Slope 6; $(-4, 3)$ **b.** Slope $-\dfrac{3}{7}$; $(5, -2)$

2. Write each equation in intercept form. For 2c, state the property you use for each step.

    a. $y = \dfrac{5}{3} - \dfrac{1}{6}(x + 4)$ **b.** $-5x + 4y + 3 = 0$

    c. $-4(y - 3) + 3(x - 1) = 8$

3. Write the equation of the line that goes through the points $(10, 8)$ and $(14, 6)$.

4. Solve each equation.

    a. $8 + \dfrac{3x + 4}{4} = 10$ **b.** $5.2(x - 1.7) + 32.4 = 3.8$

Name _____ Period _____ Date _____

1. Write an equation in point-slope form for a line, given its slope and one point that it passes through.

   a. Slope -4; $(2, -5)$

   b. Slope $\frac{9}{5}$; $(-2, 7)$

2. Write each equation in intercept form. For 2c, identify the property you use in each step of the transition.

   a. $y = -\frac{3}{2} + \frac{1}{4}(x + 3)$

   b. $3x - 5y + 4 = 0$

   c. $2(y - 3) - 5(x - 2) = 12$

3. Write the equation of the line that goes through $(10, 2)$ and $(7, 3)$ in point-slope form.

4. Solve each equation.

   a. $\frac{2x - 6}{3} + 5 = 1$

   b. $3.4 - 4.4(x + 1.8) = -16.4$

Discovering Algebra Assessment Resources
©2007 Key Curriculum Press

Name _____ Period _____ Date _____

1. The table lists the percentage of the U.S. population living in rural areas in the years given.

a. Use your calculator to make a scatter plot of the (*year, rural population*) data. Sketch the graph and describe the window you used.

b. Find the five-number summaries for the *year* data and the *rural population* data.

c. Add the quartile lines for the (*year, rural population*) data to your sketch. Give the coordinates of the two Q-points you should use for the line of fit.

d. Find the equation for the line of fit.

Year	Rural population (%)
1850	84.7
1870	74.3
1890	64.9
1910	54.3
1930	43.8
1950	36.0
1970	26.4
1990	24.8

(U.S. Census Bureau, *Encyclopedia Britannica Almanac 2005*, p. 763)

e. Write a sentence or two describing the real-world meaning of the slope of the line given by the equation in 1d.

f. Use your equation to estimate when 50% of the U.S. population lived in rural areas.

g. Use your equation to estimate the percentage of the population living in rural areas in 2000. How does your estimate compare to the actual percentage of 21.0%? What does the result tell you about using your equation to make estimates for recent years?

2. What is the main advantage of using Q-points to find a line of fit for a set of data?

Name _____ **Period** _____ **Date** _____

1. The table lists the winning times for the men's 100 m freestyle swim for Olympic games from 1952 through 2000.

   a. Use your calculator to make a scatter plot of the (*year, winning time*) data. Sketch the graph and name the window you used.

   b. Find the five-number summaries for the *year* data and the *winning time* data.

   c. Add the quartile lines for the (*year, winning time*) data to your sketch. Give the coordinates of the two Q-points you should use for the line of fit.

   d. Find the equation for the line of fit.

   e. Write a sentence or two describing the real-world meaning of the slope of the line given by the equation in 1d.

   f. Use your equation to estimate when the winning time was 60 s.

   g. Use your equation to estimate the winning time in 2004. How does your estimate compare to the actual winning time of 48.17 s?

Year	Winning time (s)
1952	57.4
1956	55.4
1960	55.2
1964	53.4
1968	52.2
1972	51.22
1976	49.99
1980	50.40
1984	49.80
1988	48.63
1992	49.02
1996	48.74
2000	48.30

(International Olympic Committee, *Encyclopedia Britannica Almanac 2005*, p. 947)

2. What is the main advantage of using Q-points to find a line of fit for a set of data?

Discovering Algebra Assessment Resources
©2007 Key Curriculum Press

Name _____ **Period** _____ **Date** _____

Answer each question and show all work clearly on a separate piece of paper.

1. Two lines are shown on the graph.

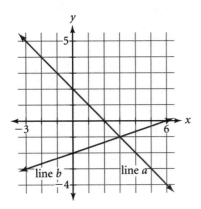

  a. Give the slope, y-intercept, and equation for each line.

  b. Name the point of intersection of the two lines.

2. The equation of a line, in point-slope form, is $y = 7 - 2(x - 5)$.

  a. Name the point on the line with an x-coordinate of 3.

  b. Name the point on the line with a y-coordinate of 5.

  c. Use the point you named in 2b to write another equation of the line in point-slope form.

3. Explain how you can find the equation of a line when you know the coordinates of two points on the line.

4. Solve the equation $\frac{5 - 11}{x + 2} = 3$, using any method. Use another method to check your solution.

5. Write each equation in the form requested.

  a. Write $y = 5x - 20$ in factored form so that the coefficient of x is $+1$.

  b. Write $y = 14.7(x - 20) + 130.6$ in intercept form.

  c. Write $y = 6.2x - 17$ in point-slope form, using the point with an x-coordinate of 8.

6. Name the property illustrated in each equation.

  a. $6 \cdot 8 = 8 \cdot 6$ **b.** $6(8 + 4) = 6 \cdot 8 + 6 \cdot 4$

(continued)

Name _____ Period _____ Date _____

7. Jamie spent the summer in Canada. Because Canada uses the metric system, he wanted to be able to convert Fahrenheit temperatures to Celsius temperatures. He remembered from science class that the relationship between the two systems is linear. He also remembered that water freezes at 32°F, or 0°C, and boils at 212°F, or 100°C.

°F	°C
32	0
212	100

   a. Show how Jamie could use this information to write an equation in point-slope form for converting Fahrenheit temperatures, F, to Celsius temperatures, C.

   b. What is the real-world meaning of the slope of the line?

   c. What is the Celsius equivalent of 68°F?

   d. On a very warm day, the temperature was 40°C. What is the Fahrenheit equivalent of this temperature?

8. Isabel, a research assistant at Maryland State University Museum, measured the metacarpal I bone (the bone from the wrist to the thumb) and the height of ten human skeletons. Anthropologists can use data such as these to conjecture a person's height based on partial skeletal remains.

(Musgrave, Jonathan H., and Harneja, Narendra K., *American Journal of Physical Anthropology* (1978) vol. 48, pp. 113–120)

Metacarpal I length (mm)	45	50	39	41	52	47	50	42	46	43
Skeletal height (cm)	174	182	157	163	183	174	176	170	170	169

   a. Use your calculator to make a scatter plot of the (*metacarpal I length, height*) data. Sketch the graph and describe the window you used.

   b. Find the five-number summaries for the *metacarpal I length* data and the *height* data.

   c. Give the coordinates of the two Q-points you should use for the line of fit.

   d. Find the slope of the line through the Q-points. What is the real-world meaning of the slope?

   e. Find the equation of the line through the Q-points.

   f. Graph the equation from 8e in the same window as the scatter plot, and sketch the result. Do you think the line is a good model for the data? Explain why or why not.

Challenge Problem

For the data in Problem 8, find an equation that you think better represents the data. Explain the method you used.

Name _____ Period _____ Date _____

Answer each question and show all work clearly on a separate piece of paper.

1. Two lines are shown on the graph.

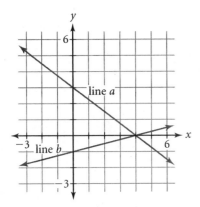

  a. Give the slope, y-intercept, and equation for each line.

  b. Name the point of intersection of the two lines.

2. The equation of a line, in point-slope form, is $y = 8 - 3(x + 3)$.

  a. Name the point on the line with an x-coordinate of 2.

  b. Name the point on the line with a y-coordinate of 11.

  c. Use the point you named in 2b to write another equation of the line in point-slope form.

3. Explain how you can find the equation of a line when you know the y-intercept and the coordinates of one other point on the line.

4. Solve the equation $\frac{3x - 11}{5} + 6 = 8$, using any method. Use another method to check your solution.

5. Write each equation in the form requested.

  a. Write $y = -22.5(x - 10) + 75.5$ in intercept form.

  b. Write $y = -6x + 18$ in factored form so that the coefficient of x is $+1$.

  c. Write $y = 7.2x - 2.4$ in point-slope form, using the point with an x-coordinate of 4.

6. Name the property illustrated in each equation.

  a. $6(4 - 5) = 6 \cdot 4 - 6 \cdot 5$ **b.** $6 + (4 + 5) = (6 + 4) + 5$

(continued)

Name _____ Period _____ Date _____

7. Jamie spent the summer in Canada. Because Canada uses the metric system, he wanted to be able to convert Celsius temperatures to Fahrenheit temperatures. He remembered from science class that the relationship between the two systems is linear. He also remembered that water freezes at 0°C, or 32°F, and boils at 100°C, or 212°F.

°C	°F
0	32
100	212

   a. Show how Jamie could use this information to write an equation for converting Celsius temperatures, C, to Fahrenheit temperatures, F.

   b. What is the real-world meaning of the slope of the line?

   c. What is the Fahrenheit equivalent of 25°C?

   d. What is the Celsius equivalent of 59°F?

8. The table shows the gestation period and average longevity of several animals.

   a. Use your calculator to make a scatter plot of the (*gestation, average longevity*) data. Sketch the graph and describe the window you used.

   b. Find the five-number summaries for the *gestation* data and the *average longevity* data.

   c. Give the coordinates of the two Q-points you should use for the line of fit.

   d. Find the slope of the line through the Q-points. What is the real-world meaning of the slope?

   e. Find the equation of the line through the Q-points.

   f. Graph the equation from 8e in the same window as the scatter plot, and sketch the result. Do you think the line is a good model for the data? Explain why or why not.

Animal	Gestation (days)	Average longevity (years)
Grizzly bear	225	25
Zebra	365	15
Red fox	52	7
Guinea pig	68	4
Horse	330	20
Rhesus monkey	166	15
Meadow mouse	21	3
Black rhinoceros	450	15
Sea lion	350	12
Sheep	154	12

(Fish and Wildlife Service, U.S. Dept. Interior, *World Almanac and Book of Facts 2005*, p. 180)

Challenge Problem

For the data in Problem 8, use a different method to find a line that represents the data. Explain the method you used.

Discovering Algebra Assessment Resources
©2007 Key Curriculum Press

Chapter 4 • Constructive Assessment Options

Choose one or more of these items to replace part of the chapter test. Let students know that they will receive from 0 to 5 points for each item depending on the correctness and completeness of their answer.

1. *(Lesson 4.2)*
   A line has an x-intercept of 12 and a y-intercept of 5.

   a. Describe a real-world situation that can be modeled by the line.

   b. Write an equation for the line in intercept form. Tell how the variables in your equation are related to the situation you described in part a.

   c. Write a problem about the situation you described that can be solved by using your equation. Give a detailed solution to your problem.

2. *(Lesson 4.3)*
   Describe completely what a line that satisfies the given conditions looks like. Then give an equation for a line that fits the conditions.

   a. The line passes through Quadrants II, III, and IV.

   b. The line has a negative slope and crosses the x-axis at 4.

   c. The line passes through Quadrants I and II only.

   d. The line passes through the origin and does not include any points where the x- and y-coordinates have the same sign.

3. *(Lesson 4.3)*
   Consider the line that passes through the points $(-3, 7)$ and $(15, -2)$. Tell whether each statement is true or false and explain how you know.

   a. An equation for the line is $y = 7 - 2(x + 3)$.

   b. An equation for the line is $y = 3 - 0.5(x - 5)$.

   c. The line does not pass through Quadrant I.

   d. The y-intercept is 11, and the x-intercept is 5.5.

4. *(Lesson 4.3)*
   A line passes through the points $(5, 12)$ and $(8, 33)$.

   a. Describe a real-world situation that can be modeled by the line.

   b. Use the two points to write an equation in point-slope form. Tell how the variables in your equation are related to the situation you described in part a.

   c. Write a problem about the situation that can be solved by using your equation. Give a detailed solution to your problem.

(continued)

5. (*Lesson 4.4*)

For homework, Julia was given equations in point-slope form and had to rewrite them in intercept form. As shown, she made mistakes rewriting three equations. For each equation, explain what she did wrong and then give the correct series of steps.

a. $y = 4 - 3(x - 6)$
$y = 4 - 3x - 6$
$y = -3x - 2$

b. $y = -5 - (x + 8)$
$y = -5 - x + 8$
$y = 3 - x$

c. $y = 3 - 7(x + 1)$
$y = -4(x + 1)$
$y = -4x - 4$

6. (*Lessons 4.2 and 4.5–4.7*)

Use complete sentences to describe two methods for fitting a linear equation to data.

7. (*Lessons 4.2 and 4.5–4.7*)

The table shows the percentage of U.S. households that had cable television in the even-numbered years 1978 through 2002.

a. Find a linear equation that fits the data. Describe the method you used and explain why you think your equation is a good fit.

b. Predict how the percentage of U.S. households with cable television will change over the next 10 to 15 years. Use your equation and the data to support your prediction.

Year	Percentage	Year	Percentage
1978	17.9	1992	61.5
1980	22.6	1994	63.4
1982	35.0	1996	66.7
1984	43.7	1998	67.4
1986	48.1	2000	67.8
1988	53.8	2002	68.9
1990	59.0		

(Nielsen Media Research, *World Almanac and Book of Facts 2005*, p. 310)

8. (*Lessons 4.5–4.7*)

The table shows the world population in billions for even-numbered years from 1970 to 2004.

Tell whether each statement is true or false, and explain how you know.

a. The world population has been increasing by about 160 million people a year since 1970.

b. Using Q-points, a model for the data is $y = 0.082(x - 1978) + 4.302$, where x is the year and y is the world population in billions.

c. According to the Q-point model, 2000 was the first year the world population was 6 billion people or more.

d. The largest two-year increase in world population occurred between 1986 and 1988.

Year	Population (billions)	Year	Population (billions)
1970	3.707	1988	5.107
1972	3.862	1990	5.282
1974	4.013	1992	5.449
1976	4.158	1994	5.611
1978	4.302	1996	5.771
1980	4.453	1998	5.928
1982	4.608	2000	6.080
1984	4.770	2002	6.227
1986	4.935	2004	6.373

(*www.census.gov/ipc/www/worldpop.html*)

Name _____ **Period** _____ **Date** _____

1. Solve the system of equations by using substitution. Be sure to verify your solution by substituting it into both original equations.

$$\begin{cases} 2x + y = 19 \\ x - y = 2 \end{cases}$$

2. Solve the system of equations by using the elimination method. Be sure to verify your solution by substituting it into both original equations.

$$\begin{cases} 2x + 3y = 9 \\ 4x - y = 11 \end{cases}$$

3. Alfonso and Joan sold sandwiches and juice boxes at a football game. The sandwiches cost $1.75 each, and each juice box cost $1.10. They sold a total of 540 items (sandwiches and juice boxes) and took in $730.50. Let *s* represent the number of sandwiches sold, and let *j* represent the number of juice boxes sold.

   a. Write an equation for the total number of items sold.

   b. Write an equation for the total cost of the items.

   c. The equations from 3a and b form a system of equations. Solve the system to find the number of sandwiches sold and the number of juice boxes sold.

4. Look back at the system of equations you wrote in Problem 3.

   a. Write a matrix to represent the system.

   b. Verify your solution in 3c by using row operations to transform your matrix into the form $\begin{bmatrix} 1 & 0 & A \\ 0 & 1 & B \end{bmatrix}$. Show each step and tell what row operation you used.

Name _____ **Period** _____ **Date** _____

1. Solve the system of equations by using substitution. Be sure to verify
your solution by substituting it into both original equations.

$$\begin{cases} 3x - y = 6 \\ x - y = -4 \end{cases}$$

2. Solve the system of equations by using the elimination method. Be sure
to verify your solution by substituting it into both original equations.

$$\begin{cases} 5x + 3y = 26 \\ 2x - y = 6 \end{cases}$$

3. Josh and Racquel sold cookies and brownies at the math club bake sale.
The cookies cost $0.35 each, and the brownies cost $0.75 each. They sold
a total of 600 items (cookies and brownies) and raised $360. Let c
represent the number of cookies sold, and let b represent the number of
brownies sold.

　a. Write an equation for the total number of items sold.

　b. Write an equation for the total cost of the items.

　c. The equations from 3a and b form a system of equations. Solve the
　　system to find the number of cookies and brownies sold.

4. Look back at the system of equations you wrote in Problem 3.

　a. Write a matrix to represent the system.

　b. Verify your solution in 3c by using row operations to transform your
　　matrix into the form $\begin{bmatrix} 1 & 0 & A \\ 0 & 1 & B \end{bmatrix}$. Show each step and tell which row
　　operations you used.

Name _____   Period _____   Date _____

1. In this graph, the scale on both axes is 1.

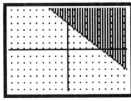

$[-10, 10, 1, -7, 7, 1]$

   a. Assume the line is solid. Write the inequality the graph represents.

   b. Assume the line is dotted. Write the inequality the graph represents.

2. Graph the system of inequalities and indicate the solution.

$$\begin{cases} y > -3 \\ y \le 2x + 1 \end{cases}$$

3. Solve the inequality $-3x + 4 > 16$, showing each step of your solution. Graph the solution on a number line.

4. Sofia wants to visit her aunt in Italy next summer. She estimates that she will need at least $600 for the trip. Her grandmother gave her $100 to put toward the trip. Sofia has a part-time job and thinks she can save $75 of her earnings each month. Write and solve an inequality to determine how many months Sofia will need to save in order to have enough money for the trip.

Name _____ **Period** _____ **Date** _____

1. In this graph, the scale on both axes is 1.

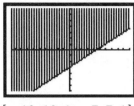

$[-10, 10, 1, -7, 7, 1]$

   a. Assume the line is solid. Write the inequality the graph represents.

   b. Assume the line is dotted. Write the inequality the graph represents.

2. Graph the system of inequalities and indicate the solution.

$$\begin{cases} y < 2 \\ y \geq 3x - 2 \end{cases}$$

3. Solve the inequality $-2x + 5 < 13$, showing each step of your solution. Graph the solution on a number line.

4. Jon wants to visit his aunt in Australia next summer. He estimates that he will need at least $1,200 for the trip. His father said he would give him $550 toward the trip. Jon has a part-time job and thinks he can save $75 of his earnings each month. Write and solve an inequality to determine how many months Jon will need to save in order to have enough money for the trip.

Discovering Algebra Assessment Resources
©2007 Key Curriculum Press

Name _____ Period _____ Date _____

1. Consider this system of equations.

$$\begin{cases} 3x + 5y = 7 \\ 2x - y = 9 \end{cases}$$

   a. Solve the system by using substitution or elimination. Check your solution by substituting it into both equations.

   b. Write both equations in intercept form. Graph the equations and verify that the point of intersection is the solution of the system.

2. Write a system of inequalities to describe the shaded area of the graph. In the inequalities, express the slopes of the lines in fraction form.

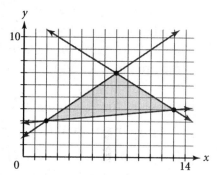

3. Consider the inequality $700 + x \geq 130 - 59x$.

   a. Solve the inequality, showing each step of your solution.

   b. Explain how you could check your solution by graphing two equations on a calculator. (Do not actually graph the equations.)

4. The Creekside Theater is putting on a play. The Hanson family bought five adult tickets and three child tickets for $131.25. The Rivera family bought three adult tickets and four child tickets for $106.25.

   a. Write a system of equations to represent this situation.

   b. Use matrices to solve the system. Show each step of your solution and tell which row operation you used. How much does an adult ticket cost? How much does a child ticket cost?

5. Complete each sentence.

   a. When two equations have the same slope, the lines they represent are

   _____ .

   b. When you solve an inequality, you need to change the direction of the inequality symbol when you _____ .

   c. If a system of linear equations has an infinite number of solutions, then the graphs of the equations _____ .

Challenge Problem

Solve the system of equations.

$$\begin{cases} 2x + 4y - z = -3 \\ x + y + z = 2 \\ -5x - y + 3z = -10 \end{cases}$$

Name _____ Period _____ Date _____

1. Consider this system of equations:

$$\begin{cases} 2x - 3y = 2 \\ 3x - y = 10 \end{cases}$$

   a. Solve the system by using substitution or elimination. Check your solution by substituting it into both equations.

   b. Write both equations in intercept form. Graph the equations and verify that the point of intersection is the solution of the system.

2. Write a system of inequalities to describe the shaded area of the graph. In the equalities, express the slopes of the lines in fraction form.

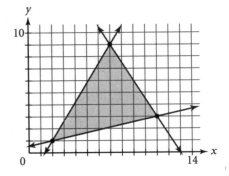

3. Consider the inequality $6 - 2x \le 9 + 8x$.

   a. Solve the inequality, showing each step of your solution.

   b. Explain how you could check your solution by graphing two equations. (Do not actually graph the equations.)

4. The Creekside Theater is putting on a play. The Hanson family bought five adult tickets and two child tickets for $129.00. The Rivera family bought two adult tickets and six child tickets for $107.50.

   a. Write a system of equations to represent this situation.

   b. Use matrices to solve the system. Show each step of your solution and tell which row operation you used. How much does an adult ticket cost? How much does a child ticket cost?

5. Complete each sentence.

   a. When the equations in a linear system have different slopes, then the system has _____ solution(s).

   b. When you solve an inequality, you need to change the direction of the inequality symbol when you _____.

   c. If a system of linear equations has no solution, then the graphs of the equations _____.

Challenge Problem

Solve the system of equations.

$$\begin{cases} 2x - 4y + z = 12 \\ x + y + z = 5 \\ -5x + 2y - 2z = -20 \end{cases}$$

Discovering Algebra Assessment Resources
©2007 Key Curriculum Press

Chapter 5 • Constructive Assessment Options

Choose one or more of these items to replace part of the chapter test. Let students know that they will receive from 0 to 5 points for each item depending on the correctness and completeness of their answer.

1. *(Lesson 5.1)*
   A door is on one wall of a classroom, and a set of windows is on the opposite wall. Sketch a graph to represent each situation, with the *x*-axis representing time and the *y*-axis representing distance from the door. You do not need to show specific scale values. Label each line with the student's name.

   a. Emily starts at the windows walking toward the door, and Alison starts at the door walking toward the windows. Each girl walks at a steady pace toward the opposite wall.

   b. Emily starts at the windows. Alison starts a few feet in front of the windows. Each girl walks toward the door at a steady pace. Emily gets to the door first.

   c. Alison starts at the door. Emily starts a few feet in front of the door. Each girl walks toward the windows at a steady pace. Alison gets to the windows first.

   d. Emily starts at the windows. Alison starts a few feet in front of the windows. Both girls walk at a steady pace toward the door, keeping the same distance between them the whole way.

2. *(Lessons 5.2–5.4)*
   Keaton solved these three systems as part of his homework. For each system, tell whether his solution is correct. If it is incorrect, explain what he did wrong and give the correct solution steps.

   a. $\begin{cases} y = 4x - 9 \\ y = -2x + 1 \end{cases}$

   $4x - 9 = -2x + 1$
   $-9 = 2x + 1$
   $-10 = 2x$
   $-5 = x$

   $y = 4(-5) - 9$
   $y = -29$

   $(-5, -29)$

   b. $\begin{cases} x - 2y = 2 \\ 3x - 5y = 7 \end{cases}$

   $x = 2 + 2y$

   $3(2 + 2y) - 5y = 7$
   $6 + 6y - 5y = 7$
   $6 + y = 7$
   $y = 1$

   $x - 2(1) = 2$
   $x = 4$

   $(4, 1)$

   c. $\begin{cases} x - y = -11 \\ x + y = 1 \end{cases}$

   $\begin{aligned} x - y &= -11 \\ x + y &= 1 \\ \hline 2x &= 12 \\ x &= 6 \end{aligned}$

(continued)

3. *(Lessons 5.1–5.4)*

Write a system of two equations that satisfies each condition. Then prove that the system satisfies the condition by solving it symbolically.

a. Both coordinates of the solution are negative integers.

b. The graphs of both equations cross the *y*-axis at 5.

c. The graphs of the equations do not intersect.

d. The solution is (0, 0).

4. *(Lessons 5.1–5.4)*

Quick Cam and Fun Photo both make prints of pictures taken with digital cameras. Quick Cam charges a $5 setup fee, plus $0.99 per print. Fun Photo charges a $3.50 setup fee, plus $1.05 per print. Tell whether each statement is true or false, and explain how you know.

a. There is no number of prints for which the cost is the same at both stores.

b. The equation $c = 0.99 + 5p$ can be used to calculate the cost, *c*, of having *p* prints made at Quick Cam.

c. It is always cheaper to have prints made at Fun Photo.

d. If Len paid $24.80 for 20 prints at one of the stores, he must have gone to Quick Cam.

5. *(Lessons 5.2–5.4)*

Write a word problem that can be solved by writing and solving a system of equations. The solution to the system must be (3, 13). Show a complete solution to your problem.

6. *(Lesson 5.5)*

Sam was absent when his class worked with linear inequalities in one variable. Sarah told him, "If you can solve equations, then you can solve inequalities. There are only a couple of new things you need to know." Write a note to Sam explaining how to solve linear inequalities. (Assume he knows how to solve equations.) Also explain how to graph an inequality on a number line.

(continued)

Discovering Algebra Assessment Resources
©2007 Key Curriculum Press

7. *(Lesson 5.7)*

Luis told his sister Rosi, "If you can guess the amount of money in my piggy bank, you can have it. The bank contains only dimes and quarters. There are no more than eight quarters and no more than four dimes. I have at least ten coins in all."

a. Write a system of inequalities for this situation.

b. Make a graph showing the solution of the system of inequalities.

c. How many different combinations of coins are possible? Explain how you found your answer.

d. If Luis has less than $2.00 in his piggy bank, how many of each coin must he have? Explain how you found your answer.

8. *(Lesson 5.7)*

Write a system of linear inequalities that satisfies the given criteria. Graph the system and indicate the solution.

a. The solution includes points in Quadrants III and IV only.

b. The solution includes points in every quadrant but Quadrant IV.

c. All the points in the solution have two positive coordinates.

d. The solution includes points in every quadrant but Quadrant I.

Name _____ Period _____ Date _____

1. In 2000, Open Road Bus Lines charged $125.00 for a ticket from Chicago to Phoenix. Since then, the price of the ticket has increased by 3% per year. Let x represent the number of years since 2000, and let y represent the ticket price.

   a. Use this recursive routine to complete the table.

   $\{0, 125\}$ [ENTER]
   $\{\text{Ans}(1) + 1, \text{Ans}(2) \cdot (1 + 0.03)\}$ [ENTER]

Year	Years since 2000, x	Ticket price, y ($)
2000		
2001		
2002		
2003		
2004		
2005		

   b. What is the constant multiplier for the y-values?

   c. Write an equation for calculating the ticket price for any year after 2000.

   d. In what year will the ticket price first exceed $160.00?

2. A box of cereal costs $4.98. Because of inflation, the price increases by 4% per year.

   a. Write an equation to model the growth in the price of the cereal.

   b. Use your equation from 2a to predict the price of the cereal three years from now.

   c. Use your equation from 2a to predict when the price will first exceed $7.50.

Name _____ Period _____ Date _____

1. In 2000, Open Road Bus Lines charged $115.00 for a ticket from Denver to San Francisco. Since then, the price of the ticket has increased by 4% per year. Let x represent the number of years since 2000, and let y represent the ticket price.

Year	Years since 2000, x	Ticket price, y ($)
2000		
2001		
2002		
2003		
2004		
2005		

   a. Use this recursive routine to complete the table.

   $\{0, 115\}$ ENTER
   $\{\text{Ans}(1) + 1, \text{Ans}(2) \cdot (1 + 0.04)\}$ ENTER

   b. What is the constant multiplier for the y-values?

   c. Write an equation for calculating the ticket price for any year after 2000.

   d. In what year will the ticket price first exceed $170.00?

2. A box of cereal costs $4.50. Because of inflation, the price increases by 6% per year.

   a. Write an equation to model the growth in the price of the cereal.

   b. Use your equation from 2a to predict the price of the cereal three years from now.

   c. Use your equation from 2a to predict when the price will first exceed $6.50.

Discovering Algebra Assessment Resources
©2007 Key Curriculum Press

Name _____ Period _____ Date _____

1. Use the properties of exponents to write each expression in the form ax^n.

   a. $4x^6 \cdot 2x^6$ b. $\left(-5x^3\right) \cdot \left(-2x^4\right)$ c. $\dfrac{72x^7}{6x^2}$ d. $(2x)(-4x)(-4x)$

   e. $\dfrac{6x^5}{3x}$ f. $3(2x)^2$

2. Write each number in standard notation.

   a. -2.4×10^4 b. 3.25×10^{-5} c. -5.5×10^{-3}

3. Write each number in scientific notation.

   a. $37{,}140{,}000$ b. 0.000801 c. -0.00001

4. Write each expression using only positive exponents.

   a. $2 \cdot x^{-1}$ b. $(2x)^{-1}$ c. $\dfrac{1}{4^{-5}}$ d. $\dfrac{x^{-2}}{y^{-5}}$

5. Use the properties of exponents to rewrite each expression.

   a. $\dfrac{7.6x^7}{3.8x^3}$ b. $x^2 \cdot (-2)^0$ c. $x^4 \cdot x^6$ d. $3^4 \cdot 2^2 \cdot 3^2 \cdot 2^3$

   e. $\dfrac{(-2y)^4}{(-2y)^3}$ f. $\left(3x^2y\right)^2(-5xy)$ g. $\dfrac{8 \times 10^9}{4 \times 10^6}$ h. $4(2x)^{-2}\left(x^2y\right)$

6. Tell whether each equation is true or false. If it is false, change the right side to make the equation true.

   a. $\left(3x^2\right)^3 = 9x^6$ b. $3\left(2x^2\right)^{-1} = -6x^{-2}$

7. Uranus is about 2.87×10^{12} m from the Sun. Light travels at approximately 3×10^8 m/s. How long does it take for the Sun's light to reach Saturn? Give your answer in seconds and to the nearest minute.

Name _____   **Period** _____   **Date** _____

1. Use the properties of exponents to write each expression in the form ax^n.

    a. $3x^5 \cdot 2x^5$ **b.** $(-7x^2) \cdot (-4x^5)$ **c.** $\dfrac{56x^9}{8x^2}$ **d.** $(3x)(-5x)(-5x)$

    e. $\dfrac{14x^3}{2x}$ **f.** $2(3x)^3$

2. Write each number in standard notation.

    a. -3.2×10^3 **b.** 4.89×10^{-4} **c.** -7.01×10^{-5}

3. Write each number in scientific notation.

    a. 5,814,000   **b.** 0.00722   **c.** -0.00004

4. Write each expression using only positive exponents.

    a. $3 \cdot x^{-2}$ **b.** $(3x)^{-1}$ **c.** $\dfrac{1}{7^{-3}}$ **d.** $\dfrac{y^{-4}}{x^{-2}}$

5. Use the properties of exponents to rewrite each expression.

    a. $\dfrac{4.5x^6}{0.5x^2}$ **b.** $(-21)^0 \cdot x^5$ **c.** $x^5 \cdot x^7$ **d.** $5^4 \cdot 7^2 \cdot 5 \cdot 7^5$

    e. $\dfrac{(3y^2)^6}{(3y^2)^5}$ **f.** $(-4xy^2)^2(3x^2y)$ **g.** $\dfrac{9 \times 10^9}{1.5 \times 10^5}$ **h.** $9(3x)^{-2}(2x^2y)$

6. Tell whether each equation is true or false. If it is false, change the right side to make the equation true.

    a. $(2x^3)^3 = 6x^6$ **b.** $2(3x^3)^{-1} = -6x^{-2}$

7. Saturn is about 1.427×10^{12} m from the Sun. Light travels at approximately 3×10^8 m/s. How long does it take for the Sun's light to reach Saturn? Give your answer in seconds and to the nearest minute.

Discovering Algebra Assessment Resources
©2007 Key Curriculum Press

Name _____ Period _____ Date _____

1. During the radioactive decay investigation, one group used the equation $y = 200(1 - 0.18)^x$ to model their data.

   a. Use the equation to complete this table.

Years, x	Atoms remaining, y
0	
1	
2	
3	
4	
5	
6	

   b. Explain what the numbers 200 and 0.18 in the equation represent in this situation.

2. Write an equation for the relationship between x and y given in the table. Then use your equation to complete the table.

x	y
-2	
-1	
0	64
1	12.8
2	2.56
3	0.512
4	

Name _____ Period _____ Date _____

1. During the radioactive decay investigation, one group used the equation $y = 150(1 - 0.16)^x$ to model their data.

   a. Use the equation to complete this table.

Years, x	Atoms remaining, y
0	
1	
2	
3	
4	
5	
6	

   b. Explain what the numbers 150 and 0.16 in the equation represent in this situation.

2. Write an equation for the relationship between x and y given in the table. Then use your equation to complete the table.

x	y
-2	
-1	
0	1000
1	700
2	490
3	343
4	

Discovering Algebra Assessment Resources
©2007 Key Curriculum Press

Name _____ Period _____ Date _____

1. Use the properties of exponents to rewrite each expression.

   a. $24x^5 \cdot 2x^2$

   b. $\left(5x^3y^2\right)^2$

   c. $\dfrac{72x^6}{3x}$

   d. $5^x5^y3^z$

   e. $\dfrac{1.4 \times 10^{14}}{2.8 \times 10^{16}}$

   f. $\left(3x^7y^3\right)\left(-12x^4y\right)$

2. A rubber ball rebounds to 85% of the height from which it is dropped.

   a. How high is the first bounce if the ball is dropped from a height of 200 cm?

   b. Record the height of each bounce in the table.

   c. Write a recursive routine that generates the heights of the bounces.

   d. Write an equation that generates the heights of the bounces.

   e. On which bounce will the height first be less than 70 cm?

Bounce number	Height (cm)
0	200
1	
2	
3	
4	
5	

3. Write each number in standard notation.

   a. -4.3×10^5

   b. 5.25×10^{-4}

4. Write each number in scientific notation.

   a. 31,540,000,000

   b. -0.00000502

5. Find the x-value that makes each equation true.

   a. $0.000712 = 7.12 \times 10^x$

   b. $25 \times 10^{-5} = 2.5 \times 10^x$

   c. $0.0047 = 4.7 \times 10^x$

6. Use the properties of exponents to answer each question.

   a. Explain why $\dfrac{8^5}{8^5} = 1$.

   b. Write an equation equivalent to $y = \dfrac{1}{10^x}$.

7. Assume that the values of paintings by a certain artist increase by 7% each year. For each question, write an expression in the form $A(1 + r)^x$. Then evaluate the expression to answer the question.

   a. If a painting is worth $5,000 today, how much was it worth three years ago?

   b. If a painting was worth $3,000 two years ago, how much is it worth today?

   c. If a painting is worth $2,000 today, how much will it be worth in 40 years?

8. What are the advantages of using scientific notation to express very large and very small numbers?

Name _____ Period _____ Date _____

1. Use the properties of exponents to rewrite each expression.

  a. $12x^3 \cdot 3x^5$ **b.** $(7x^2y^3)^3$ **c.** $\dfrac{45x^6}{3x^2}$

  d. $7^x 5^y 7^z$ **e.** $\dfrac{1.2 \times 10^8}{4.8 \times 10^{12}}$ **f.** $(5x^4y)(-6x^3y^5)$

2. A rubber ball rebounds to 75% of the height from which it is dropped.

  a. How high is the first bounce if the ball is dropped from a height of 300 cm?

  b. Record the height of each bounce in the table.

  c. Write a recursive routine that generates the heights of the bounces.

  d. Write an equation that generates the heights of the bounces.

  e. On which bounce will the height first be less than 20 cm?

Bounce number	Height (cm)
0	300
1	
2	
3	
4	
5	

3. Write each number in standard notation.

  a. 2.8×10^7 **b.** 4.3×10^{-3}

4. Write each number in scientific notation.

  a. 781,000,000   **b.** -0.0000533

5. Find the x-value that makes each equation true.

  a. $0.00624 = 6.24 \times 10^x$ **b.** $377 \times 10^{-3} = 3.77 \times 10^x$ **c.** $0.00074 = 7.4 \times 10^x$

6. Use the properties of exponents to answer each question.

  a. Explain why $\dfrac{6^{-3}}{6^{-3}} = 1$.   **b.** Write an equation equivalent to $y = 5^{-x}$.

7. Assume that the values of houses in a particular neighborhood increase by 8% each year. For each question, write an expression in the form $A(1 + r)^x$. Then evaluate the expression to answer the question.

  a. If a house is worth $200,000 today, how much was it worth four years ago?

  b. If a house was worth $175,000 three years ago, how much is it worth today?

  c. If a house is worth $300,000 today, how much will it be worth in ten years?

8. What are the advantages of using scientific notation to express very large and very small numbers?

Discovering Algebra Assessment Resources
©2007 Key Curriculum Press

Chapter 6 • Constructive Assessment Options

Choose one or more of these items to replace part of the chapter test. Let students know that they will receive from 0 to 5 points for each item depending on the correctness and completeness of their answer.

1. *(Lessons 6.1, 6.2)*
   Divide the tables, recursive routines, and equations into groups so the items in each group represent the same relationship. Show all your work and explain how you found your answers.

   a.

x	y
0	2
1	4
2	8
3	16
4	32

   b.

x	y
0	16
1	8
2	4
3	2
4	1

   c.

x	y
0	16
1	4
2	1
3	0.25
4	0.0625

   d.

x	y
0	2
1	1
2	0.5
3	0.25
4	0.125

   e. $\{0, 2\}$ [ENTER]
   $\{\text{Ans}(1) + 1, \text{Ans}(2) \cdot (1 + 0.5)\}$ [ENTER], [ENTER], . . .

   f. $\{0, 16\}$ [ENTER]
   $\{\text{Ans}(1) + 1, \text{Ans}(2) \cdot (1 - 0.75)\}$ [ENTER], [ENTER], . . .

   g. $\{0, 2\}$ [ENTER]
   $\{\text{Ans}(1) + 1, \text{Ans}(2) \cdot (1 - 0.5)\}$ [ENTER], [ENTER], . . .

   h. $\{0, 16\}$ [ENTER]
   $\{\text{Ans}(1) + 1, \text{Ans}(2) \cdot (1 - 0.25)\}$ [ENTER], [ENTER], . . .

   i. $y = 16(1 - 0.25)^x$ **j.** $y = 2(1 + 1)^x$

   k. $y = 2(1 + 0.5)^x$ **l.** $y = 2(1 - 0.5)^x$

2. *(Lesson 6.2)*
   Do the following for parts a and b:

   i. Describe a real-world exponential growth or decay situation that fits the conditions.

   ii. Write an equation for the situation, explaining what each variable in the equation represents.

   iii. Write a question about your situation that can be answered by using your equation, and give the answer.

   a. The starting value is 12, and the growth rate is 10%.

   b. The value after two time periods is 20, and the value after three time periods is 18.

(continued)

3. *(Lessons 6.2, 6.6)*

A bus company raises the prices of its tickets by 3.4% per year. In 2005, the price of a ticket from Dallas to New Orleans was $80.00.

   a. Write an equation that can be used to calculate the price of a ticket from Dallas to New Orleans for any year. Use *y* to represent the price of the ticket, and use *x* to represent the number of years after 2005.

   b. Write two questions about the ticket price that can be answered by using your equation. Answering one question should require substituting a positive value for *x*, and answering the other question should require substituting a negative value for *x*. Give the answers and show how you found them.

4. *(Lesson 6.3)*

As part of her homework assignment, Kristi had to use the properties of exponents to rewrite expressions. She made mistakes on these three problems. For each problem, describe what Kristi did wrong and give the correct answer.

   a. $\left(x^3 y^4\right)^2 = x^5 y^6$
      b. $\left(3x^2\right)\left(5x^7\right) = 8x^9$
      c. $\left(x^4\right)^3\left(x^7\right) = x^{14}$

5. *(Lesson 6.6)*

Kelly was absent when her class learned about zero and negative exponents. Write a note to Kelly explaining what she needs to know about zero and negative exponents. Include examples to help her understand why the meanings of zero and negative exponents make sense.

6. *(Lesson 6.7)*

The table shows the number of people in the world per automobile at five-year intervals starting in 1950.

   a. Write an exponential equation to model the data. Show all your work.

   b. In a scatter plot of the data, what does the point $(10, 31.0)$ represent?

   c. Based on the data, what conclusion can you draw about how the number of automobiles is changing relative to the world population? Explain how you arrived at your conclusion.

   d. What do you think the trend in the number of people per automobile will be for the next 50 years? Use the data to support your answer.

Years after 1950, x	People per automobile, y
0	48.2
5	38.1
10	31.0
15	23.9
20	19.1
25	15.7
30	13.9
35	12.9
40	11.9
45	11.7

(Brown, Flavin, and Renner, *Vital Signs 1997*, Worldwatch Institute, 1997, pp. 75 and 81)

(continued)

7. *(Lesson 6.7)*

Shown are the paper plates the groups in Mr. Stein's class will be using for the Radioactive Decay investigation. Each group will start the activity with 100 counters. For each plate, sketch a graph and write an equation to approximate the results the group can expect to get. (Let x represent the number of years, and let y represent the number of atoms remaining.) Sketch all the graphs on the same set of axes.

a.

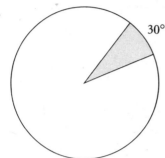

b.

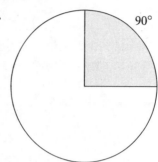

c.

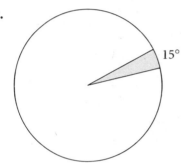

d.

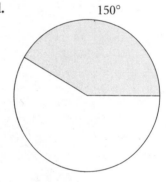

8. *(Lesson 6.8)*

A ball is dropped and allowed to bounce until it stops. The equation $y = 1.8(1 - 0.23)^x$ gives the height of the ball in meters after x bounces.

a. What does the number 1.8 in the equation represent in this situation?

b. What does the number 0.23 in the equation represent in this situation?

c. If some of the air is let out of the ball and it is dropped from a greater height, how will the numbers in the equation change? Explain your answer.

d. If air is added to the ball and it is dropped from a lesser height, how will the numbers in the equation change? Explain your answer.

Name _____ Period _____ Date _____

1. Sketch the following.

    a. A graph of a function

    b. A graph of a relation that is not a function

2. Tell whether each relation in the form (*input, output*) represents a function, and explain how you know.

    a. (*person, Social Security number*)   **b.** (*first name, last name*)

    c. (*city, Zip code*)   **d.** (*state, governor*)

3. Consider the equation $y = x^2 - 3$.

    a. Complete this table of values for the equation.

x	-3	-2	-1	0	1	2	3
y							

    b. Use the values in the table to sketch a graph of the equation.

    c. Decide whether the equation represents a function, and explain how you decided.

    d. For the domain $-3 \le x \le 3$, what is the range?

4. Explain how to use the vertical line test to determine whether a graph represents a function.

5. Does a vertical line represent a function? Explain.

6. For each set of ordered pairs, determine whether they represent a function and state the domain and range.

    a. $(-2, 3), (4, 1), (3, -1), (0, -1), (4, 0)$

    b. $(-3, 3), (-1, 2), (0, 3), (5, 0), (1, 8)$

Name _____   Period _____   Date _____

1. Sketch the following.

    a. A graph of a function

    b. A graph of a relation that is not a function

2. Tell whether each relation in the form (*input, output*) represents a function, and explain how you know.

    a. (*person, height*)   **b.** (*person, first name*)

    c. (*president, country*)   **d.** (*age, person*)

3. Consider the equation $y = x^2 + 2$.

    a. Complete this table of values for the equation.

x	-3	-2	-1	0	1	2	3
y							

    b. Use the values in the table to sketch a graph of the equation.

    c. Decide whether the equation represents a function, and explain how you decided.

    d. For the domain $-3 \leq x \leq 3$, what is the range?

4. Explain how to use the vertical line test to determine whether a graph represents a function.

5. Does a horizontal line represent a function? Explain.

6. For each set of ordered pairs, determine whether they represent a function and state the domain and range.

    a. $(-2, 3), (-3, 1), (3, 2), (0, -1), (4, 0)$

    b. $(-3, 3), (-1, 2), (0, 1), (5, 0), (-1, 4)$

                           Discovering Algebra Assessment Resources

Name _____ Period _____ Date _____

1. Write a story to fit this graph. Begin your story "Sara's dog, Chico, was resting on the front lawn." Identify the independent and dependent variables.

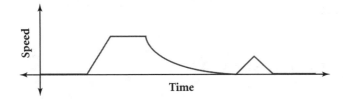

2. If $f(x) = -\frac{4}{3}x + 5$ and $g(x) = x^2 - 3x - 5$, find:

   a. $f(6)$ **b.** $f(-2)$ **c.** x, when $f(x) = -9$

   d. $g(1)$ **e.** $g(0)$ **f.** $g(-2)$

3. Use this graph of $y = f(x)$ to answer 3a–e.

   a. Find $f(-1)$.

   b. Find $f(5)$.

   c. For what x-values does $f(x) = 3$?

   d. For what x-values is $f(x) > 4$?

   e. What range corresponds to the domain shown in the graph?

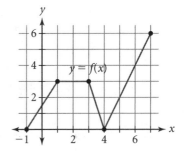

4. Sketch a graph of a function that fits each description.

   a. continuous and always increasing with a slower and slower rate of change

   b. linear, discrete, and decreasing

5. Identify the independent and dependent variables in each relationship, and justify your choices.

   a. The relationship between the number of minutes spent on a long-distance call and the cost of the call

   b. The relationship between the amount of flour used for a cookie recipe and the number of cookies made

Name _____ Period _____ Date _____

1. Write a story to fit this graph. Begin your story "Sara's dog, Chico, was resting on the front lawn." Identify the independent and dependent variables.

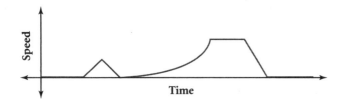

2. If $f(x) = -\frac{5}{3}x - 4$ and $g(x) = x^2 + 6x - 7$, find:

   a. $f(6)$ b. $f(-2)$ c. x, when $f(x) = -10$

   d. $g(2)$ e. $g(-3)$ f. $g(0)$

3. Use this graph of $y = f(x)$ to answer 3a–e.

   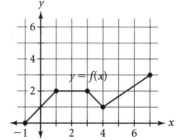

   a. Find $f(0)$.

   b. Find $f(4)$.

   c. For what x-values does $f(x) = 2$?

   d. For what x-values is $f(x) < 1$?

   e. What range corresponds to the domain shown in the graph?

4. Sketch a graph of a function that fits each description.

   a. continuous and always decreasing with a slower and slower rate of change

   b. linear, discrete, and increasing

5. Identify the independent and dependent variables in each relationship, and justify your choices.

   a. The relationship between the number of gallons of gas needed to fill a car's gas tank and the number of miles it has traveled since being filled

   b. The relationship between a child's height and his or her age

Discovering Algebra Assessment Resources
©2007 Key Curriculum Press

Name _____ **Period** _____ **Date** _____

1. Evaluate both sides of each statement to determine whether to replace the box with $=$, $<$, or $>$.

a. $|4| + |7| \,\square\, |4 + 7|$

b. $\left|\dfrac{18}{-6}\right| \,\square\, -\dfrac{18}{6}$

c. $|-5| \cdot |-6| \,\square\, |-30|$

d. $|2^{-3}| \,\square\, 2^{|-3|}$

2. Consider the function that fits this description: For x-values greater than or equal to 0, the function is the same as $y = x$. For x-values less than 0, the function is the same as $y = -x$.

a. Sketch the graph of the function.

b. What familiar function has the same graph you drew for 2a?

3. If possible, solve each equation or inequality.

a. $|x| = 9$

b. $|x| = 0$

c. $|x| = -2$

d. $|x - 4.5| = 0$

e. $|x| \geq 7$

f. $x^2 = 0.49$

g. $x^2 - 3 = 33$

h. $(x + 9)^2 = 144$

4. Sam says that $y = |x|$ and $y = x^2$ are not functions, because there are output values that correspond to two different input values. For example, for the relationship $y = |x|$ the output 5 corresponds to inputs -5 and 5, and for the relationship $y = x^2$ the output 9 corresponds to inputs -3 and 3. Is Sam correct? Explain why or why not.

5. a. Complete the table and sketch a graph of the function $f(x) = (x - 4)^2$ on the domain $-2 \leq x \leq 10$.

x	-2	-1	0	1	2	3	4	5	6	7	8	9	10
$f(x)$													

b. What is the range of $f(x)$ for the given domain?

Name _____ Period _____ Date _____

1. Evaluate both sides of each statement to determine whether to replace the box with $=$, $<$, or $>$.

  a. $|5| - |8|$ ☐ $|5 - 8|$ **b.** $-\left|\dfrac{18}{6}\right|$ ☐ $\dfrac{18}{6}$

  c. $|-5| \cdot |7|$ ☐ $|-35|$ **d.** $|2^{-4}|$ ☐ $|16^{-1}|$

2. Consider the function that fits this description: For x-values greater than or equal to 0, the function is the same as $y = x$. For x-values less than 0, the function is the same as $y = -x$.

  a. Sketch the graph of the function.

  b. What familiar function has the same graph you drew for 2a?

3. Solve each equation for x.

  a. $|x| = 4$ **b.** $|x| = 0$ **c.** $|x| = -8$ **d.** $|x + 6.2| = 0$

  e. $|x| \leq 5$ **f.** $x^2 = 1.21$ **g.** $(x - 7)^2 = 169$ **h.** $x^2 - 2 = 14$

4. Sam says that $y = -|x|$ and $y = -x^2$ are not functions because there are many output values that correspond to two different input values. For example, for the relationship $y = -|x|$ the output -5 corresponds to inputs -5 and 5, and for the relationship $y = -x^2$ the output -9 corresponds to inputs -3 and 3. Is Sam correct? Explain why or why not.

5. a. Complete the table and sketch a graph of the function $f(x) = (x + 2)^2$ on the domain $-7 \leq x \leq 3$.

x	-7	-6	-5	-4	-3	-2	-1	0	1	2	3
$f(x)$											

  b. What is the range of $f(x)$ for the given domain?

Name _____ Period _____ Date _____

Answer each question and show all work clearly on a separate piece of paper.

1. Find the value of each expression.

    a. $|5 + (-7)|$ **b.** $-\left|\dfrac{-10}{-5}\right|$ **c.** $|-14 - 3|$

    d. $\left|-5^{|-2|}\right|$ **e.** $\sqrt{(-6)^2}$

2. Explain how to find the absolute value of a number. Be sure to discuss positive numbers, negative numbers, and zero.

3. Tell whether each table represents a function, and explain how you know.

a.

Input, x	Output, y
0	13
1	11
2	9
3	7
4	5
5	3

b.

Domain, x	Range, y
-3	9
-2	4
-1	1
0	0
1	1
2	4
3	9

c.

Domain, x	Range, y
2	8
3	11
5	12
7	18
9	20
11	23
2	-8

4. How are the graphs of $y = x^2$ and $y = |x|$ similar? How are they different?

5. Susan made up the following coding rule: Take each letter of the alphabet and advance it five letters. Does this rule describe a function? If so, use function notation to represent the rule (use the numbers 1 through 26 to represent A through Z). If not, explain why not.

6. A relation has the domain $-3 \le x \le 5$ and the range $-2 \le y \le 4$, and the x-value -1 corresponds to the y-value -1.

    a. Draw the graph of a function that fits this description.

    b. Draw the graph of a relation that fits this description and is *not* a function.

(continued)

Name _____ **Period** _____ **Date** _____

7. The graph shows Darnell's energy level during the school day.

a. When was his energy level highest?

b. When was his energy level rising fastest?

c. When was his energy level lowest? Give a possible reason why his energy level might have been so low.

d. When was his energy level decreasing?

e. What is the dependent variable in this situation?

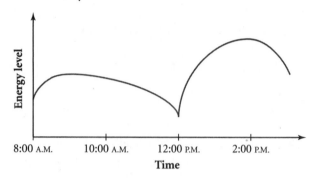

8. The equation $p(t) = 800(1 - 0.092)^t$ describes a bacteria population where t represents time in hours.

a. How many bacteria were in the population initially?

b. How does the bacteria population change from one hour to the next?

c. Which variable is the independent variable?

d. Graph the equation and give the window you use. Is the relationship a function? Why or why not?

e. Use your graph and the trace feature to find how long it takes for the bacteria population to decrease to half its original size.

9. Solve each equation or inequality for x.

a. $|2x + 1| = 15$

b. $3(x - 6)^2 + 11 = 8$

c. $|x - 4| > 3$

d. $(x - 3.6)^2 = 64$

Discovering Algebra Assessment Resources
©2007 Key Curriculum Press

Name _____ Period _____ Date _____

Answer each question and show all work clearly on a separate piece of paper.

1. Find the value of each expression.

  a. $|-5 + 8|$

  b. $-\left|\dfrac{12}{-2}\right|$

  c. $|-5 - 8|$

  d. $\left|-2^{|-3|}\right|$

  e. $\sqrt{(-8)^2}$

2. Explain how to find the absolute value of a number. Be sure to discuss positive numbers, negative numbers, and zero.

3. Tell whether each table represents a function, and explain how you know.

a.

Input, x	Output, y
0	−3
1	−1
2	1
3	5
4	7
5	9

b.

Domain, x	Range, y
−4	5
−4	1
−4	3
−4	−2
−4	0
−4	7
−4	8

c.

Domain, x	Range, y
−3	2
−2	2
−1	2
0	2
1	2
2	2
3	2

4. How are the graphs of $y = x^2$ and $y = |x|$ similar? How are they different?

5. Susan made up the following coding rule: Take each letter of the alphabet and move it back three letters. Does this rule describe a function? If so, use function notation to represent the rule (use the numbers 1 through 26 to represent A through Z). If not, explain why not.

6. A relation has the domain $-2 \le x \le 4$ and the range $-3 \le y \le 5$, and the x-value 0 corresponds to the y-value 2.

  a. Draw the graph of a function that fits this description.

  b. Draw the graph of a relation that fits this description and is *not* a function.

(continued)

Name _____   **Period** _____   **Date** _____

7. The graph shows Darnell's energy level during the school day.

   a. When was his energy level highest?

   b. When was his energy level rising fastest?

   c. When was his energy level lowest? Give a possible reason why his energy level might have been so low.

   d. When was his energy level decreasing?

   e. What is the dependent variable in this situation?

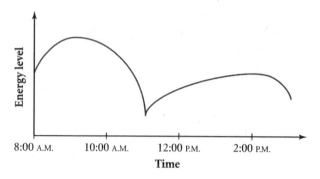

8. The equation $p(t) = 650(1 - 0.088)^t$ describes a bacteria population where t represents time in hours.

   a. How many bacteria were in the population initially?

   b. How does the bacteria population change from one hour to the next?

   c. Which variable is the independent variable?

   d. Graph the equation and give the window you use. Is the relationship a function? Why or why not?

   e. Use your graph and the trace feature to find how long it takes for the bacteria population to decrease to half its original size.

9. If possible, solve each equation or inequality.

   a. $|2x - 3| = 11$ b. $3(x + 5)^2 + 11 = 9$

   c. $|x + 7| > 3$ d. $(x + 1.8)^2 = 81$

Discovering Algebra Assessment Resources
©2007 Key Curriculum Press

Chapter 7 • Constructive Assessment Options

Choose one or more of these items to replace part of the chapter test. Let students know that they will receive from 0 to 5 points for each item, depending on the correctness and completeness of their answer.

1. *(Lesson 7.1)*
Create a code that is a function. Explain your code in words and by making a grid. Choose two words and code them.

2. *(Lessons 7.1, 7.2)*
Sketch a graph that fits each description, and give the domain and range of the relationship your graph represents.

a. a graph that passes through all four quadrants and represents a function

b. a graph that passes through all four quadrants and does not represent a function

c. a graph that passes through Quadrants I, II, and III only and represents a function

d. a graph that passes through Quadrants I, II, and III only and does not represent a function

3. *(Lesson 7.2)*
The inverse of a relationship is obtained by interchanging the x- and y-values. For example, the inverse of the relationship $(3, 2), (4, 0), (-5, -6)$ is $(2, 3), (0, 4), (-6, -5)$, and the inverse of the relationship $y = 2x + 1$ is $x = 2y + 1$.

a. Tell whether each relationship is a function. Then, give the inverse of the relationship and tell whether it is a function. Explain your answers.

   i. *(high school student, high school teacher)*   **ii.** *(perimeter, square)*

   iii. *(rectangle, area)*   **iv.** *(city, area code)*

b. Give an example of a function whose inverse is also a function. Explain how you know your example meets these conditions.

c. Give an example of a function whose inverse is not a function. Explain how you know your example meets these conditions.

4. *(Lesson 7.3)*
Label the axes with variable names and scale values, and write a story that could be modeled by this graph. Your story should account for each segment of the graph and should mention specific values, including rates.

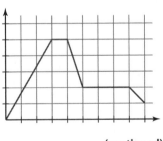

(continued)

5. *(Lessons 7.3)*

Explain the following terms, using complete sentences: *independent variable, dependent variable, domain, range, linear function, nonlinear function, increasing function, decreasing function.* You may use equations and graphs in your explanations. Assume that the person reading your explanation is taking algebra.

6. *(Lesson 7.3)*

Sketch a graph for each situation. Write a few sentences explaining your graph.

a. the number of students in your school's cafeteria from the start to the end of a typical school day

b. the number of students in the hallway of your school from the start to the end of a typical school day

c. the number of students in your school's gym from the start to the end of a typical school day

7. *(Lesson 7.4)*

The inverse of a function is obtained by interchanging the x- and y-values. For example, the inverse of $y = 4x - 8$ is $x = 4y - 8$ or, solving for y, $y = 0.25x + 2$. One way to determine whether two functions are inverses is to let one be $f(x)$ and let the other be $g(x)$ and then find $f(g(x))$ and $g(f(x))$. If both results are equal to x, the functions are inverses. For example, let $f(x) = 4x - 8$ and let $g(x) = 0.25x + 2$. To find $f(g(x))$, substitute $g(x)$ for x in the function $f(x)$:

$$f(g(x)) = 4(0.25x + 2) - 8 = x + 8 - 8 = x$$

To find $g(f(x))$, substitute $f(x)$ for x in the function $g(x)$:

$$g(f(x)) = 0.25(4x - 8) + 2 = x - 2 + 2 = x$$

Because $f(g(x)) = x$ and $g(f(x)) = x$, the functions are inverses.

Determine whether the given functions are inverses. Show all your work.

a. $y = 3x + 6$ and $y = \frac{1}{3}x + 2$ **b.** $y = 2x - 4$ and $y = \frac{1}{2}x + 2$

Discovering Algebra Assessment Resources
©2007 Key Curriculum Press

Chapters 4–7 • Exam

Form A

Name _____ Period _____ Date _____

Answer each question and show all work clearly on a separate piece of paper.

1. Write the equation of each line in intercept form ($y = a + bx$).
   a. the line with equation $y + 3 = \frac{3}{4}(x - 2)$
   b. the line through $(-4, 5)$ and $(2, 17)$

2. The Pampered Pet Hotel cares for dogs and cats while their owners are away. The daily fee for boarding a dog at the hotel is different from the fee for boarding a cat. On Tuesday 11 dogs and 14 cats stayed at the hotel, and the hotel took in \$573.25. On Friday 22 dogs and 9 cats stayed at the hotel, and the hotel took in \$790.25.
   a. Let d be the cost of boarding a dog, and let c be the cost of boarding a cat. Write a system of equations to represent this situation.
   b. Solve the system of equations you found in 2a. How much does it cost to board a cat at the hotel? How much does it cost to board a dog?

3. Solve each inequality.
   a. $2(4 - 3x) < 24$
   b. $6 - 5x \geq 4(x - 3)$

4. Use the properties of exponents to rewrite each expression.
   a. $\left(2a^2b^4\right)^5$
   b. $\dfrac{x^7y^3z^5}{x^4z}$
   c. $3^x \cdot 4^y \cdot 3^{-y}$

5. Write each expression using only positive exponents.
   a. $2^{-1}c^{-4}d^2$
   b. $\dfrac{x^{-7}}{y^{-3}}$
   c. $(3p)^{-3}$

6. The population of Jamesville increases by 5% each year; the current population is 20,000. The population of Thomasville decreases by 8% each year; the current population is 75,000.
   a. For each town, write an equation you could use to estimate the population x years from now.
   b. Use the equations from 6a to estimate the populations of the towns five years from now. Round your answers to the nearest hundred.
   c. Use the equations from 6a to estimate the populations of the towns ten years ago. Round your answers to the nearest hundred.
   d. Use a calculator graph or table to help you estimate when the populations of the two towns will be equal.

(continued)

Name _____   Period _____   Date _____

7. Write a system of inequalities for the solution shown on the graph.

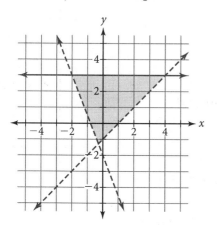

8. Tell whether each table or recursive routine represents a linear relationship, an exponential relationship, or neither, and explain how you know.

    a. $\{0, 64\}$ [ENTER], $\{\text{Ans}(1) + 1, \text{Ans}(2) - 32\}$ [ENTER], [ENTER], . . .

    b. $\{0, 11\}$ [ENTER], $\{\text{Ans}(1) + 1, \text{Ans}(2) \cdot 0.75\}$ [ENTER], [ENTER], . . .

    c.

x	0	1	2	3	4
y	2	6	18	54	162

    d.

x	0	1	2	3	4
y	12.75	17.5	22.25	27	31.75

9. Tell whether each relation is a function, and explain how you know. Assume that x is the input variable and y is the output variable.

    a. $y = x^2$ **b.** $|y| = x$

    c.

x	2	1	0	1	2
y	−4	−2	0	2	4

    d.

x	−2	−1	0	1	2
y	9	2	1	2	9

    e.

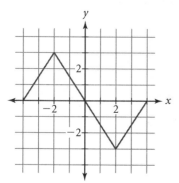

    f.

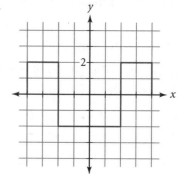

(continued)

Discovering Algebra Assessment Resources
©2007 Key Curriculum Press

Name _____ Period _____ Date _____

10. Consider this graph of the function $y = f(x)$.

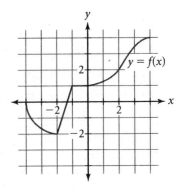

   a. Give the domain and range of the function.

   b. What is $f(2)$?

   c. For what x-values does $f(x) = 1$?

   d. Use terms such as *increasing, decreasing, linear, nonlinear,* and *rate of change* to describe the behavior of the function.

11. Solve each equation.

   a. $|2\dot{x} + 4| = 14$ **b.** $(x - 3)^2 = 121$ **c.** $12 - |x + 4.5| = 14$

12. The table shows the number of hits and the number of runs by players on the 2004 Seattle Mariners. Data are shown only for players who had 75 or more at bats.

2004 Seattle Mariners

Player	Hits	Runs	Player	Hits	Runs
I. Suzuki	262	101	D. Wilson	80	23
R. Ibanez	146	67	W. Bloomquist	46	27
R. Winn	179	84	R. Aurilia	63	27
B. Jacobsen	44	17	M. Olivo	70	46
J. Cabrera	97	38	J. Lopez	48	28
E. Martinez	128	45	J. Leone	22	15
B. Boone	149	74	S. Spiezio	79	38
D. Hansen	22	14	H. Bocachica	22	9

(*seattle.mariners.mlb.com*)

   a. Define variables and use Q-points to find an equation for a line of fit for the data.

   b. What is the real-world meaning of the slope of the line?

   c. How many runs does this model predict a player with 120 hits would have?

   d. If a player scored 75 runs, about how many hits does this model predict he had?

Chapters 4–7 • Exam

Form B

Name _____ Period _____ Date _____

Answer each question and show all work clearly on a separate piece of paper.

1. Write the equation of each line in intercept form $(y = a + bx)$.
   a. the line with equation $y - 5 = \frac{3}{4}(x + 2)$
   b. the line through $(-4, 5)$ and $(8, -1)$

2. The Pampered Pet Hotel cares for dogs and cats while their owners are away. The daily fee for boarding a dog at the hotel is different from the fee for boarding a cat. On Tuesday 14 dogs and 7 cats stayed at the hotel, and the hotel took in $586.25. On Friday 11 dogs and 21 cats stayed at the hotel, and the hotel took in $751.25.

   a. Let d be the cost of boarding a dog, and let c be the cost of boarding a cat. Write a system of equations to represent this situation.

   b. Solve the system of equations you found in 2a. How much does it cost to board a cat at the hotel? How much does it cost to board a dog?

3. Solve each inequality.
   a. $7(7 - 5x) > 28$
   b. $10 - 4x < 2(x - 7)$

4. Use the properties of exponents to rewrite each expression in simplest terms.

   a. $(2a^2b^3)^4$
   b. $\dfrac{x^3y^2z^7}{z^3z^3}$
   c. $7^x \cdot 4^y \cdot 7^{2x}$

5. Write each expression using only positive exponents.

   a. $2^{-2}cd^{-5}$
   b. $\dfrac{x^{-2}}{y^{-4}}$
   c. $(2p)^{-5}$

6. The population of Jamesville increases by 4% each year; the current population is 24,000. The population of Thomasville decreases by 7% each year; the current population is 72,000.

   a. For each town, write an equation you could use to estimate the population x years from now.

   b. Use the equations from 6a to estimate the populations of the towns five years from now. Round your answers to the nearest hundred.

   c. Use the equations from 6a to estimate the populations of the towns ten years ago. Round your answers to the nearest hundred.

   d. Use a calculator graph or table to help you estimate when the populations of the two towns will be equal.

(continued)

Discovering Algebra Assessment Resources
©2007 Key Curriculum Press

Name _____   **Period** _____   **Date** _____

7. Write a system of inequalities for the solution shown on the graph.

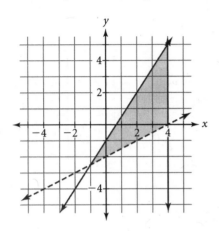

8. Tell whether each table or recursive routine represents a linear relationship, an exponential relationship, or neither; explain how you know.

a. $\{0, 64\}$ [ENTER], $\{Ans(1) + 1, Ans(2) \cdot 32\}$ [ENTER], [ENTER], . . .

b. $\{0, 11\}$ [ENTER], $\{Ans(1) + 1, Ans(2) + 0.75\}$ [ENTER], [ENTER], . . .

c.

x	0	1	2	3	4
y	2	5	8	11	14

d.

x	0	1	2	3	4
y	729	243	81	27	9

9. Tell whether each relation is a function, and explain how you know. Assume that x is the input variable and y is the output variable.

a. $y^2 = x$

b. $y = |x|$

c.

x	−8	−4	0	4	8
y	2	1	0	1	2

d.

x	8	4	0	4	8
y	4	2	0	−2	−4

e.

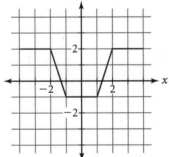

f.

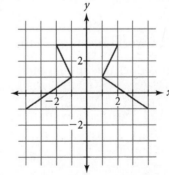

(continued)

Name _____ Period _____ Date _____

10. Consider this graph of the function $y = f(x)$.

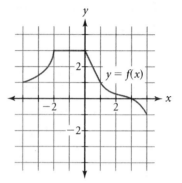

  a. Give the domain and range of the function.

  b. What is $f(-2)$?

  c. For what x-values is $f(x) < 1$?

  d. Use terms such as *increasing, decreasing, linear, nonlinear,* and *rate of change* to describe the behavior of the function.

11. Solve each equation.

  a. $|2x - 6| = 18$ **b.** $12 - |x - 3.5| = 19$ **c.** $(x + 4)^2 = 225$

12. The table shows the number of hits and the number of runs by players on the 2004 World Champion Boston Red Sox. Data are shown only for players who had 100 or more at bats.

2004 Boston Red Sox

Player	Hits	Runs	Player	Hits	Runs
N. Garciaparra	50	24	B. Mueller	113	75
T. Nixon	47	24	D. Mirabelli	45	27
M. Ramirez	175	108	G. Kapler	79	51
J. Damon	189	123	M. Bellhorn	138	93
D. Ortiz	175	94	K. Youkilis	54	38
K. Millar	151	74	D. McCarty	39	24
J. Varitek	137	67	D. Mientkiewicz	93	47
O. Cabrera	67	33	P. Reese	54	32

(*boston.redsox.mlb.com*)

  a. Define variables and use Q-points to find an equation for a line of fit for the data.

  b. What is the real-world meaning of the slope of the line?

  c. How many runs does this model predict a player with 120 hits would have?

  d. If a player scored 85 runs, how many hits would this model predict he had?

Discovering Algebra Assessment Resources
©2007 Key Curriculum Press

Name _____ Period _____ Date _____

1. Use the figure to answer 1a–c.

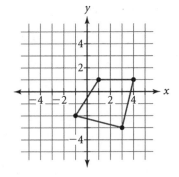

   a. Name the coordinates of the vertices of the quadrilateral.

   b. Sketch the image that would result from the translation $(x, y + 3)$. Label the image "Image a."

   c. Sketch the image that would result from the translation $(x - 4, y - 1)$. Label the image "Image b."

2. In 2a and 2b the dashed triangle is the image of the solid triangle after a transformation. Describe each transformation, then define the coordinates of any point in the image using (x, y) as the coordinates of any point in the original.

a.

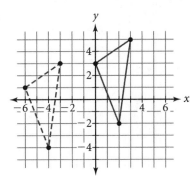

b.

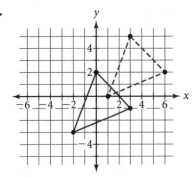

3. Describe each graph as a transformation of $y = |x|$ or $y = x^2$. Then write its equation.

a.

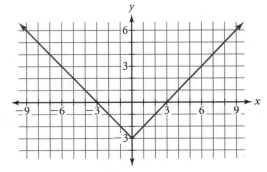

b.

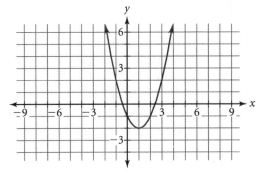

c.

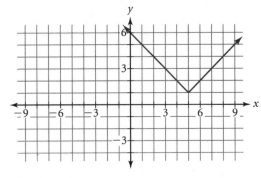

1. Use the figure to answer 1a–c.

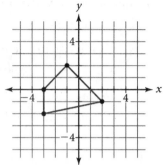

   a. Name the coordinates of the vertices of the quadrilateral.

   b. Sketch the image that would result from the translation $(x + 3, y)$. Label the image "Image a."

   c. Sketch the image that would result from the translation $(x - 2, y + 3)$. Label the image "Image b."

2. In 2a and 2b the dashed triangle is the image of the solid triangle after a transformation. Describe each transformation, then define the coordinates of any point in the image using (x, y) as the coordinates of any point in the original.

   a.

   b.

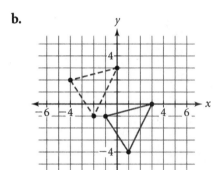

3. Describe each graph as a transformation of $y = |x|$ or $y = x^2$. Then write its equation.

   a.

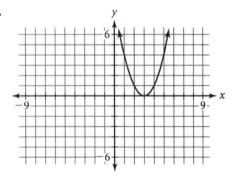

   b.

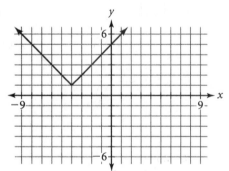

   c.

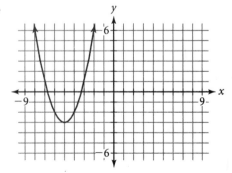

Discovering Algebra Assessment Resources
©2007 Key Curriculum Press

Name _____ Period _____ Date _____

1. The vertices of the quadrilateral shown here are $(1, 1)$, $(4, 1)$, $(3, -3)$, and $(-1, -2)$.

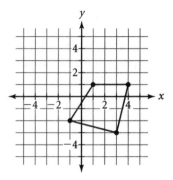

   a. Sketch the image of the quadrilateral after a vertical stretch by a factor of 1.5 followed by a reflection across the y-axis.

   b. Define the coordinates of any point in the image using (x, y) as the coordinates of any point in the original quadrilateral.

2. Describe each graph as a transformation of $y = x^2$. Then write its equation.

   a.
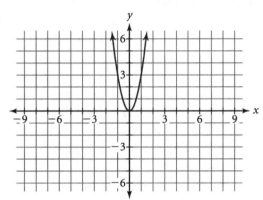

   b.
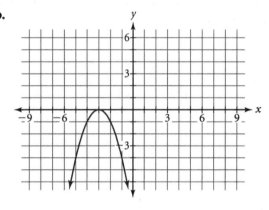

   c.
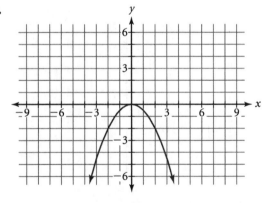

   d.
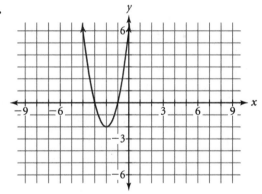

3. Use words such as *translation, reflection, stretch, shrink,* and *factor* to describe how the graph of each function is related to the graph of $y = |x|$.

   a. $y + 0.5 = |x + 2|$ b. $y = -2 \cdot |x - 1|$

4. Use words such as *translation, reflection, stretch, shrink,* and *factor* to describe how the graph of each function is related to the graph of $y = f(x)$.

   a. $y = 3 \cdot f(-x)$ b. $y = -f(-x)$

Name _____ **Period** _____ **Date** _____

1. The vertices of the quadrilateral shown here are $(2, -1)$, $(-3, -2)$, $(-3, 0)$, and $(-1, 2)$.

   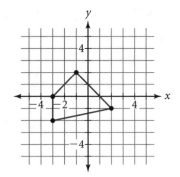

   a. Sketch the image of the quadrilateral after a vertical stretch by a factor of 2.5 followed by a reflection across the y-axis.

   b. Define the coordinates of any point in the image using (x, y) as the coordinates of any point in the original quadrilateral.

2. Describe each graph as a transformation of $y = x^2$. Then write its equation.

   a.
   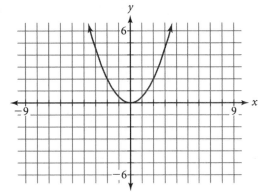

   b.
   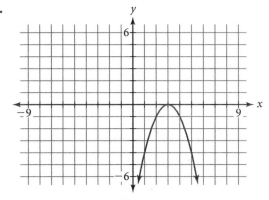

   c.
   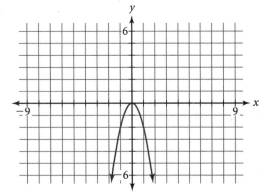

   d.
   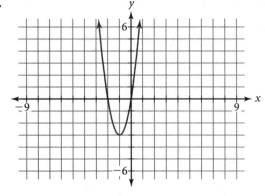

3. Use words such as *translation, reflection, stretch, shrink,* and *factor* to describe how the graph of each function is related to the graph of $y = |x|$.

   a. $y = |x - 5| - 2$ b. $y = 2 \cdot |x + 3|$

4. Use words such as *translation, reflection, stretch, shrink,* and *factor* to describe how the graph of each function is related to the graph of $y = f(x)$.

   a. $y = -f(x + 4)$ b. $y = 4f(-x) + 2$

Discovering Algebra Assessment Resources
©2007 Key Curriculum Press

Name _____ Period _____ Date _____

1. Describe each graph as a transformation of $y = \frac{1}{x}$. Then write
its equation.

a.

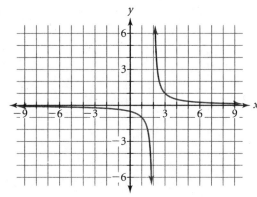

b.

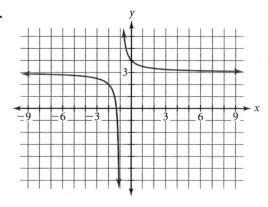

2. If the graph of $y = \frac{a}{x}$ is in Quadrants I and III, in which quadrants is the
graph of $y = -\frac{a}{x}$?

3. Consider the function $y + 5 = \frac{2}{x + 3}$.

   a. Describe it as a transformation of the parent function $y = \frac{1}{x}$.

   b. Sketch its graph.

   c. List values that are not part of its domain.

4. The matrix $[A] = \begin{bmatrix} 0 & 3 & 3 & 0 \\ 0 & 0 & 1 & 1 \end{bmatrix}$ represents the vertices of a
geometric figure.

   a. Sketch the figure. What type of figure is it?

   b. Describe the transformation represented by the product $\begin{bmatrix} 1 & 0 \\ 0 & 2 \end{bmatrix} \cdot [A]$.

   Give the coordinates of the vertices of the image in matrix form.

   c. Describe the transformation represented by the product
   $\begin{bmatrix} -1 & 0 \\ 0 & -1 \end{bmatrix} \cdot [A]$. Give the coordinates of the vertices of the
   image in matrix form.

5. Perform each operation. Express each answer in reduced form. State any
restrictions on the variable.

   a. $\frac{11x}{3} - \frac{7x}{6}$

   b. $\frac{2(x - 4)}{(x + 1)^2} \cdot \frac{x + 1}{4}$

   c. $12x \div \frac{4x^3}{3}$

Name _____ Period _____ Date _____

1. Describe each graph as a transformation of $y = \frac{1}{x}$. Then write its equation.

a.

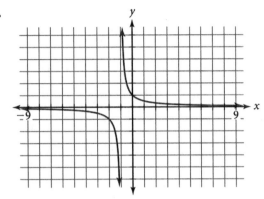

b.

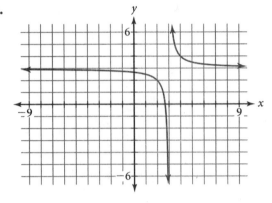

2. If the graph of $y = -\frac{a}{x}$ is in Quadrants II and IV, in which quadrants is the graph of $y = \frac{a}{x}$?

3. Consider the function $y - 4 = \frac{2}{x+1}$.

   a. Describe it as a transformation of the parent function $y = \frac{1}{x}$.

   b. Sketch its graph.

   c. List values that are not part of its domain.

4. The matrix $[A] = \begin{bmatrix} -1 & 0 & 3 & 2 \\ 0 & 2 & 2 & 0 \end{bmatrix}$ represents the vertices of a geometric figure.

   a. Sketch the figure. What type of figure is it?

   b. Describe the transformation represented by the product $\begin{bmatrix} 1 & 0 \\ 0 & 0.5 \end{bmatrix} \cdot [A]$. Give the coordinates of the vertices of the image in matrix form.

   c. Describe the transformation represented by the product $\begin{bmatrix} -1 & 0 \\ 0 & -1 \end{bmatrix} \cdot [A]$. Give the coordinates of the vertices of the image in matrix form.

5. Perform each operation. Express each answer in reduced form. State any restrictions on the variable.

   a. $\frac{13x}{3} - \frac{5x}{6}$

   b. $\frac{3(x+3)}{(x-4)^2} \cdot \frac{x-4}{6}$

   c. $20x \div \frac{5x^3}{4}$

Discovering Algebra Assessment Resources
©2007 Key Curriculum Press

Name _____ Period _____ Date _____

Answer each question and show all work clearly on a separate piece of paper.

1. Write an equation for each graph.

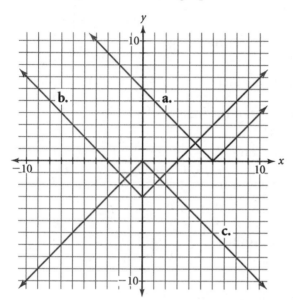 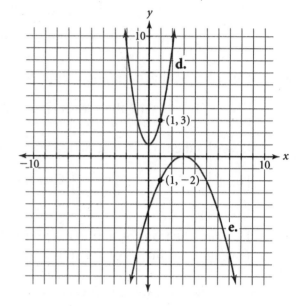

2. Describe each function as a transformation of the parent function $y = \frac{1}{x}$.

   a. $y - 4 = \dfrac{1}{x - 1}$ **b.** $y = \dfrac{3}{x + 2}$

3. Describe how the graph of $y = x^2 + 1$ will be transformed if you substitute as directed.

   a. $(y - 3)$ for y **b.** $(x - 3)$ for x

   c. $-x$ for x **d.** $\dfrac{y}{2}$ for y

4. Write an equation for a function whose graph fits each description.

   a. A rational function with asymptotes at $x = 3$ and $y = -2$.

   b. An absolute-value function with a vertex at $(2, 5)$ and a vertical stretch of 3.

(continued)

Name _____ **Period** _____ **Date** _____

5. Consider the square at right.

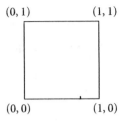

(0, 1)   (1, 1)

(0, 0)   (1, 0)

   a. Write a matrix $[B]$ to represent the square.

   b. Describe the transformation represented by the product
   $\begin{bmatrix} 0.5 & 0 \\ 0 & 0.5 \end{bmatrix} \cdot [B]$. Give the coordinates of the vertices of the image.

   c. Describe the transformation represented by the product
   $\begin{bmatrix} 2 & 0 \\ 0 & -2 \end{bmatrix} \cdot [B]$. Give the coordinates of the vertices of the image.

   d. Describe the transformation represented by the sum
   $[B] + \begin{bmatrix} -3 & -3 & -3 & -3 \\ 2 & 2 & 2 & 2 \end{bmatrix}$. Give the coordinates of the vertices of
   the image.

   e. Describe the transformation represented by the product $\begin{bmatrix} 1 & 0 \\ 0 & 1 \end{bmatrix} \cdot [B]$.
   Give the coordinates of the vertices of the image.

6. Perform each operation. Express each answer in reduced form. State any
restrictions on the variable.

   a. $\dfrac{8x^2}{15} + \dfrac{3x^2}{10}$

   b. $\dfrac{2x - 5}{3x} - \dfrac{x + 1}{2x}$

   c. $\dfrac{4x^2y}{6x^5} \cdot \dfrac{-3xy}{2}$

   d. $\dfrac{x + 3}{x - 4} \div \dfrac{x - 1}{2x - 8}$

7. When his niece was born, Mr. Hernandez opened an account to help
pay for her college education. The account earns 4% interest each year.
Mr. Hernandez has not deposited or withdrawn any money since
he opened the account. Today, five years after the account was opened,
the balance is $1,520.82.

   a. Write an equation you could use to calculate the balance in the
   account x years from now.

   b. How could you translate the graph of the equation from 7a so that it
   represents the balance in the account x years after it was opened?

   c. Use your answer from 7b to write an equation for the amount of
   money in the account x years after it was opened.

   d. What was Mr. Hernandez's initial deposit?

Discovering Algebra Assessment Resources
©2007 Key Curriculum Press

Name _____   Period _____   Date _____

Answer each question and show all work clearly on a separate piece of paper.

1. Write an equation for each graph.

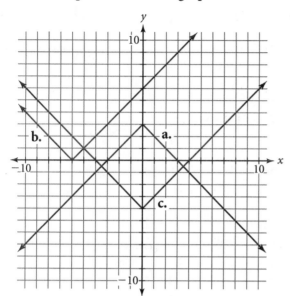
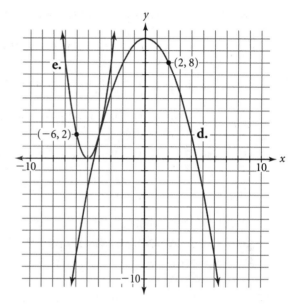

2. Describe each function as a transformation of the parent function $y = \frac{1}{x}$.

   a. $y + 5 = \dfrac{1}{x + 2}$ b. $y = \dfrac{0.5}{x - 3}$

3. Describe how the graph of $y = x^2 + 1$ will be transformed if you substitute as directed.

   a. $(y + 4)$ for y b. $(x + 3)$ for x

   c. $-x$ for x d. $0.5y$ for y

4. Write an equation for a function whose graph fits each description.

   a. A rational function with asymptotes at $x = -2$ and $y = 3$.

   b. An absolute-value function with a vertex at $(-1, -3)$ and a vertical shrink of 0.5.

(continued)

Name _____ **Period** _____ **Date** _____

5. Consider the square at right.

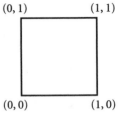

(0, 1)   (1, 1)

(0, 0)   (1, 0)

   a. Write a matrix $[B]$ to represent the square.

   b. Describe the transformation represented by the product $\begin{bmatrix} 3 & 0 \\ 0 & 3 \end{bmatrix} \cdot [B]$.
Give the coordinates of the vertices of the image.

   c. Describe the transformation represented by the product
$\begin{bmatrix} -3 & 0 \\ 0 & 3 \end{bmatrix} \cdot [B]$. Give the coordinates of the vertices of the image.

   d. Describe the transformation represented by the sum
$[B] + \begin{bmatrix} 2 & 2 & 2 & 2 \\ -1 & -1 & -1 & -1 \end{bmatrix}$. Give the coordinates of the vertices of
the image.

   e. Describe the transformation represented by the product $\begin{bmatrix} 0 & 1 \\ 1 & 0 \end{bmatrix} \cdot [B]$.
Give the coordinates of the vertices of the image.

6. Perform each operation. Express each answer in reduced form. State any
restrictions on the variable.

   a. $\dfrac{13x^2}{15} + \dfrac{3x^2}{10}$

   b. $\dfrac{3x + 1}{3x} - \dfrac{x + 3}{2x}$

   c. $\dfrac{-6x^3y^2}{5x^6y} \cdot \dfrac{10xy}{3}$

   d. $\dfrac{x - 3}{x + 4} \div \dfrac{x + 1}{2x + 8}$

7. When his niece was born, Mr. Hernandez opened an account to help
pay for her college education. The account earns 5% interest each year.
Mr. Hernandez has not deposited or withdrawn any money since he
opened the account. Today, seven years after the account was opened, the
balance is $1,336.75.

   a. Write an equation you could use to calculate the balance in the
account x years from now.

   b. How could you translate the graph of the equation from 7a so that it
represents the balance in the account x years after it was opened?

   c. Use your answer from 7b to write an equation for the amount of
money in the account x years after it was opened.

   d. What was Mr. Hernandez's initial deposit?

Discovering Algebra Assessment Resources
©2007 Key Curriculum Press

Chapter 8 • Constructive Assessment Options

Choose one or more of these items to replace part of the chapter test.
Let students know that they will receive from 0 to 5 points for each item,
depending on the correctness and completeness of their answer.

1. *(Lessons 8.1–8.4)*

Graph your initials on a coordinate grid, then, apply at least two
transformations (one after the other) to your initials and graph the final
image. At least one of your transformations should *not* be a translation.
Describe the transformations in words.

2. *(Lessons 8.1–8.4)*

Parts a and b show the graph of a function $f(x)$ and the image of the
graph after a series of transformations. Write an equation in the form
$y = k + a \cdot f(x - h)$ for each image, and explain how you arrived at
your equation.

a.

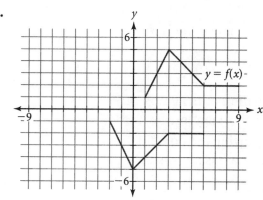

b.

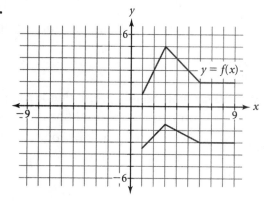

3. *(Lessons 8.2–8.4)*

The graph of $y = k + a \cdot f(x + h)$ is a transformation of the graph of
$y = f(x)$. Describe completely how the values of h, k, and a affect the
graph of $y = f(x)$. You may use equations and graphs in your explanation.

4. *(Lesson 8.6)*

As you work this problem, make sure your graphs are in a
"friendly window."

a. Each pair of functions includes a linear function and a rational
function. Graph the functions in each pair, one at a time. Look closely
at each graph. Explain how the graphs in each pair are similar and
how they are different.

    i. $f(x) = x + 3$ and $g(x) = \dfrac{x^2 + x - 6}{x - 2}$

    ii. $f(x) = x + 1$ and $g(x) = \dfrac{x^2 + 3x + 2}{x + 2}$

    iii. $f(x) = x - 2$ and $g(x) = \dfrac{x^2 - x - 2}{x + 1}$

b. Write the equation of a rational function that has a graph similar to
the graph of $f(x) = x - 4$.

(continued)

5. *(Lesson 8.6)*

Here is the graph of the function $y = \frac{1}{x^2}$.

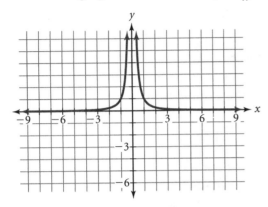

a. Describe the graph by giving the domain, range, and asymptotes, and by telling when the graph is increasing and when it is decreasing.

b. Use what you know about transformations to sketch the graph of each equation.

    i. $y = -3 + \dfrac{1}{(x-2)^2}$ **ii.** $y = \dfrac{-1}{(x+3)^2}$

c. Give the equation of a graph that is a transformation of the graph of $y = \frac{1}{x^2}$. (Your equation should be different from the equations in part b.) Describe the graph of your equation by giving the domain, range, and asymptotes, and by telling when the graph is increasing and when it is decreasing.

6. *(Lesson 8.7)*

On each grid, Triangle 1 is the original figure, and Triangle 2 is its image.

i.

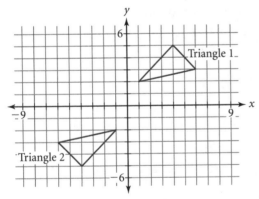

ii.

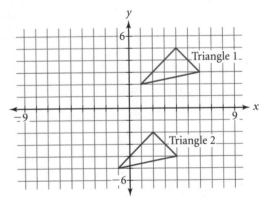

a. Write a matrix to represent Triangle 1.

b. For each grid, write a matrix equation that represents the transformation of Triangle 1 to Triangle 2.

Discovering Algebra Assessment Resources
©2007 Key Curriculum Press

Name _____ **Period** _____ **Date** _____

1. Solve the equation $(x - 1)^2 - 3 = 13$ symbolically.

2. Use a graph and table to approximate solutions to the equation $-x^2 + 2x + 6 = 2$ to the nearest hundredth.

3. This parabola has the equation $y = -0.25x^2 + 0.5x + 2$. Find the coordinates of its vertex. Explain how you found your answer.

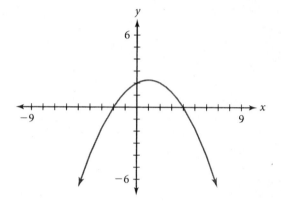

4. A ball is dropped from the top of a tall building. The ball's height, in meters, t seconds after it is dropped is $h(t) = -4.9t^2 + 30$.

a. Find $h(1)$ and give a real-world meaning for this value.

b. Use a graph to find out when the ball is 10 meters above the ground. Give your answer to the nearest hundredth of a second.

c. How tall is the building? How do you know?

d. When does the ball hit the ground? Give your answer to the nearest hundredth of a second.

5. Give an example of each number described in 5a–c.

a. an integer that is not a whole number

b. a rational number that is also an integer

c. a real number that is not rational

d. What is the name for the type of number in 5c?

Name _____ **Period** _____ **Date** _____

1. Solve the equation $(x - 2)^2 - 1 = 13$ symbolically. Leave your answer in radical form.

2. Use a graph and table to approximate solutions to the equation $x^2 + 3x - 1 = 4$ to the nearest hundredth.

3. This parabola has the equation $y = 0.2x^2 + 0.6x - 2$. Find the coordinates of its vertex. Explain how you found your answer.

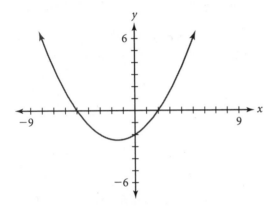

4. A ball is dropped from the top of a tall building. The ball's height, in meters, t seconds after it is dropped is $h(t) = -4.9t^2 + 20$.

   a. Find $h(1.5)$ and give a real-world meaning for this value.

   b. Use a graph to find out when the ball is 8 meters above the ground. Give your answer to the nearest hundredth of a second.

   c. How tall is the building? How do you know?

   d. When does the ball hit the ground? Give your answer to the nearest hundredth of a second.

5. Give an example of each number described in 5a–c.

   a. an integer that is also a whole number

   b. a rational number that is not an integer

   c. an irrational number

   d. What is the name for the type of number that includes all possible answers to 5a, b, and c?

Discovering Algebra Assessment Resources
©2007 Key Curriculum Press

Name _____   Period _____   Date _____

1. Expand each expression and combine like terms.

   a. $(x - 3)^2$ **b.** $(x + 1)(x + 3)$ **c.** $(2x - 1)(x + 4)$

2. Rewrite each equation in general form.

   a. $y = (x - 3)^2 + 5$ **b.** $y = 2(x - 1)^2 - 2.5$

3. Consider the quadratic equation $y = x^2 + 2x + 3$.

   a. Graph the equation.

   b. Name the coordinates of the vertex.

   c. Write the equation in vertex form.

   d. Verify that the equation you wrote in 3c is correct by expanding it to general form.

4. Solve the equation $x(x - 4)(x - 5) = 0$ without graphing it.

5. Tell whether each statement is true or false. If the statement is false, change the right side to make it true.

   a. $x^2 + 8x + 15 = (x + 3)(x + 5)$

   b. $x^2 - 16 = (x - 4)(x - 4)$

   c. $3x^2 - 27 = 3(x + 3)(x - 3)$

   d. $x^2 + x - 6 = (x + 3)(x + 2)$

6. Explain how you could prove to a friend that the equation $y = x^2 + 4$ has no real roots.

7. Rewrite the equation $y = x^2 - 3x - 28$ in factored form.

8. Reduce each rational expression. State any restrictions on the variable.

   a. $\dfrac{(x + 3)(x + 1)}{(x + 1)(x - 4)}$ **b.** $\dfrac{x^2 + 6x + 8}{x^2 - 16}$

Name _____ Period _____ Date _____

1. Expand each expression and combine like terms.

    a. $(x - 5)^2$ **b.** $(x + 2)(x + 3)$ **c.** $(x - 1)(3x + 4)$

2. Rewrite each equation in general form.

    a. $y = (x + 2)^2 + 7$ **b.** $y = 3(x - 2)^2 - 1.5$

3. Consider the quadratic equation $y = x^2 + 6x + 5$.

    a. Graph the equation.

    b. Name the coordinates of the vertex.

    c. Write the equation in vertex form.

    d. Verify that the equation you wrote in 3c is correct by expanding it to general form.

4. Solve the equation $x(x + 2)(x - 8) = 0$ without graphing it.

5. Tell whether each statement is true or false. If the statement is false, change the right side to make it true.

    a. $x^2 + 9x + 14 = (x + 2)(x + 7)$

    b. $x^2 - 25 = (x - 5)(x - 5)$

    c. $4x^2 - 16 = 4(x + 2)(x - 2)$

    d. $x^2 - x - 6 = (x - 3)(x - 2)$

6. Explain how you could prove to a friend that the equation $y = x^2 + 2x + 4$ has no real roots.

7. Rewrite the equation $y = x^2 + 2x - 15$ in factored form.

8. Reduce each rational expression. State any restrictions on the variable.

    a. $\dfrac{(x + 3)(x - 1)}{(x - 2)(x + 3)}$ **b.** $\dfrac{x^2 + 6x + 8}{x^2 - 4}$

Discovering Algebra Assessment Resources
©2007 Key Curriculum Press

Name _____ Period _____ Date _____

1. Solve the quadratic equation $3(x + 2)^2 - 9 = 0$. Give your answer in radical form.

2. Solve the quadratic equation $x^2 + 4x - 1 = 4$ by completing the square.

3. Solve the quadratic equation $3x^2 + x - 6 = 0$ by using the quadratic formula. Give your answer in radical form.

4. The volume of this cube is 6319 cm³. Write and solve an equation to find x. Give your answer to the nearest hundredth.

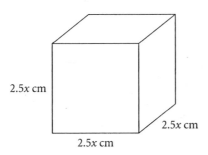

2.5x cm

2.5x cm

2.5x cm

5. How does the graph of $y = 0.5(x - 2)^3 + 4$ compare to the graph of the parent function $y = x^3$?

6. Write the expression $x^3 + x^2 - 6x$ in factored form.

7. The width of a rectangle is 8 cm less than the length. The area of the rectangle is 240 cm².

   a. Write an equation for the area of the rectangle in terms of the length, l.

   b. Solve the equation in 7a.

   c. Give the dimensions of the rectangle.

Name _____ **Period** _____ **Date** _____

1. Solve the quadratic equation $2(x + 3)^2 - 10 = 0$. Give your answer in radical form.

2. Solve the quadratic equation $x^2 - 2x - 3 = 12$ by completing the square.

3. Solve the quadratic equation $5x^2 + x - 3 = 0$ by using the quadratic formula. Give your answer in radical form.

4. The volume of this cube is 5284 cm³. Write and solve an equation to find x. Give your answer to the nearest hundredth.

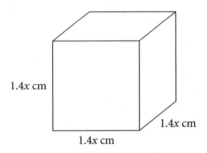

1.4x cm

1.4x cm

1.4x cm

5. How does the graph of $y = 2(x + 5)^3 - 3$ compare to the graph of the parent function $y = x^3$?

6. Write the expression $x^3 + 4x^2 - 5x$ in factored form.

7. The width of a rectangle is 11 cm less than the length. The area of the rectangle is 180 cm².

   a. Write an equation for the area of the rectangle in terms of the length, l.

   b. Solve the equation in 7a.

   c. Give the dimensions of the rectangle.

Discovering Algebra Assessment Resources
©2007 Key Curriculum Press

Name _____ Period _____ Date _____

Answer each question and show all work clearly on a separate piece of paper.

1. A tennis ball is dropped from the top of a tall building. The ball's height, in meters, t seconds after it is released is $h(t) = -4.9t^2 + 200$.

   a. Find $h(3)$ and give a real-world meaning for this value.

   b. When is the ball 30 meters above the ground? Give your answer to the nearest hundredth of a second.

   c. When does the ball hit the ground? Give your answer to the nearest hundredth of a second.

2. Tell whether each statement is true or false. If the statement is false, change the right side to make it true. Give the corrected right side in the same form as the original. For example, if the right side is given in factored form, write the corrected version in factored form.

   a. $x^2 + 5x - 24 = (x + 3)(x - 8)$ **b.** $2(x - 1)^2 + 3 = 2x^2 - 4x + 5$

   c. $(x + 3)^2 = x^2 + 9$ **d.** $(x + 2)(x - 5) = x^2 - 10$

3. Consider the equation $y = (x - 6)(x + 2)$.

   a. Find the x-intercepts and the vertex of the graph of the equation.

   b. Write the equation in vertex form.

   c. Write the equation in general form.

4. Write the equation for this parabola in vertex form.

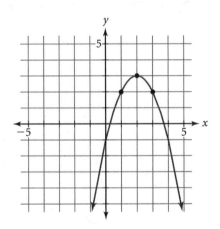

5. Solve each equation by using the quadratic formula.

   a. $2x^2 - 7x + 5 = 0$ **b.** $x^2 - 3x + 4 = 0$

6. Solve the equation $2x^3 - 8x = 0$ by factoring.

(continued)

Name _____ Period _____ Date _____

7. Solve the equation $x^2 - 4x - 1 = 0$ by completing the square. Leave your answer in radical form.

8. Is it possible for two different quadratic functions to have the same roots? Explain.

9. Write an equation in factored form that matches the graph shown below.

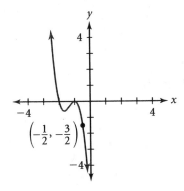

10. Multiply the terms and express the answer in reduced form. State any restrictions on the variable.

$$\frac{3}{x - 2} \cdot \frac{x^2 - 4}{3x + 3}$$

Discovering Algebra Assessment Resources
©2007 Key Curriculum Press

Chapter 9 • Test

Form B

Name _____ Period _____ Date _____

Answer each question and show all work clearly on a separate piece of paper.

1. A tennis ball is dropped from the top of a tall building. The ball's height, in meters, t seconds after it is released is $h(t) = -4.9t^2 + 175$.

   a. Find $h(4)$ and give a real-world meaning for this value.

   b. When is the ball 55 meters above the ground? Give your answer to the nearest hundredth of a second.

   c. When does the ball hit the ground? Give your answer to the nearest hundredth of a second.

2. Tell whether each statement is true or false. If the statement is false, change the right side to make it true. Give the corrected right side in the same form as the original. For example, if the right side is given in factored form, write the corrected version in factored form.

   a. $x^2 + 4x - 45 = (x - 5)(x + 9)$
   b. $3(x - 2)^2 + 5 = 3x^2 - 12x - 27$

   c. $(x - 3)^2 = x^2 - 9$
   d. $(x + 5)(x - 2) = x^2 + 3x - 10$

3. Consider the equation $y = (x + 3)(x - 7)$.

   a. Find the x-intercepts and the vertex of the graph of the equation.

   b. Write the equation in vertex form.

   c. Write the equation in general form.

4. Write the equation for this parabola in vertex form.

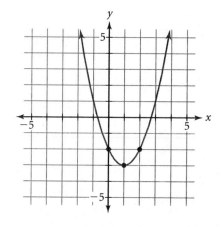

5. Solve each equation by using the quadratic formula.

   a. $3x^2 - 7x + 4 = 0$
   b. $x^2 - 4x + 5 = 0$

6. Solve the equation $3x^3 - 27x = 0$ by factoring.

(continued)

Name _____   **Period** _____   **Date** _____

7. Solve the equation $x^2 - 4x - 3 = 0$ by completing the square. Leave your answer in radical form.

8. Is it possible for two different quadratic functions to have the same roots? Explain.

9. Write an equation in factored form that matches the graph shown below.

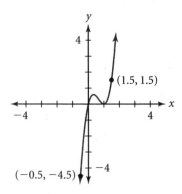

10. Multiply the terms and express the answer in reduced form. State any restrictions on the variable.

$$\frac{4}{x-3} \cdot \frac{x^2 - 2x - 3}{4x + 8}$$

Chapter 9 • Constructive Assessment Options

Choose one or more of these items to replace part of the chapter test. Let students know that they will receive from 0 to 5 points for each item, depending on the correctness and completeness of their answer.

1. *(Lessons 9.1–9.4)*
   Write a quadratic equation for each set of conditions. You may write the equations in any form you wish.

   a. The graph of the equation is in Quadrants III and IV only, and has its vertex on the *y*-axis.

   b. The equation has only one real root, and its graph crosses the *y*-axis at $(0, 4)$.

   c. The graph of the equation opens downward, is in all four quadrants, and has its vertex in Quadrant II.

2. *(Lessons 9.1–9.4)*
   You have worked with three different forms of quadratic equations: factored form, vertex form, and general form. Describe the three forms and explain what each tells you about the graph of the equation. You may use examples and graphs in your explanation.

3. *(Lesson 9.2)*
   To raise money for their trips, members of the ski club sell hot dogs at after-school sporting events. Currently they charge $2.00 per hot dog and sell about 40 hot dogs per event. They would like to increase their income. The club treasurer estimates that they will sell five more hot dogs for every 10¢ they lower the price and five fewer hot dogs for every 10¢ they raise the price.

   a. Use the given information to complete the table at right.

   b. Make a scatter plot with *Number of 10¢ increases* on the *x*-axis and *Income* on the *y*-axis.

   c. Find an equation that fits the data in your scatter plot. (*Hint:* Start by writing expressions for the *Price per hot dog* and the *Number of hot dogs sold* in terms of the *Number of 10¢ increases.*)

Number of 10¢ increases	Price per hot dog	Number of hot dogs sold	Income
−15	$0.50		
−10			
−5			
0	$2.00	40	$80.00
2			
4			
6			

   d. How much should the ski club charge per hot dog in order to maximize its income? Explain how you found your answer.

(continued)

4. *(Lesson 9.5)*

The height, y, of a ball x seconds after it is dropped from a height of 100 m can be modeled by the equation $y = -4.9x^2 + 100$. Write and answer three questions about this situation. Show all your work.

5. *(Lesson 9.5)*

Camilla threw a softball straight up in the air. The table at right shows the height of the ball in feet at different times after she released it.

Tell whether each statement is true or false and explain how you know. (*Hint:* Find the equation for the height of Camilla's ball, using the fact that the general equation for the height, y, of a thrown ball x seconds after it is released is $y = -16x^2 + bx + c$.)

Time (s)	Height (ft)
0.4	19.44
1.0	30.00
1.2	30.96
1.4	30.64
2.0	22.00
2.2	16.56

a. Camilla released the ball from a height of 6 ft.

b. There were two times when the ball was at a height of 4 ft.

c. The ball was in the air for less than 3 s.

d. The maximum height of the ball was less than 35 ft.

6. a. Graph the equations $y = x^2 - 8x + 11$ and $y = 2x + 2$ on the same coordinate axes. How many points of intersection do the graphs have?

b. Algebraically solve the system $y = x^2 - 8x + 11$ and $y = 2x + 2$. Use the quadratic formula in your solution. At what step in your solution can you tell how many times the two graphs will intersect? Explain your thinking.

c. Find the equation of a line parallel to $y = 2x + 2$ that does not intersect the parabola. Algebraically solve the system $y = x^2 - 8x + 11$ and this new linear equation. Use the quadratic formula in your solution. At what step in your solution can you tell that the line and parabola do not intersect? Explain your thinking.

d. Use your work from parts b and c to write the equation of a line parallel to $y = 2x + 2$ that intersects the parabola in exactly one point. Explain your method.

Name _____   Period _____   Date _____

1. The table at right shows how the 690 students at Bentley High School get to school. If you were to graph these data in a circle graph, what would be the number of degrees in each sector?

Method	Number of students
Bus	380
Walk	160
Car	80
Bike	70

2. The table below shows the number of times 160 shoppers at a downtown mall used public transportation during the previous week. Make a relative frequency bar graph that displays this information.

Number of times	0	1	2	3	4	5
Number of people	86	34	8	9	5	18

3. Use the information on the spinner at right to complete each statement.

   a. $P(\$1) =$

   b. $P(\$5) =$

   c. $P(\geq\$4) =$

   d. $P(<\$4) =$

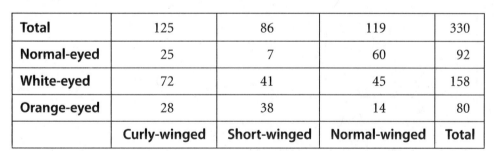

4. Biologist Edna Switt is conducting a fruit fly experiment. She captures a fly from her breeding jar, examines it for eye color and wing characteristics, and then releases it back into her jar. Her findings are in the table below.

Total	125	86	119	330
Normal-eyed	25	7	60	92
White-eyed	72	41	45	158
Orange-eyed	28	38	14	80
	Curly-winged	Short-winged	Normal-winged	Total

Use her data to find the following probabilities for the next fly she captures from the jar.

a. P(white-eyed, curly-winged) =

b. P(normal-winged) =

c. P(not normal-winged) =

d. P(white-eyed or orange-eyed, short-winged) =

Name _____ Period _____ Date _____

1. The table at right shows how the 540 students at Bentley High School get to school. If you were to graph these data in a circle graph, what would be the number of degrees in each sector?

Method	Number of students
Bus	220
Walk	150
Car	70
Bike	100

2. The table below shows the number of times 220 shoppers at a downtown mall used public transportation during the previous week. Make a relative frequency bar graph that displays this information.

Number of times	0	1	2	3	4	5
Number of people	114	48	12	11	7	28

3. Use the information on the spinner at right to complete each statement below.

   a. $P(\$2) =$ **b.** $P(\$8) =$

   c. $P(\geq\$4) =$ **d.** $P(<\$4) =$

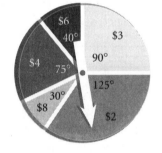

4. Biologist Cathy Navarro is conducting a fruit fly experiment. She captures a fly from her breeding jar, examines it for eye color and wing characteristics, and then releases it back into her jar. Her findings are in the table below.

	Curly-winged	Short-winged	Normal-winged	Total
Total	109	74	97	280
Normal-eyed	21	6	50	77
White-eyed	62	37	28	127
Orange-eyed	26	31	19	76

Use her data to find the following probabilities for the next fly she captures from her jar.

a. $P(\text{white-eyed, curly-winged}) =$

b. $P(\text{normal-winged}) =$

c. $P(\text{not normal-winged}) =$

d. $P(\text{white-eyed or orange-eyed, short-winged}) =$

Discovering Algebra Assessment Resources
©2007 Key Curriculum Press

Name _____ Period _____ Date _____

1. Jessica is studying the behavior of her pet worm. She releases it at the center of a circle and keeps track of which quadrant it enters.

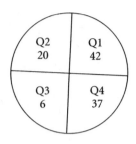

   a. Is the worm's behavior random? Explain.

   b. What is the experimental probability that the next time she releases her worm it will enter Q2?

2. The executive committee of the Bentley High School Trivia Club has five members. They must select a chairperson, a secretary, and a treasurer. Is the answer to the question "How many possibilities are there?" a permutation or a combination? Now answer the question.

3. Every day Fernando wears a shirt with six buttons. He matches each button to its corresponding hole, but does so in a different order each day. For how many days can he button up his shirt in a different order before he repeats himself?

4. Evaluate the following without a calculator. Show your calculations.

   a. $_7P_3$

   b. $_7C_3$

5. a. What is the probability that a random arrangement of four books on a shelf is in alphabetical order by author?

   b. What is the probability that, in a random arrangement of four books on a shelf, at least the first two are in alphabetical order by author?

6. A bag contains a red, a blue, a yellow, a white, and a green ball. Three balls are drawn out without replacement.

   a. What is the probability that the red, blue, and yellow balls are selected?

   b. What is the probability that the three balls in 6a are selected in the exact order listed (red, blue, yellow)?

Name _____ Period _____ Date _____

1. Angela is studying the behavior of a garden snail. She releases it at the center of a circle and keeps track of which quadrant it enters.

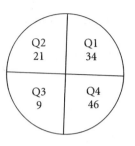

   a. Is the snail's behavior random? Explain.

   b. What is the experimental probability that the next time she releases the snail it will enter Q4?

2. The executive committee of the Bentley High School Math Club has six members. They must select a chairperson, a secretary, and a treasurer. Is the answer to the question "How many possibilities are there?" a permutation or a combination? Now answer the question.

3. Every day Fernando wears a shirt with five buttons. He matches each button to its corresponding hole, but does so in a different order each day. For how many days can he button up his shirt in a different order before he repeats himself?

4. Evaluate the following without a calculator. Show your calculations.

   a. $_7P_4$ b. $_7C_4$

5. a. What is the probability that a random arrangement of five books on a shelf is in alphabetical order by author?

   b. What is the probability that, in a random arrangement of five books on a shelf, at least the first three are in alphabetical order by author?

6. A bag contains a red, a blue, a yellow, a white, and a green ball. Three balls are drawn out without replacement.

   a. What is the probability that the red and yellow balls are selected?

   b. What is the probability that the two balls in 6a are selected in the order listed (red, yellow)?

Discovering Algebra Assessment Resources
©2007 Key Curriculum Press

Name _____ Period _____ Date _____

1. Marcus has been playing table tennis with his father. The tree diagram summarizes the results of recent two-game matches between Marcus and his father.

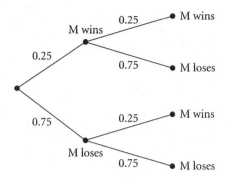

a. List all of the possible outcomes, assuming the order of wins or losses does not matter.

b. $P(\text{Marcus wins both games}) =$

c. $P(\text{Marcus wins 1 and loses 1}) =$

d. $P(\text{Marcus loses both games}) =$

2. Using the spinner shown, how much money should one expect to win in ten spins?

3. In Sucker, a random game of chance, the probability of winning is 30%. If you win, you get 100 points. If you lose, you give up 50 points.

a. What is your expected point gain or loss after one game? After ten games?

b. What is the probability of winning three games in a row?

c. If you win three games in a row, what is your expected gain or loss on the fourth game?

Name _____   Period _____   Date _____

1. Danielle is learning to play cribbage from her father. The tree diagram
summarizes the results of recent two-game matches between Danielle
and her father.

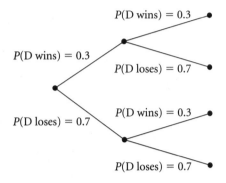

    a. List all of the possible outcomes, assuming the order of wins or losses
does not matter.

    b. P(Danielle wins both games) =

    c. P(Danielle wins 1 and loses 1) =

    d. P(Danielle loses both games) =

2. Using the spinner shown, how much money should one expect
to win in ten spins?

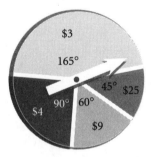

3. In Sucker, a random game of chance, the probability of winning is 35%.
If you win, you get 100 points. If you lose, you give up 60 points.

    a. What is your expected point gain or loss after one game? After
ten games?

    b. What is the probability of winning three games in a row?

    c. If you win three games in a row, what is your expected gain or loss
on the fourth game?

Discovering Algebra Assessment Resources
©2007 Key Curriculum Press

Name _____ Period _____ Date _____

1. The table shows the number of women's shoes of each type sold one day at the Smart Shoe Shoppe. Make a relative frequency bar graph that displays this information.

Type of shoe	Tennis shoes	Loafers	Heels	Low dress shoes	Walking shoes
Number of pairs sold	18	12	6	9	15

2. Mario tagged a total of 147 squirrels. He tagged 38 tan male squirrels, 10 tan female squirrels, 82 gray male squirrels, and 17 gray female squirrels.

   a. If this distribution accurately reflects the squirrel population, what is the probability that the next squirrel Mario captures will be a gray squirrel?

   b. $P(\text{not a gray squirrel}) =$

   c. If there are 4500 squirrels in the total population, about how many are female?

3. A bag contains blue, yellow, red, and orange blocks. Tai randomly chose a block from the bag, recorded the color, and then returned the block to the bag. He did this a total of ten times. He chose six blue blocks, two yellow blocks, one red block, and one orange block.

   a. Based on Tai's results, find the experimental probability of selecting a blue block and the experimental probability of selecting a red block.

   b. Tai dumped out the blocks and found that there were 16 blue blocks, 10 yellow blocks, 8 red blocks, and 6 orange blocks. What is the theoretical probability of selecting a blue block? A red block?

   c. Are the experimental probabilities you found in 3a equal to the theoretical probabilities you computed in 3b? Explain why or why not.

   d. If Tai randomly selects 200 blocks from the bag (replacing the block before he draws a new one), about how many times can he expect to choose each color?

4. Ms. Gonzales gave her algebra class a test. Students could do any three of five parts, and any two of four questions from the parts they chose. How many different tests could a student write?

(continued)

Name _____ **Period** _____ **Date** _____

5. Pile It On Pizza offers a pizza special with your choice of any 5 of their 12 toppings.

   a. How many different specials can Pile It On Pizza make?

   b. Sherry likes all the toppings except anchovies, feta cheese, and onion. How many specials are available that would make Sherry happy?

   c. Sherry ordered a pizza special but forgot to specify the toppings she wanted. In such a situation, Pile It On randomly selects five toppings. What is the probability that Sherry will be satisfied with the results?

6. Sal is an outside shooter. On average she makes 40% of her three-point shots. In a typical game she takes two three-point shots for every 5 minutes that she plays.

   a. What are the possible outcomes for a typical 5-minute period of the game, assuming she only takes three-point shots?

   b. What are the probabilities of each of the outcomes?

   c. What is Sal's expected point value from three-pointers for each 5 minutes she plays?

   d. Sal typically plays 40 minutes a game. How many points should the coach expect from her outside shooting?

7. Should this game be named "Spinner of Fortune" or "Spinner of Misfortune"? Explain.

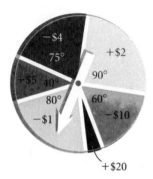

Discovering Algebra Assessment Resources
©2007 Key Curriculum Press

Name _____   Period _____   Date _____

1. The table shows the number of women's shoes of each type sold one day at the Smart Shoe Shoppe. Make a relative frequency bar graph that displays this information.

Type of shoe	Tennis shoes	Loafers	Heels	Low dress shoes	Walking shoes
Number of pairs sold	19	15	4	8	25

2. Mario tagged a total of 153 squirrels. He tagged 13 tan male squirrels, 57 tan female squirrels, 17 gray male squirrels, and 66 gray female squirrels.

   a. If this distribution accurately reflects the squirrel population, what is the probability that the next squirrel Mario captures will be a gray squirrel?

   b. $P(\text{not a gray squirrel}) =$

   c. If there are 3500 squirrels in the total population, about how many are female?

3. A bag contains blue, yellow, red, and orange blocks. Tai randomly chose a block from the bag, recorded the color, and then returned the block to the bag. He did this a total of ten times. He chose three blue blocks, one yellow block, four red blocks, and two orange blocks.

   a. Based on Tai's results, find the experimental probability of selecting a blue block and the experimental probability of selecting a red block.

   b. Tai dumped out the blocks and found that there were eight blue blocks, three yellow blocks, eight red blocks, and five orange blocks. What is the theoretical probability of selecting a blue block? A yellow block?

   c. Are the experimental probabilities you found in 3a equal to the theoretical probabilities you computed in 3b? Explain why or why not.

   d. If Tai randomly selects 360 blocks from the bag (replacing the block before he draws a new one), about how many times can he expect to choose each color?

4. Ms. Gonzales gave her algebra class a test. Students could do any two of five different parts, and any three of four questions from the parts they chose. How many different tests could a student write?

(continued)

Name _____   Period _____   Date _____

5. Pile It On Pizza offers a pizza special with your choice of any 6 of their 11 toppings.

   a. How many different specials can Pile It On Pizza make?

   b. Sherry likes all the toppings except anchovies, feta cheese, and onion. How many specials are available that would make Sherry happy?

   c. Sherry ordered a pizza special but forgot to specify the toppings she wanted. In such a situation, Pile It On randomly selects six toppings. What is the probability that Sherry will be satisfied with the results?

6. Sofia is an outside shooter. On average she makes 45% of her three-point shots. In a typical game she takes three three-point shots every 7 minutes that she plays, and no two-point shots.

   a. What are the possible outcomes for a 7-minute period of a typical game?

   b. What are the probabilities of each of the outcomes?

   c. What is Sofia's expected point value from three-pointers for each 7 minutes she plays?

   d. Sofia typically plays 35 minutes a game. How many points should the coach expect from her outside shooting?

7. Should this game be named "Spinner of Fortune" or "Spinner of Misfortune"? Explain.

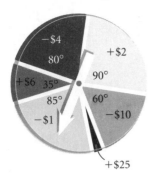

Discovering Algebra Assessment Resources
©2007 Key Curriculum Press

Chapter 10 • Constructive Assessment Options

1. (*Lessons 10.2, 10.3*)

Mrs. Garcia's class conducted a probability experiment. Each group was given a bag containing 45 tiles. All the bags contained the same number of blue tiles, and the rest of the tiles were yellow. For each trial, a tile was drawn from the bag, its color was recorded, and the tile was returned to the bag. Here are the results.

Group	Trials conducted	Blue tiles drawn
1	10	5
2	50	32
3	15	8
4	100	66
5	35	28
6	150	110

Use these data to predict the bag's contents as accurately as possible. Explain how you made your prediction and why you think it is accurate.

2. (*Lessons 10.2, 10.3*)

A bag contains blue and yellow tiles. For each trial, a tile is drawn from the bag, its color is recorded, and then it is returned to the bag. In this scatter plot, the x-variable is the number of trials, and the y-variable is the ratio of the number of blue tiles drawn to the number of trials.

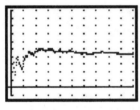

$[-5, 200, 20, -0.1, 1, 0.1]$

a. There are 70 tiles in the bag. Based on the results shown in the graph, how many tiles of each color do you predict are in the bag? Explain your answer.

b. If the results for hundreds of more trials were added to the scatter plot, what would the scatter plot look like? Explain your answer.

(continued)

3. (*Lesson 10.4*)
You are a member of a group with nine other people. Show the formula
you use and the work you do to calculate each answer.

a. Three people who serve as president, vice president, and secretary
form the executive committee. How many different executive
committees are possible?

b. The group is lined up for a picture. In how many different ways can
the members be lined up?

c. If one person is chosen at random to deliver a speech, what is the
probability that it will be you?

d. If three members are chosen randomly to attend a conference, what is
the probability that you will be one of them?

e. At every meeting a person is chosen at random to bring refreshments
to the next meeting. What is the probability that you will *not* be
chosen at five consecutive meetings?

4. (*Lessons 10.5, 10.6*)
A tetrahedron is a pyramid with four triangular faces. In a game of Toss
It, you toss a tetrahedron die with one red face. If the red face is one of
the three visible faces, you toss again. If the red face is hidden (facing
down against the table), your turn is over. For each toss after the first,
you earn three points.

a. Make a tree diagram showing all of the information.

b. What is the probability that a turn will end in one toss? In two tosses?
In three tosses? In four tosses? In n tosses?

c. Write an expression that gives the expected point value for a turn that
lasts at most four tosses.

d. Write an expression that gives the expected point value for a turn that
lasts at most n tosses.

e. Write a recursive routine that generates pairs of numbers that show
the maximum number of tosses in a turn and its corresponding
expected point value. Start with the pair {1, 0}. {1, 0} means that a
turn with a maximum of one toss has an expected point value of zero.
As n gets larger, what happens to the expected point value?

5. (*Lesson 10.6*)
Design a spinner game with an expected value of $10. The spinner's
circle must have at least four sectors of different sizes, and each sector
must have a different dollar value.

a. Give the angle measures of each sector and the point value of
each sector.

b. Write an equation that shows the calculation of the expected value.

Discovering Algebra Assessment Resources
©2007 Key Curriculum Press

Name _____ Period _____ Date _____

1. The equation of line l is $3x + 2y = 6$.

   a. Write the equation of line l in intercept form. What is the slope of line l?

   b. Write the equation of a line parallel to line l.

   c. Write the equation of a line perpendicular to line l.

2. Consider quadrilateral $ABCD$ with vertices $A(-1, -3)$, $B(3, -2)$, $C(2, 2)$, and $D(-2, 1)$.

   a. Find the slope of each of the sides.

   b. Classify quadrilateral $ABCD$ using the most specific term that describes it. Explain your thinking.

   c. Are the diagonals of the quadrilateral perpendicular? Explain how you know.

3. Segment AB has endpoints $(-2, 6)$ and $(4, 0)$. Write the equation of the line that is the perpendicular bisector of $\overline{AB}$.

4. Find the exact solution to the equation $(x + 3)^2 - 12 = 2$. Give the decimal approximation to the nearest thousandth.

5. Find the exact side lengths of $\triangle ABC$.

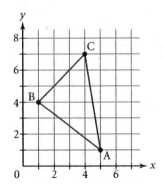

6. What is the slope of the y-axis? What is the slope of the line with equation $y = -4$?

Name _____   Period _____   Date _____

1. The equation of line l is $5x - 3y = 6$.

   a. Write the equation of line l in intercept form. What is the slope of line l?

   b. Write the equation of a line parallel to line l.

   c. Write the equation of a line perpendicular to line l.

2. Consider quadrilateral $ABCD$ with vertices $A(2, 4)$, $B(8, 4)$, $C(5, -2)$, and $D(-1, -2)$.

   a. Find the slope of each of the sides.

   b. Classify quadrilateral $ABCD$ using the most specific term that describes it. Explain your thinking.

   c. Are the diagonals of the quadrilateral perpendicular? Explain how you know.

3. The endpoints of $\overline{CD}$ are $(-5, -2)$ and $(7, 10)$. Write the equation of the perpendicular bisector of $\overline{CD}$.

4. Find the exact solution to the equation $(x - 5)^2 - 8 = 2$. Give the decimal approximation to the nearest thousandth.

5. Find the exact side lengths of $\triangle ABC$.

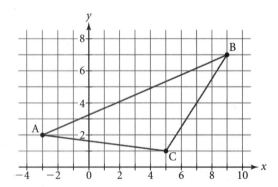

6. What is the slope of the x-axis? What is the slope of the line with equation $x = -4$?

Discovering Algebra Assessment Resources
©2007 Key Curriculum Press

Name _____ **Period** _____ **Date** _____

1. Find the area of the largest square in this diagram. Then find the exact length of each side of the triangle.

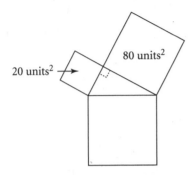

20 units² →

80 units²

2. Mr. Jones leans a 13 ft ladder against the side of his house so that the foot of the ladder is 5 ft from the base of the house. How far up the side of the house does the ladder reach?

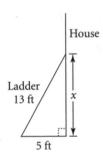

House

Ladder
13 ft

x

5 ft

3. Rewrite each expression with as few square root symbols as possible and no parentheses.

   a. $2\sqrt{3} + 2\sqrt{2} + 3\sqrt{3} - 5\sqrt{2}$

   b. $\dfrac{\sqrt{72}}{\sqrt{2}}$

   c. $\sqrt{2}\left(\sqrt{3}\right) + 3\sqrt{6}$

4. Rewrite each radical expression so that the number under the square root symbol has no perfect-square factors. Check each answer by finding decimal approximations.

   a. $\sqrt{75}$

   b. $\sqrt{72}$

5. Explain how to construct a line segment that is $\sqrt{20}$ units long.

Name _____ Period _____ Date _____

1. Find the missing area of the top square in this diagram. Then find the exact length of each side of the triangle.

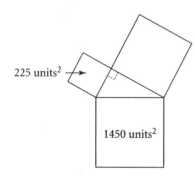

225 units^2

1450 units^2

2. Mr. Jones leans a 13 ft ladder against the side of his house so that the top of the ladder reaches 12 ft up the side of the house. How far is the base of the ladder from the house?

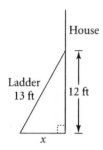

House

Ladder 13 ft

12 ft

x

3. Rewrite each expression with as few square root symbols as possible and no parentheses.

a. $2\sqrt{5} + 3\sqrt{3} + 3\sqrt{3} - 5\sqrt{5}$

b. $\dfrac{\sqrt{36}}{\sqrt{3}}$

c. $\sqrt{3}\left(\sqrt{5}\right) + 2\sqrt{15}$

4. Rewrite each radical expression so that the number under the square root symbol has no perfect-square factors. Check each answer by finding decimal approximations.

a. $\sqrt{108}$

b. $\sqrt{98}$

5. Explain how to construct a line segment that is $\sqrt{13}$ units long.

Discovering Algebra Assessment Resources
©2007 Key Curriculum Press

Name _____   Period _____   Date _____

1. Solve each equation.

    a. $\sqrt{x+7} = x - 5$ **b.** $\sqrt{x^2 + x + 6} = x + 1$

2. Find the distance between points $(3, 1)$ and $(-2, 2)$.

3. Use trigonometric equations to find the values of x and y to the nearest tenth.

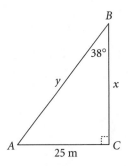

4. Use a trigonometric equation to find the measure of angle A to the nearest degree.

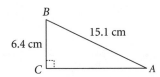

5. Given $\triangle ABC$, with measurements as shown, answer each question.

    a. Find altitude h. Round answers to the nearest 0.1 cm.

    b. Find the area of $\triangle ABC$. Round your answer to the nearest 0.1 cm².

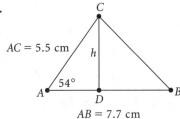

Name _____ Period _____ Date _____

1. Solve each equation.

    a. $\sqrt{x + 5} = x - 1$
                         b. $\sqrt{x^2 - 3x + 6} = x - 1$

2. Find the distance between points $(5, 3)$ and $(-3, 2)$.

3. Use trigonometric ratios to find the values of x and y to the nearest tenth.

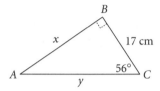

4. Use a trigonometric equation to find the measure of angle B to the nearest degree.

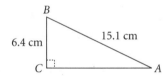

5. Given $\triangle ABC$ with measurements as marked in the figure, answer each question.

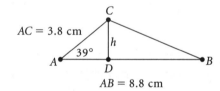

    a. Find altitude h. Round answers to the nearest 0.1 cm.

    b. Find the area of $\triangle ABC$. Round your answer to the nearest 0.1 cm^2.

Name _____   Period _____   Date _____

Answer each question and show all work clearly on a separate piece of paper.

1. Consider $\triangle ABC$ with vertices $A(1, 2)$, $B(5, 10)$, and $C(-7, 6)$.

   a. Show that $\triangle ABC$ is a right triangle.

   b. Find the exact length of each side of the triangle. Rewrite any radical expressions so they have no perfect-square factors.

2. The length of the hypotenuse of a right triangle is 41 cm, and the length of one leg is 9 cm. What is the length of the other leg?

3. A triangle has side lengths 4 cm, 5 cm, and 7 cm.

   a. Is the triangle a right triangle? Explain why or why not.

   b. Give side lengths of another triangle that is similar to the given triangle.

4. Rewrite each expression with as few square root symbols as possible and no parentheses. The expression may already be in this form.

   a. $2\sqrt{3} - 5\sqrt{3}$

   b. $\sqrt{2} \cdot \sqrt{8}$

   c. $\sqrt{2} + \sqrt{8}$

   d. $\sqrt{2} + \sqrt{6}$

   e. $\left(10\sqrt{14}\right)^2$

   f. $\dfrac{\sqrt{24}}{\sqrt{6}}$

5. A square has a diagonal with length 15 in. What is the length of each side of the square? Give your answer to the nearest tenth of an inch.

6. A hot-air balloon is tied down with two long ropes. One of the ropes is 150 ft long and makes an angle of 70° with the ground. How high above the ground is the balloon? Round your answer to the nearest foot.

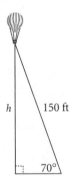

7. Write a trigonometric equation and solve it to find the measure of angle A.

$5\sqrt{3}$ m   10 m

Name _____ Period _____ Date _____

Answer each question and show all work clearly on a separate piece of paper.

1. Consider $\triangle ABC$ with vertices $A(1, 4)$, $B(9, -2)$, and $C(-2, 0)$.

   a. Show that $\triangle ABC$ is a right triangle.

   b. Find the exact length of each side of the triangle. Rewrite radical expressions so they have no perfect-square factors.

2. The length of the hypotenuse of a right triangle is 55 cm, and the length of one leg is 13 cm. What is the length of the other leg? Round your answer to the nearest hundredth of a centimeter.

3. A triangle has side lengths 5 cm, 12 cm, and 15 cm.

   a. Is the triangle a right triangle? Explain why or why not.

   b. Give side lengths of another triangle that is similar to the given triangle.

4. Rewrite each expression with as few square root symbols as possible and no parentheses. The expression may already be in this form.

   a. $5\sqrt{7} - 7\sqrt{7}$ **b.** $\sqrt{3} \cdot \sqrt{12}$ **c.** $\sqrt{3} + \sqrt{27}$

   d. $\sqrt{3} + \sqrt{15}$ **e.** $\left(5\sqrt{10}\right)^2$ **f.** $\dfrac{\sqrt{64}}{\sqrt{8}}$

5. A square has a diagonal with length 36 in. What is the length of each side of the square? Give your answer to the nearest tenth of an inch.

6. A hot-air balloon is tied down with two long ropes. One of the ropes is 120 ft long and makes an angle of 65° with the ground. How high above the ground is the balloon? Round your answer to the nearest foot.

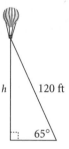

7. Write a trigonometric equation and solve it to find the measure of angle A.

A

10 m

D 5 m B

Chapter 11 • Constructive Assessment Options

Choose one or more of these items to replace part of the chapter test. Let students know that they will receive from 0 to 5 points for each item, depending on the correctness and completeness of their answer.

1. *(Lesson 11.1)*
   Write a pair of equations that meets each set of conditions.

   a. The graphs of the equations are parallel lines that pass through Quadrants I and II only.

   b. The graphs of the equations are perpendicular lines with an intersection point on the negative x-axis.

   c. The graphs of the two equations are perpendicular lines, and one of the lines is parallel to the y-axis.

2. *(Lesson 11.4)*
   A 16 ft ladder leans against a building on one side of an alley so that the top of the ladder is 13 ft above the ground. Then, while the feet of the ladder remain fixed, the top of the ladder is pushed until it leans against the building on the opposite side of the alley. The top of the ladder is now 10 ft above the ground. How wide is the alley? Round your answer to the nearest hundredth of a foot. Explain how you found your answer, showing all your work.

3. *(Lesson 11.4)*
   Write a word problem that can be solved by using the Pythagorean Theorem. Give a complete solution to your problem.

4. *(Lesson 11.5)*
   As part of his homework assignment, Matt had to rewrite radical expressions. For each problem, tell whether Matt's answer is correct. If it is incorrect, explain what he did wrong and give the correct expression.

   a. $5\sqrt{2} + \sqrt{2} - 3\sqrt{2} = 2\sqrt{2}$

   b. $\sqrt{40} = 4\sqrt{10}$

   c. $\sqrt{3}(2\sqrt{3}) = 6$

   d. $3\sqrt{12} + 7\sqrt{3} = 13\sqrt{3}$

5. *(Lesson 11.6)*
   Explain in detail how the distance formula is derived from the Pythagorean Theorem. You may use illustrations and graphs in your explanation.

(continued)

6. *(Lessons 11.1, 11.2, 11.6)*

Draw a square, *ABCD*, with a side length of *p*. Set up coordinate axes so that $\overline{AB}$ is on the positive *x*-axis and point *A* is at the origin.

   a. What are the coordinates of the four vertices?

   b. Use the coordinates from part a to check that *ABCD* meets the criteria for the definition of a square (four congruent sides and four right angles).

   c. Find the midpoint of each diagonal. What can you conclude?

   d. Find the slope of each diagonal. What can you conclude?

   e. Find the length of each diagonal. What can you conclude?

   f. Combine your conclusions from parts c, d, and e into one conjecture about the diagonals of any square. Is this statement a conjecture or is it a theorem that you have now proved with deductive reasoning? Explain your answer.

7. *(Lessons 11.1, 11.6)*

In this problem, you will consider three types of quadrilaterals.

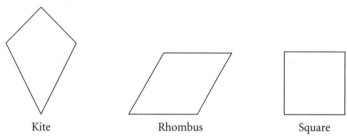

Kite   Rhombus   Square

A *kite* is a quadrilateral with two pairs of congruent adjacent sides.

A *rhombus* is a quadrilateral with four congruent sides.

A *square* is a quadrilateral with four congruent sides and four right angles.

   a. Give the coordinates of the vertices of a kite. None of the sides should be parallel to the *x*- or *y*-axis. Prove that the figure fits the definition of a kite.

   b. Give the coordinates of the vertices of a rhombus that is not a square. None of the sides should be parallel to the *x*- or *y*-axis. Prove that the figure fits the definition of a rhombus and that it is not a square.

   c. Give the coordinates of the vertices of a square. None of the sides should be parallel to the *x*- or *y*-axis. Prove that the figure fits the definition of a square.

8. *(Lessons 11.7, 11.8)*

Find the least and greatest possible values of the sine and cosine functions and explain your reasoning. (*Hint:* Draw right triangles with acute angles of various sizes.)

Name _____ **Period** _____ **Date** _____

Answer each question and show all work clearly on a separate piece of paper.

1. Describe each graph as a transformation of the graph of $y = x^2$ or $y = |x|$. Then give the equation for the graph.

a.

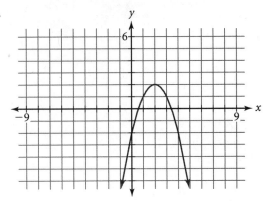

b.

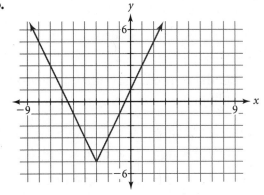

2. Here is a graph of the function $y = g(x)$.

   a. Sketch the graph of $y = g(-x) - 4$.

   b. Sketch the graph of $y = -g(x - 4) + 2$.

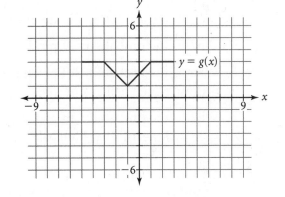

3. Find the roots of each quadratic equation without making a table or a graph.

   a. $y = (x + 11)(x - 4)$

   b. $y = x^2 - 12x + 36$

   c. $y = x^2 + 7x - 4$

   d. $y = -5x^2 - 2x + 3$

4. The height of a golf ball is given by the equation $h = -16t^2 + 56t$, where t is time measured in seconds and h is height measured in feet.

   a. How long is the ball in the air?

   b. What is the maximum height reached by the ball, and when does the ball reach this height?

   c. When is the ball at a height of 32 ft? Round your answers to the nearest tenth of a second.

(continued)

Name _____ Period _____ Date _____

5. This relative frequency circle graph shows the preferences that a number of people have for certain types of desserts.

Dessert preferences

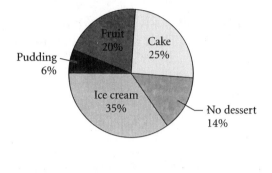

a. What is the size of the angle for the ice cream sector?

b. If 350 people were polled, how many preferred no dessert?

c. If 90 people preferred fruit, how many preferred pudding?

6. a. How many different seven-digit numbers can be made using the digits 1 through 7? No digit can be used more than once.

b. How many different four-digit numbers can be made using the digits 1 through 7? No digit can be used more than once.

7. Two red and three blue balls are in a bag.

a. What is the probability of picking a blue ball?

b. What is the probability of picking a blue ball, replacing it, and then picking a blue ball again?

c. What is the probability of picking a blue ball, not replacing it, and then picking another blue ball?

8. Draw a right triangle on a coordinate grid so that none of the sides are horizontal or vertical. Prove that your triangle is a right triangle, and then find the length of the hypotenuse.

9. Kate is flying a kite. She is holding the spool of kite string 4 ft above the ground. She has let out all 200 ft of string. When her friend Gus stands 100 ft away from her, the kite is directly over his head.

a. Find the height of the kite above the ground to the nearest foot.

b. Find the angle of elevation of the kite (that is, the angle the kite string forms with the horizontal).

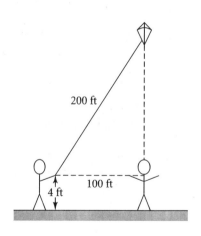

Discovering Algebra Assessment Resources
©2007 Key Curriculum Press

Name ————————————————————— Period ——————— Date ———————

Answer each question and show all work clearly on a separate piece of paper.

1. Describe each graph as a transformation of the graph of $y = x^2$ or $y = |x|$. Then give the equation for the graph.

a.

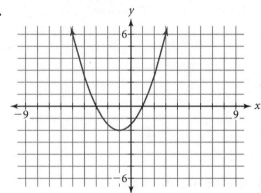

b.

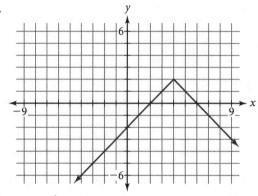

2. Here is a graph of the function $y = g(x)$.

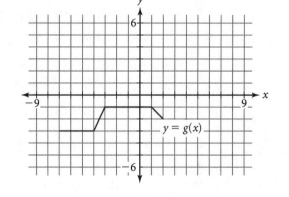

   a. Sketch the graph of $y = g(-x) + 5$.

   b. Sketch the graph of $y = -g(x + 2) + 3$.

3. Find the roots of each quadratic equation without making a table or a graph.

   a. $y = (x - 9)(x + 3)$

   b. $y = x^2 + 10x + 25$

   c. $y = x^2 - 5x + 2$

   d. $y = -3x^2 + 2x + 5$

4. The height of a golf ball is given by the equation $h = -16t^2 + 72t$, where t is time measured in seconds and h is height measured in feet.

   a. How long is the ball in the air?

   b. What is the maximum height reached by the ball, and when does the ball reach this height?

   c. When is the ball at a height of 48 ft? Round your answers to the nearest tenth of a second.

(continued)

Name _____   Period _____   Date _____

5. The relative frequency circle graph shows the preferences that a number
of people have for certain types of desserts.

Dessert preferences

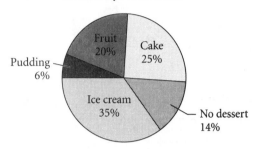

a. What is the size of the angle for the fruit sector?

b. If 250 people were polled, how many preferred no dessert?

c. If 100 people preferred cake, how many preferred pudding?

6. a. How many different six-digit numbers can be made using the
digits 1 through 6? No digit can be used more than once.

b. How many different three-digit numbers can be made using the
digits 1 through 6? No digit can be used more than once.

7. Two red and three blue balls are in a bag.

a. What is the probability of picking a red ball?

b. What is the probability of picking a red ball, replacing it, and then
picking a red ball again?

c. What is the probability of picking a red ball, not replacing it, and
picking another red ball?

8. Draw a right triangle on a coordinate grid so that none of the sides are
horizontal or vertical. Prove that your triangle is a right triangle, and
then find the length of the hypotenuse.

9. Kate is flying a kite. She is holding the spool of kite string
4 ft above the ground. She has let out all 250 ft of string. When
her friend Gus stands 120 ft away from her, the kite is directly
over his head.

a. Find the height of the kite above the ground to the nearest foot.

b. Find the angle of elevation of the kite (that is, the angle the
kite string forms with the horizontal).

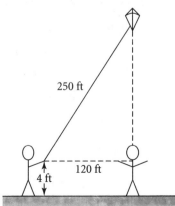

Discovering Algebra Assessment Resources
©2007 Key Curriculum Press

Name ——————————————————————————— Period ——————— Date ———————

Answer each question and show all work clearly on a separate piece of paper.

1. Here are the test scores for Ms. Caruso's two algebra classes.

   First period:
   45, 55, 62, 64, 65, 65, 67, 69, 70, 75, 92, 95, 97, 97, 98, 99, 99, 100, 100

   Third period:
   70, 74, 75, 75, 75, 80, 82, 85, 85, 85, 87, 88, 89, 89, 90, 90, 91, 92

   a. Find the mean of the scores for each class to the nearest tenth.

   b. Find the five-number summary for each class.

   c. On the same axis, make a box plot for each class.

   d. Which class do you think did better on the test? Use statistics to defend your answer.

2. At Sal's Sandwich Bar, customers make their own sandwiches. The price is determined by the weight of the sandwich in ounces.

   a. Ali's 14 oz sandwich cost $3.78. How much will Tom pay for his 17 oz sandwich?

   b. Ruth has $5.67 to spend at the sandwich bar. What is the most her sandwich can weigh?

3. Rosco's Cab Company charges a fixed fee plus an amount per quarter-mile for each ride. This table shows the number of quarter-miles driven and the total fare for five of Rosco's customers.

   a. Find the fixed fee and the amount charged per quarter-mile.

   b. Write an equation for calculating the total fare, f, for a trip of q quarter-miles.

   c. What would be the fare for a 7.5-mile trip?

   d. If the fare for a trip is $25.25, how long was the trip in miles?

Quarter-miles driven	Total fare
6	$4.90
20	$12.60
25	$15.35
40	$23.60
48	$28.00

(continued)

Name _____ **Period** _____ **Date** _____

4. This table shows the number of trips taken for leisure by U.S. residents in the years 1994 through 2003. Only trips of at least 50 miles, one-way, are included.

Year	Number of trips (millions)	Year	Number of trips (millions)
1994	800.9	1999	848.6
1995	820.0	2000	865.7
1996	828.8	2001	895.5
1997	862.8	2002	912.3
1998	862.6	2003	929.5

(*World Almanac and Book of Facts 2005*, p. 743)

   a. Let x represent the year, and let y represent the number of trips. Use Q-points to find an equation that models these data.

   b. What does the slope of the model mean in this situation?

   c. Use your model to predict the number of trips taken for leisure by U.S. residents in 2006.

5. Solve this system of equations.

$$\begin{cases} 4x + y = 7 \\ 2y + 3 = 3x - 16 \end{cases}$$

6. Write the system of inequalities for the solution shown on the graph at right.

7. Nine years ago, Mr. Mancini bought an antique vase at an auction. An appraiser told him that the value of the vase had increased by about 7% each year since Mr. Mancini purchased it and that it is now worth about $700.

   a. To the nearest dollar, what was the value of the vase when Mr. Mancini purchased it?

   b. If the value continues to increase by 7% per year, how much will the vase be worth 10 years from now?

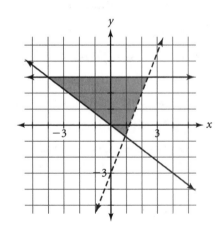

(continued)

Discovering Algebra Assessment Resources
©2007 Key Curriculum Press

Name _____ **Period** _____ **Date** _____

8. At right is a graph of the function $y = f(x)$.

   a. What is the domain of the function? What is the range?

   b. What is $f(-2)$?

   c. For what x-values does $f(x) = 2$?

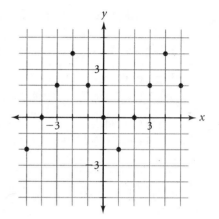

9. Consider the quadratic equation $y = 3x^2 - 12x + 8$.

   a. Find the roots of the equation by using the quadratic formula. Leave your answers in exact form.

   b. Rewrite the equation in vertex form.

10. At right is a graph of the function $y = f(x)$.

   a. Sketch a graph of $y = -f(x + 3) + 2$.

   b. Sketch a graph of $y = 3 \cdot f(-x)$.

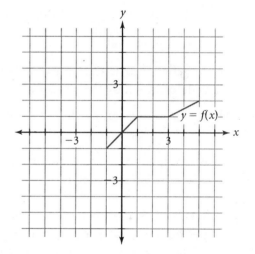

11. An Olympic soccer field has a length of 100 meters and a width of 70 meters. To the nearest meter, what is the distance from one corner of the field to the opposite corner?

12. Eight tokens, all of identical size, are put into a bag. The tokens are labeled 1 through 8 to indicate how many points they are worth. A group of tokens are drawn out together.

   a. What is the number of three-token groups that can be picked?

   b. What is the number of three-token groups that contain the eight-point token?

   c. What is the probability of a three-token group including the eight-point token?

   d. What is the probability that if two tokens are drawn without replacement, both will have point values greater than 5?

   e. What is the expected point value of a single token drawn from the bag?

Name _____ Period _____ Date _____

Answer each question and **show all** work clearly on a separate piece of paper.

1. Here are the test scores for Ms. Caruso's two algebra classes.

   First period:
   70, 74, 74, 75, 75, 78, 84, 85, 85, 85, 85, 86, 89, 89, 90, 91, 92, 92

   Third period:
   45, 54, 60, 65, 65, 65, 67, 68, 75, 75, 92, 95, 97, 98, 98, 98, 99, 100, 100

   a. Find the mean of the scores for each class to the nearest tenth.

   b. Find the five-number summary for each class.

   c. On the same axis, make a box plot for each class.

   d. Which class do you think did better on the test? Use statistics to
      defend your answer.

2. At Sal's Sandwich Bar, customers make their own sandwiches. The price
   is determined by the weight of the sandwich in ounces.

   a. Ali's 14 oz sandwich cost $4.48. How much will Tom pay for his
      17 oz sandwich?

   b. Ruth has $6.08 to spend at the sandwich bar. What is the most her
      sandwich can weigh?

3. Rosco's Cab Company charges a fixed fee plus an amount
   per quarter-mile for each ride. This table shows the number
   of quarter-miles driven and the total fare for five of
   Rosco's customers.

   a. Find the fixed fee and the amount charged per quarter-mile.

   b. Write an equation for calculating the total fare, f, for a trip
      of q quarter-miles.

   c. What would be the fare for a 7.5-mile trip?

   d. If the fare for a trip is $29.70, how long was the trip in miles?

Quarter-miles driven	Total fare
6	$5.65
20	$14.75
25	$18.00
40	$27.75
48	$32.95

(continued)

Discovering Algebra Assessment Resources
©2007 Key Curriculum Press

Name _____ **Period** _____ **Date** _____

4. This table shows the number of trips taken for leisure by U.S. residents in the years 1994 through 2003. Only trips of at least 50 miles, one-way, are included.

Year	Number of trips (millions)	Year	Number of trips (millions)
1994	800.9	1999	848.6
1995	820.0	2000	865.7
1996	828.8	2001	895.5
1997	862.8	2002	912.3
1998	862.6	2003	929.5

(*World Almanac and Book of Facts 2005*, p. 743)

a. Let x represent the year, and let y represent the number of trips. Use Q-points to find an equation that models these data.

b. What does the slope of the model mean in this situation?

c. Use your model to predict the number of trips U.S. residents will take for leisure in 2009.

5. Solve this system of equations.

$$\begin{cases} 2x + y = 3 \\ 2y - 5 = -3 - 6x \end{cases}$$

6. Write the system of inequalities for the solution shown on the graph at right.

7. Seven years ago, Mr. Mancini bought an antique vase at an auction. An appraiser told him that the value of the vase had increased by about 9% each year since Mr. Mancini purchased it and that it is now worth about $600.

a. To the nearest dollar, what was the value of the vase when Mr. Mancini purchased it?

b. If the value continues to increase by 9% per year, how much will the vase be worth 12 years from now?

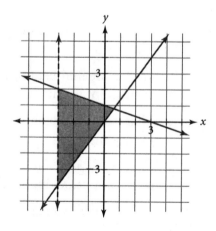

Name _____   Period _____   Date _____

8. At right is a graph of the function $y = f(x)$.

   a. What is the domain of the function? What is the range?

   b. What is $f(-2)$?

   c. For what x-values does $f(x) = 0$?

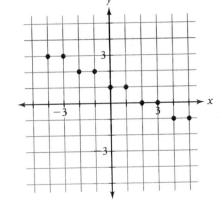

9. Consider the quadratic equation $y = -2x^2 - 4x + 5$.

   a. Find the roots of the equation by using the quadratic formula. Leave your answers in exact form.

   b. Rewrite the equation in vertex form.

10. At right is a graph of the function $y = f(x)$.

   a. Sketch a graph of $y = f(-x) + 4$.

   b. Sketch a graph of $y = -2 \cdot f(x + 5)$.

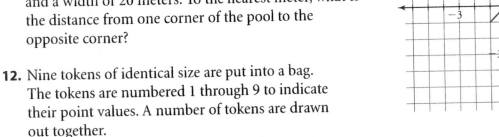

11. An Olympic water-polo pool has a length of 30 meters and a width of 20 meters. To the nearest meter, what is the distance from one corner of the pool to the opposite corner?

12. Nine tokens of identical size are put into a bag. The tokens are numbered 1 through 9 to indicate their point values. A number of tokens are drawn out together.

   a. What is the number of three-token groups that can be drawn from the bag?

   b. What is the number of three-token groups that contain the seven-point token?

   c. What is the probability that a three-token group includes the seven-point token?

   d. What is the probability that if two tokens are drawn, they will both have point values higher than 6?

   e. What is the expected point value of a single token drawn from the bag?

Discovering Algebra Assessment Resources
©2007 Key Curriculum Press

CHAPTER 0 · Test   **Form A**

1. a.

Stage number	Total length		Decimal form
	Multiplication form	**Exponent form**	
0	1	$5^0 \cdot \left(\frac{1}{3}\right)^0 = \left(\frac{5}{3}\right)^0$	1
1	$5 \cdot \frac{1}{3}$	$5^1 \cdot \left(\frac{1}{3}\right)^1 = \left(\frac{5}{3}\right)^1$	1.67
2	$5 \cdot 5 \cdot \frac{1}{3} \cdot \frac{1}{3}$	$5^2 \cdot \left(\frac{1}{3}\right)^2 = \left(\frac{5}{3}\right)^2$	2.78
3	$5 \cdot 5 \cdot 5 \cdot \frac{1}{3} \cdot \frac{1}{3} \cdot \frac{1}{3}$	$5^3 \cdot \left(\frac{1}{3}\right)^3 = \left(\frac{5}{3}\right)^3$	4.63

b. $\left(\frac{5}{3}\right)^7$; 35.72   **c.** Stage 5   **d.** Stage 9

2. a.

Starting value	2	−1	10
First recursion	−2.2	−3.4	1
Second recursion	−3.88	−4.36	−2.6
Third recursion	−4.552	−4.744	−4.04
Fourth recursion	−4.8208	−4.8976	−4.616
Fifth recursion	−4.92832	−4.95904	−4.8464

b. Yes; −5

3. a. In each new triangle, connect the midpoint of the hypotenuse to the midpoints of the legs.

    b. $\frac{1}{4}$ **c.** $\frac{1}{16}; \frac{1}{64}$

    d. $\frac{1}{4} + \frac{2}{16} + \frac{3}{64} = \frac{16}{64} + \frac{8}{64} + \frac{3}{64} = \frac{27}{64}$

4. a. 4   **b.** 8   **c.** 2^6

CHAPTER 0 · Test   **Form B**

1. a.

Stage number	Total length		Decimal form
	Multiplication form	**Exponent form**	
0	1	$9^0 \cdot \left(\frac{1}{5}\right)^0 = \left(\frac{9}{5}\right)^0$	1
1	$9 \cdot \frac{1}{5}$	$9^1 \cdot \left(\frac{1}{5}\right)^1 = \left(\frac{9}{5}\right)^1$	1.80
2	$9 \cdot 9 \cdot \frac{1}{5} \cdot \frac{1}{5}$	$9^2 \cdot \left(\frac{1}{5}\right)^2 = \left(\frac{9}{5}\right)^2$	3.24
3	$9 \cdot 9 \cdot 9 \cdot \frac{1}{5} \cdot \frac{1}{5} \cdot \frac{1}{5}$	$9^3 \cdot \left(\frac{1}{5}\right)^3 = \left(\frac{9}{5}\right)^3$	5.83

b. $\left(\frac{9}{5}\right)^7$; 61.22   **c.** Stage 4   **d.** Stage 8

2. a.

Starting value	2	−1	10
First recursion	−3.6	−4.2	−2
Second recursion	−4.72	−4.84	−4.4
Third recursion	−4.944	−4.968	−4.88
Fourth recursion	−4.9888	−4.9936	−4.976
Fifth recursion	−4.99776	−4.99872	−4.9952

b. Yes; −5

3. a. Draw a 3-by-3 checkerboard pattern (with gray squares in the corners and the center) in each white square.

    b. $\frac{1}{9}$ **c.** $\frac{1}{81}; \frac{1}{729}$

    d. $\frac{1}{9} + \frac{2}{81} + \frac{3}{729} = \frac{27}{243} + \frac{6}{243} + \frac{1}{243} = \frac{34}{243}$

4. a. 16   **b.** 64   **c.** 4^6

SCORING RUBRICS

1. 5 Points

a. Answer includes a fractal pattern correctly drawn to Stage 3 and a clear, correct rule for generating the pattern. Sample answer: At the endpoints of each segment from the previous stage, draw segments half as long as the segments drawn at the previous stage. Each previous segment should be the perpendicular bisector of the new segments drawn at its endpoints.

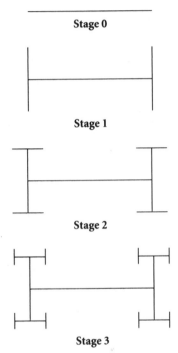

Stage 0

Stage 1

Stage 2

Stage 3

b. Answer includes two questions, one involving fractions and the other involving exponents. Questions are answered correctly. Sample questions and answers are based on the example from part a:

Q: If the length of the segment at Stage 0 is 1, what is the length of each new segment at Stage 5?
A: $\left(\frac{1}{2}\right)^5$

Q: What is the number of new segments at Stage n?
A: 2^n

3 Points

a. The fractal pattern is drawn correctly, but the rule is not clearly defined, or the rule is correct, but Stage 3 of the fractal pattern is not drawn correctly or is missing.

b. Questions meet the given criteria, but the answers are missing or are incorrect.

1 Point

a. The fractal pattern is correct at least through Stage 2, but no rule is given.

b. Questions do not meet the given criteria, but the answers given are correct, or only one correct question and answer are given.

2. 5 Points

a. Answer includes correctly drawn stages and a clear, correct rule for generating the pattern. Sample answer: Draw a square. Insert a 3-by-3 checkerboard of white and gray squares, with white squares in the corners and the center, in each white square of the previous stage.

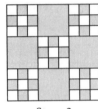 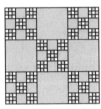

Stage 2   Stage 3

b. Answer includes two questions—one involving gray squares and one involving white squares—along with the correct answers. Sample questions and answers:

Q: What is the number of new white squares at Stage n? **A:** 5^n

Q: What is the number of new gray squares at Stage 5? **A:** $5^4 \cdot 4$, or 2500

3 Points

a. Stages 2 and 3 are drawn correctly, but the rule is not clearly defined, or the rule is correct, but Stage 3 is missing or is drawn incorrectly.

b. Questions meet the given criteria, but one of the answers is missing or is incorrect.

1 Point

a. The fractal pattern is mostly correct, but the rule is not given.

b. The questions do not fit the given criteria, but the answers given are correct, or only one correct question and answer are given.

3. Parts d and e are challenging. You might assign them as part of a group assessment or give extra credit for complete solutions. Encourage students to draw the figures on grid-paper, especially if you assign parts d and e.

5 Points

Work and answers are clearly organized for all parts.

a.

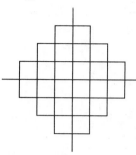

Stage 3   Stage 4

b. Stage 0 is 1.

Stage 1 is 2.

Stage 2 is 4.

Stage 3 is 8.

Stage 4 is 16.

c. Stage 0 is $1 = 2^0$

Stage 1 is $2 = 2^1$

Stage 2 is $4 = 2^2$

Stage 3 is $8 = 2^3$

Stage 4 is $16 = 2^4$

…

Stage 8 is 2^8 or 256.

d. Areas should be shown as simplified fractions or decimals.

The area enclosed in Stage 2 is $4\left(\frac{1}{4} \cdot \frac{1}{4}\right) = \frac{1}{4}$, or 0.25.

The area enclosed in Stage 3 is $24\left(\frac{1}{8} \cdot \frac{1}{8}\right) = \frac{24}{64} = \frac{3}{8}$, or 0.375.

The area enclosed in Stage 4 is $112\left(\frac{1}{16} \cdot \frac{1}{16}\right) = \frac{112}{256} = \frac{7}{16}$, or 0.4375.

e. The area increases with each stage and approaches $\frac{1}{2}$ or 0.5. In general, the enclosed area of Stage n is $\frac{2^{n-1} - 1}{2^n}$, which gets closer to $\frac{1}{2}$ as n increases. Explanations may vary.

Sample explanations:

As the stage number increases, the enclosed area gets closer to the area of a square or diamond having half the area of a square with the original Stage 0 segment as a side. See the sketch below. The outer square has area 1, so the inner area of enclosed squares has an area of almost $\frac{1}{2}$.

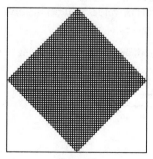

Stage 6

The decimal areas increase with each stage and seem to get closer to 0.5. The fractional areas of $\frac{1}{4}$, $\frac{3}{8}$, and $\frac{7}{16}$ show a pattern: The numerator is always one less than half the denominator, so the value of the fraction is a little less than $\frac{1}{2}$. As the number of the stage increases, the areas become closer to $\frac{1}{2}$.

3 Points

a. Answer is correct, but work is poorly organized or incomplete, or answer is incorrect due to a minor calculation error.

b. Answer is correct, but work is poorly organized or incomplete, or answer is incorrect due to a minor calculation error.

c. Some numbers are expressed in exponential form but not all of them. Stage 0 may not be given correctly. Stage 4 may be given as 4^2. The length for Stage 8 is attempted but may not be correct.

d. The enclosed areas for Stage 2 and Stage 3 are correct. The answer for Stage 4 is not correct or not attempted.

e. The student observes that the enclosed area increases and seems to approach $\frac{1}{2}$, but no meaningful explanation is given.

1 Point

a. Answer is attempted, but incorrect.

b. Answer is incorrect, or answer is correct, but no work or explanation is given.

c. Some of the numbers are expressed in exponent form, others are not. The length for Stage 8 is not attempted.

d. The enclosed areas for Stage 2 and Stage 3 are attempted but not correct. The Stage 4 answer is not attempted.

e. Part e is not attempted.

4. 5 Points

a. Answer includes correct attractor values for 0.2, 0.5, 0.75, 0.9, and at least two other N-values. Some examples:

N	Attractor
0.2	2.5
0.5	4
0.75	8
0.9	20
0.1	$2.\overline{2}$

N	Attractor
0.25	$2.\overline{6}$
0.4	$3.\overline{3}$
0.6	5
0.7	$6.\overline{6}$
0.8	10

b. *Attractor value* $= \dfrac{2}{1 - N}$

3 Points

a. The table has correct entries for only four or five *N*-values.

b. The rule is attempted, with some correct work shown, but the rule is not correct.

1 Point

a. The table has correct entries for only two or three *N*-values.

b. An incorrect rule is given, and no work is shown.

5. 5 Points

a. Four correct expressions are given. Correct expressions will have $A < 1$ and be of the form $A \cdot \square + B$, where $B = 2 - 2A$. Possible expressions include $0.1 \cdot \square + 1.8$, $0.2 \cdot \square + 1.6$, $0.7 \cdot \square + 0.6$, and $0.6 \cdot \square + 0.8$.

b. Rule correctly states that $A < 1$ and the expression must be in the form $A \cdot \square + B$, where $B = 2 - 2A$ (or, equivalently, where $A = \frac{2-B}{2}$ or $A = 1 - \frac{B}{2}$).

3 Points

a. Only two or three correct expressions are given.

b. The rule is attempted, with some correct work shown, but the rule is not correct.

1 Point

a. Only one correct expression is given.

b. An incorrect rule is given, and no work is shown.

CHAPTER 1 · Quiz 1   **Form A**

1.

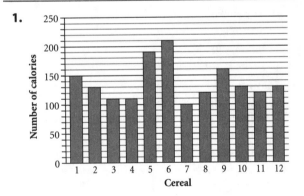

2.

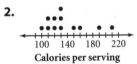

3. Mean: $138.\overline{3}$ calories; median: 130 calories; mode: 130 calories

---

CHAPTER 1 · Quiz 1   **Form B**

1.

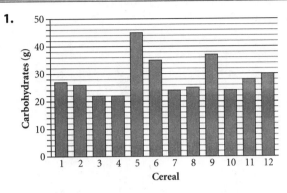

2.

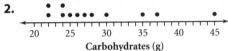

3. Mean: 28.75 g; median: 26.5 g; modes: 22 and 24 g

CHAPTER 1 · Quiz 2   **Form A**

1. Mean: Find the sum of the data values and divide by the number of data values.
Median: Arrange the data in ascending or descending order. Find the middle number. If there is an even number of data values, find the mean of the two data values in the middle.
Mode: Find the value or values that occur most frequently.

2. Mean: 73.8; median: 74; mode: 74; five-number summary: 65, 72, 74, 76, 78

3.

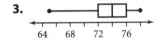

CHAPTER 1 · Quiz 2   **Form B**

1. Mean: Find the sum of the data values and divide by the number of data values.
Median: Arrange the data in ascending or descending order. Find the middle number. If there is an even number of data values, find the mean of the two data values in the middle.
Mode: Find the value or values that occur most frequently.

2. Mean: $34.2\overline{7}$; median: 34; modes: 32 and 34; five-number summary: 30, 32, 34, 36, 41

3.

1. 63, 63, 87

2. a. $A(-3, 4)$; $B(-4, 0)$; $C(-4, -3)$; $D(3, -4)$; $E(0, 0)$; $F(4, 3)$

   b. Point C

3. a. Answers will vary. A bin width of 3, 4, or 5 probably works best.

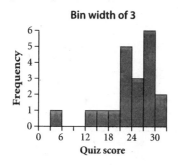

Bin width of 3

b. 3, 21.5, 24, 28.5, 30

c. Answers will vary. One possible answer: 25–30 points: A; 20–24 points: B; 15–19 points: C; 10–14 points: D; less than 10 points: F. Even though this assignment of grades means that the median grade in the class is a B, calculus students are strong mathematics students, and the material is challenging, so the teacher can be somewhat generous with As and Bs. If a student gets less than half of the possible points, he or she will get a grade lower than a C.

4. $[B] = \begin{bmatrix} 0.98 & 1.73 \\ 1.18 & 1.98 \\ 1.38 & 2.18 \end{bmatrix}$ (Answers are rounded to the nearest cent.)

1. 42, 42, 57

2. a. $A(3, -2)$; $B(0, 0)$; $C(4, 4)$; $D(0, -3)$; $E(-4, 1)$; $F(-3, -4)$

   b. Point E

3. a. Answers will vary. A bin width of 5 works well.

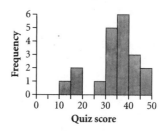

b. 12, 30, 35, 39, 48

c. Answers will vary. One possible answer: 40–50 points: A; 35–39 points: B; 30–34 points: C; 25–29 points: D; less than 25 points: F. Even though this assignment of grades means that the median grade in the class is a B, calculus students are strong mathematics students, and the material is challenging, so the teacher can be somewhat generous with As and Bs. If a student gets less than half of the possible points, he or she will get a grade of F.

4. $[B] = \begin{bmatrix} 1.69 & 2.03 \\ 2.14 & 2.48 \\ 2.59 & 2.93 \end{bmatrix}$ (Answers are rounded to the nearest cent.)

CHAPTER 1 · Test   Form A

1. a. sometimes   **b.** always   **c.** sometimes
   d. never   **e.** sometimes

2. a. A dot plot   **b.** Mean: 7; median: 7; mode: 7
   c. 6, 6.5, 7, 7.25, 8.5

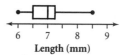

Length (mm)

   d. 0.75

   e. Yes. 1.5(IQR) = 1.125; Q3 + 1.125 = 8.375. Therefore, 8.5 is an outlier.

   f. 2.5

   g. The mean, median, and mode will each be increased by 1. The IQR and the range will not be changed.

3. a. Points A and B **b.** Points G, H, and I
   c. $C(0, 3)$; $F(4, 0)$; $J(0, -2)$

4. a. Five-number summaries: Group 1: 60, 64, 65.5, 70, 75, Group 2: 63, 65, 67, 69, 72; mean heights: Group 1: 66.8 in., Group 2: 67.1 in.

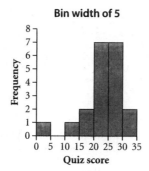

Height (in.)

b. Answers will vary as to which group is taller. Students could argue that Group 1 has more taller people in it. However, Group 2 has a larger median (and mean) height, with less spread among the heights. But the means of the two groups are not too far apart. Group 1 has some tall people but also some short people.

5. Answers will vary. A bin width of 2 gives eight bins—enough to show the patterns in the data.

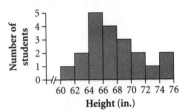

6. a. Between points *E* and *F*

b. Between points *D* and *E* she might have been waiting at a stoplight. Between points *F* and *G* she was probably slowing down because she was near a school.

c. Answers will vary. One possible answer: The driver started out at home, got up to speed, and leveled off. She slowed down and stopped at a stoplight. When the light turned green, she speeded up but then slowed down because she was near a school. She drove more slowly for a while and then slowed to a stop at the school.

7. $[A] - [B] = \begin{bmatrix} 76 & 69 \\ 108 & 115 \\ 108 & 105 \\ 91 & 88 \end{bmatrix}$

CHALLENGE PROBLEM

During the last three months she must save a total of $500 - (53 \cdot 3 + 47 \cdot 4) = \$153$. Because $153/3 = 51$, she must save a mean of $51 during each of the last three months. It is not possible to calculate her savings for any one month because you are given mean amounts for each group of months, not individual amounts.

CHAPTER 1 · Test   Form B

1. a. sometimes   **b.** never   **c.** never
   d. sometimes   **e.** sometimes

2. a. A dot plot
   b. Mean: 2.1; median: 1.5; mode: 1
   c. 0, 1, 1.5, 3, 7

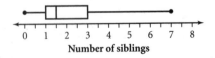

d. 2

e. Yes. 1.5(IQR) = 3; Q3 + 3 = 6. Therefore, 7 is an outlier.

f. 7

g. The mean, median, and mode will each be increased by 3. The IQR and the range will not be changed.

3. a. Points *J* and *K*   **b.** Points *G* and *H*
   c. $B(-3, 0)$; $E(6, 0)$; $I(0, -4)$

4. a. Five-number summaries: Group 1: 61, 62, 67, 68, 69; Group 2: 56, 60, 64, 72, 75; mean heights: Group 1: 65.6 in.; Group 2: 65 in.

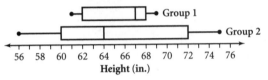

b. Answers will vary as to which group is taller. Students could argue that Group 2 has more taller people in it. However, Group 1 has a larger median (and mean) height, with less spread among the heights. But the means of the two groups are not too far apart. Group 2 has some tall people but also some very short people.

5. Answers will vary. A bin width of 2 gives ten bins—enough to show the patterns in the data.

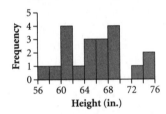

6. a. Between points *H* and *I*

b. Between points *B* and *C* she walked back home. She may have forgotten her homework and returned to get it. Between points *E* and *F* she stopped walking. She may have stopped to talk to someone.

c. Answers will vary. One possible answer: Jamila left home and walked at a steady pace. She realized she forgot her homework and went back to get it. She started out again, walking more quickly this time. She stopped to talk to a neighbor for a few minutes. Then she walked at a steady pace. She dropped a pen and had to backtrack a little to pick it up. She realized it was getting late and walked quickly the rest of the way.

7. $[A] + [B] = \begin{bmatrix} 18 & 22 \\ 10 & 11 \\ 11 & 10 \\ 22 & 23 \end{bmatrix}$

Discovering Algebra Assessment Resources / Answers
©2007 Key Curriculum Press

During the last four days the total number of visitors must be $2500 - (224 \cdot 4 + 328 \cdot 2) = 948$. Because $948/4 = 237$, a mean of 237 visitors per day must come to the gallery on each of the last four days. It is not possible to calculate the exact number of visitors on any one day because you are given mean numbers for each group of days, not individual numbers.

CHAPTER 1 · Constructive Assessment Options

SCORING RUBRICS

1. 5 Points

Answers should include most of the following points:

- Dot plots and stem plots show individual data values.

- Stem plots and histograms group data values into intervals.

- Box plots and histograms do not show individual data values.

- Histograms show the number of data values in each equal interval.

- Stem plots, dot plots, and histograms show the "shape" of a data set.

- The shape of a histogram depends on the bin width.

- Box plots let you see the spread of the data and the range for 25% intervals of the data.

- Dot plots and stem plots allow you to identify the mode of the data quickly.

- Box plots allow you to locate the median of the data quickly.

- All the graphs except the histogram reveal the minimum and maximum values.

3 Points

Answer mentions that dot plots and stem plots show every data value, while box plots and histograms do not. Answer also includes at least three other points from the list above.

1 Point

Answer mentions only one or two points from the list above.

2. 5 Points

Descriptions are correct. Sample data sets meet the constraint. Box plots are neat and accurate.

a. Sample answer: The values cluster toward the lower end of the range, but there are a few higher values that pull the mean above the median. One such data set is {1, 1, 1, 2, 2, 3, 5, 9, 10, 10}, which has a median of 2.5 and a mean of 4.4.

b. Sample answer: The values cluster toward the upper end of the range, but there are a few lower values that pull the mean below the median. One such data set is {1, 1, 1, 2, 7, 8, 9, 9, 10, 10}, which has a median of 7.5 and a mean of 5.8.

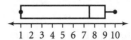

c. Sample answer: The values are fairly evenly distributed. High numbers are balanced out by low numbers. One such data set is {1, 2, 3, 4, 5, 5, 6, 6, 8, 10}, which has a mean of 5 and a median of 5.

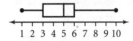

3 Points

Descriptions are given, but they are not clear or are incomplete. Sample data sets meet the constraint. Box plots are neat and accurate.

a. Sample description: There are more low numbers than high numbers.

b. Sample description: There are more high numbers than low numbers.

c. Sample description: Most of the values are the same.

1 Point

Sample data and box plots are correct for one or two box plots, but general descriptions are incorrect or missing.

3. 5 Points

a. The minimum and the lower quartile are equal. The upper quartile and the maximum are equal. The median is equal to either the lower quartile or the upper quartile.

b. The minimum, lower quartile, median, upper quartile, and maximum are equal.

c. The lower quartile, median, and upper quartile are equal.

d. The lower quartile, median, upper quartile, and maximum are equal.

3 Points

Answers are mostly correct, but some information is missing.

1 Point

Some answers are correct, but many of the answers are inadequate or are missing.

4. 5 Points

a. No, because the box plot shows only the five-number summary values. You can determine only that she was either 25 or 26 years old.

b. Answer demonstrates a thorough understanding of the five-number summary values. Sample answer:

The three youngest astronauts were either 25 or 26 years old.

The astronauts with the middle six ages were 26, 27, or 28 years old.

The three oldest of the youngest ten astronauts were either 28 or 29 years old.

c. The youngest was 25. The third youngest was 26. The fifth was 27. The sixth, seventh, and eighth were 28. The tenth was 29.

3 Points

a. Answer correctly states that the age cannot be determined, but explanation is unclear.

b. Answer demonstrates a partial understanding of the five-number summary values. Sample answer: Most of the ages are between 26 and 28.

c. The correct age is given for only three or four astronauts.

1 Point

a. Answer is correct, but no explanation is given.

b. Answer provides some correct information but does not demonstrate an understanding of the median or of quartiles. Sample answer: The numbers are between 25 and 29.

c. The correct age is only given for two astronauts.

5. 5 Points

Answer should include at least five correct observations. Sample observations:

The maximum value is almost the same for all the samples.

All the medians are close to 1995, so about half the coins in each sample have mint years of 1995 or earlier and half have mint years of 1995 or later.

For all the coins, the third quartile is less than or equal to 2002, indicating that about 75% of the mint years are earlier than 2002.

None of the samples include coins newer than 2005.

All the samples include coins with mint years in the 1970s except for the dimes.

The dimes have the smallest interquartile range (less than 10 years), and the quarters have the largest (about 20 years).

The spread and distribution of values for the nickels and quarters are very similar.

3 Points

At least three correct observations are given.

1 Point

Only one or two correct observations are given.

6. 5 Points

Matches are correct, and clear explanations are given.

a. i. Sample explanation: From the histogram, you can see that the data set has ten values. The (data value representing the) lower quartile is the third value, which is in the second bar of the histogram. This value is 1 unit greater than the minimum. The median is halfway between the fifth and sixth values, so it is between the values represented by the third and fourth bars. This value is 2.5 units greater than the minimum. Only box plot i has a lower quartile 1 unit greater than the minimum and a median 2.5 units greater than the minimum.

b. iii. Sample explanation: The (data value representing the) first quartile is in the second bar and is 1 unit greater than the minimum. The median is between the second and third bars and is 1.5 units greater than the minimum. Only box plot iii has a lower quartile 1 unit greater than the minimum and a median 1.5 units greater than the minimum.

c. ii. Sample explanation: The (data value representing the) first quartile is in the second bar and is 2 units greater than the minimum. Only box plot ii has a lower quartile 2 units greater than the minimum.

3 Points

Matches are correct, but explanations are missing or involve incorrect reasoning.

1 Point

Only one match is correct.

7. 5 Points

For each graph, the answer includes four correct observations and a description of information that can be found from that graph but not from the other two graphs.

a. Sample answer: The gold-medal times have generally decreased over the years. The fastest time was in 1996. The slowest time was in 1908. The times range from a little over 19 s to a little under 23 s. The scatter plot is the only graph that lets you see the year value corresponding to each time value.

b. Sample answer: The range of times is between about 19.3 s and 22.6 s. The median time is about 20.5 s. About 25% of the times are less than 20 s. The interquartile range is about 1.6 s. The box plot is the only plot that allows you to quickly find the median time.

Discovering Algebra Assessment Resources / Answers
©2007 Key Curriculum Press

c. Sample answer: Six of the winning times are greater than 20 s but less than 20.5 s. Fifteen of the winning times are greater than or equal to 19 s but less than 21 s. Only one person has finished in less than 19.5 s. Only one person has won the gold medal with a time of 22.5 s or greater. The histogram is the only graph that allows you to quickly find the number of times in each 0.5 s interval.

3 Points
Answers include only three correct observations for each graph.

1 Point
Answers include only one correct observation for each graph.

8. 5 Points
Listed points are correct. Descriptions are clear and accurate. Graph is drawn correctly.

a. Sample answer: $(-5, -3)$, $(0, 2)$, $(2, 4)$, $(3, 5)$; the points lie on a line that is parallel to and 2 units above the line $y = x$.

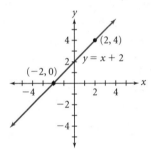

b. Sample answer: $(-3, -6)$, $(-1, -2)$, $(0, 0)$, $(1, 2)$, $(2, 4)$; the points lie on a line that passes through the origin and is steeper than $y = x$.

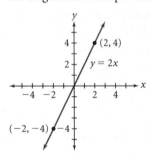

c. Sample answer: $(-2, -7)$, $(-1, -4)$, $(0, -1)$, $(2, 5)$, $(4, 11)$; the points lie on a line that is much steeper than the line of $y = x$ and that passes through $(0, -1)$.

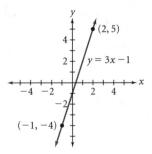

3 Points
Listed points are correct. Description is unclear, but graph is accurate.

1 Point
Listed points are correct. Description and graph are incorrect.

CHAPTER 2 · Quiz 1   **Form A**

1. a. $\frac{2}{3} > \frac{7}{12}$ **b.** $\frac{11}{15} > \frac{2}{3}$ **c.** $\frac{5}{7} < \frac{20}{27}$
   d. $\frac{11}{15} < \frac{20}{27}$ **e.** $\frac{10}{14} = \frac{25}{35}$

2. a. $x = 35$ **b.** $y = 98$ **c.** $z = 49.5$

3. About 765 deer

4. a. $\frac{35}{100} = \frac{12}{x}$; $x \approx 34.3$ **b.** $\frac{500}{400} = \frac{x}{100}$; 125%

5. About 110 students

6. a. $\frac{1}{2.54} = \frac{67}{a}$; $a = 170.18$ cm

   b. $\frac{1}{2.54} = \frac{b}{13.5}$; $b \approx 5.3$ in.

7. 88 ft/s

CHAPTER 2 · Quiz 1   **Form B**

1. a. $\frac{2}{3} < \frac{7}{9}$ **b.** $\frac{2}{3} > \frac{16}{25}$ **c.** $\frac{14}{18} = \frac{21}{27}$
   d. $\frac{21}{33} < \frac{13}{18}$ **e.** $\frac{16}{25} > \frac{21}{33}$

2. a. $x = 15$ **b.** $y = 81$ **c.** $z = 26.25$

3. About 390 deer

4. a. $\frac{48}{100} = \frac{57.6}{x}$; $x = 120$ **b.** $\frac{600}{150} = \frac{x}{100}$; 400%

5. About 150 students

6. a. $\frac{1}{2.54} = \frac{62.5}{a}$; $a = 158.75$ cm

   b. $\frac{1}{2.54} = \frac{b}{20}$; $b \approx 7.9$ in.

7. $13.\overline{63}$ mi/h, or about 13.6 mi/h

CHAPTER 2 · Quiz 2   **Form A**

1. a. $3.89   **b.** $19.45   **c.** Cashews   **d.** 3 lb

2. a. Estimates will vary. The actual equivalent is 40.50 Australian dollars.

b. 1.35 Australian dollars per U.S. dollar

c. $y = 1.35x$

d. 40.50 Australian dollars

e. 53.33 U.S. dollars

3. a. Direct variation; y increases at a constant rate; the graph is a straight line through the origin.

b. Inverse variation; the variables have a constant product ($x \cdot y = 36$).

c. Inverse variation; this is the graph of $xy = k$, a curve that does not cross either axis.

d. Direct variation; the ratio of the variables is constant; the relationship can be represented by $y = 3x$, which is a direct-variation equation.

e. Neither; it looks like a direct variation, but it does not go through the origin.

f. Inverse variation; the equation is of the form $y = \frac{k}{x}$ (in this case, $k = 24$).

g. Direct variation; the equation is of the form $y = kx$ (in this case, $k = 12$).

CHAPTER 2 · Quiz 2   Form B

1. a. $3.27

b. $16.35

c. Walnuts

d. 4.5 lb

2. a. Estimates will vary. The actual equivalent is 16.50 British pounds.

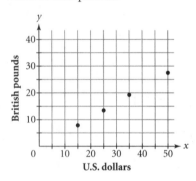

b. 0.55 pound per dollar

c. $y = 0.55x$

d. 16.50 British pounds

e. $130.91

3. a. Direct variation; y changes at a constant rate; the graph is a straight line through the origin.

b. Direct variation; the ratio of the variables is constant; the relationship can be represented by $y = 6x$, which is a direct-variation equation.

c. Neither; it looks like a direct variation, but it does not go through the origin.

d. Inverse variation; the variables have a constant product ($xy = 12$).

e. Inverse variation; this is the graph of $xy = k$, a curve that does not cross either axis.

f. Direct variation; the equation is of the form $y = kx$ (in this case, $k = -24$).

g. Inverse variation; the equation is of the form $y = \frac{k}{x}$ (in this case, $k = 15$).

CHAPTER 2 · Quiz 3   Form A

1. a. 51   **b.** 81   **c.** 62

d. 2   **e.** $\frac{576}{-12.2} \approx -47.2$

2. a. $2\left(\frac{x + 12}{4} - 7\right)$ **b.** -5.5

3. a. Pick a number. Add 9. Multiply by 3. Add 6. Divide by 3. Subtract your original number.

b. Starting numbers will vary. The result will be 11 for any starting number.

c. Dividing by 3 undoes the multiplication by 3. Subtracting N undoes picking the original number.

4. a. $x = 56$ **b.** $x = -1.5$

CHAPTER 2 · Quiz 3   Form B

1. a. -15 **b.** -36 **c.** 36

d. -9 **e.** 1

2. a. $3\left(\frac{x - 8}{-4} + 11\right)$ **b.** 35.25

3. a. Pick a number. Add 7. Multiply by 5. Add 10. Divide by 5. Subtract your original number.

b. Starting numbers will vary. The result will be 9 for any starting number.

c. Dividing by 5 undoes the multiplication by 5. Subtracting N undoes picking the original number.

4. a. $x = 36$ **b.** $x = -11.2$

CHAPTER 2 · Test   Form A

1. a. $P = 21.25$ **b.** $x = 10.\overline{6}$

2. 15 cups of white rice, 6 cups of wild rice

3. About 320 seals

4. 22.5 mi/h

5. a. $5.76   **b.** 14 oz

6. a. Dividing each gram value by the corresponding ounce value shows that there are about 28.3 grams per ounce. The equation $y = 28.3x$ relates weight in ounces, x, to weight in grams, y.

b. Direct variation   **c.** About 24.7 oz

7. a. 6 in.   **b.** 4 in.   **c.** about 7.7 in.

   d. Inverse variation; the product is constant.

8. a. 1   **b.** −8

9. a. $x = 1.9$ **b.** $x = -6$

CHALLENGE PROBLEM

$x = 2.4$ in.; inverse variation; the product of the left nickels and the left distance is constant.

CHAPTER 2 · Test   Form B

  1. a. $P = 23.4375$

    b. $x = 5.\overline{81}$

  2. 21 cups of white rice, 9 cups of wild rice

  3. About 269 seals

  4. About 318.3 ft/s

  5. a. $4.48

    b. 26 oz

  6. a. Dividing each kilometer value by the corresponding mile value shows that there are about 1.6 kilometers per mile. The equation $y = 1.6x$ relates length in miles, x, to length in kilometers, y.

    b. Direct variation

    c. 1200 km

  7. a. 2 in.   **b.** 9 in.   **c.** About 8.5 in.

    d. Inverse variation; the product is constant.

  8. a. 22.75

    b. −8

  9. a. $x = -0.525$

    b. $x = 9$

CHALLENGE PROBLEM

$x = 3$ in.; inverse variation; the product of the left nickels and the left distance is constant.

CHAPTER 2 · Constructive Assessment Options

SCORING RUBRICS

1. 5 Points

Answer correctly explains what Jacki did wrong and why her reasoning is incorrect. Correct solutions to both problems are given. Sample answer: Jacki sets up the proportions correctly but solves them incorrectly. She finds the difference between the two denominators. Then she adds that number to the numerator

of the first ratio to get the numerator of the second ratio. This does not make sense; finding equivalent ratios involves multiplying both parts of the ratio by the same number. Here are the steps for solving the first problem.

$$\frac{2}{3} = \frac{x}{12} \qquad \text{Original proportion.}$$

$$12 \cdot \frac{2}{3} = x \qquad \text{Multiply by 12 to undo the division.}$$

$$8 = x \qquad \text{Multiply and divide.}$$

There are eight boys in the class.

Here are the steps for solving the second problem.

$$\frac{8}{12} = \frac{x}{112} \qquad \text{Original proportion.}$$

$$112 \cdot \frac{8}{12} = x \qquad \text{Multiply by 112 to undo the division.}$$

$$75 \approx x \qquad \text{Multiply and divide.}$$

There are 75 students in the math club.

3 Points

Answer correctly explains what Jacki did wrong, but the explanation of why her reasoning does not make sense is not completely correct or is unclear. Solutions to problems are mostly correct.

1 Point

Answer correctly explains what Jacki did wrong, but the explanation of why her reasoning does not make sense is missing or is incorrect. Solutions to problems are missing or are incorrect.

2. 5 Points

Answers and explanations are correct.

  a. True. Possible explanation: Because about 2 drachmas are the same weight as about 9 g, the drachma must be heavier.

  b. False. Possible explanation: The number of grams is more than four times greater than the number of drachmas, so 15 drachmas is about 65 g, and 65 drachmas is about 280 g.

  c. False. Possible explanation: The ratio is $\frac{2.2 \text{ drachmas}}{9.4 \text{ g}}$, which is equal to about $\frac{1 \text{ drachma}}{4.3 \text{ g}}$, not $\frac{4.3 \text{ drachmas}}{1 \text{ g}}$.

  d. True. Possible explanation: Using the values in the table, we find that the number of grams divided by the number of drachmas is about 4.3. Because $100 \div 23 \approx 4.3$, the statement is true.

3 Points

Answers are correct, but one or two of the explanations are vague or incorrect.

1 Point

Answers are correct, but no explanations are given, or one or two answers are incorrect, but the correct answers have good, clear explanations.

3. 5 Points

a. Let x and y represent the variables. Then find the ratios of y-values to corresponding x-values. The ratios should be the same or very close (if the ratios are not exactly the same, find the mean or median of the ratios). If k is the common ratio, then the equation is $\frac{y}{x} = k$, or $y = kx$.

b. Answer mentions solving the equation, tracing a graph, and using a calculator table, and provides a detailed explanation of each method. Sample answer: You can substitute the known x- or y-value into the equation and solve to find the other value. If the x-value is known, you just need to multiply it by k to find the y-value. If the y-value is known, you need to divide it by k to find the x-value.

You can graph the equation (by hand or by using a calculator). The graph will be a line. If you know the x-value, find the point on the line whose x-coordinate is that value. The corresponding y-coordinate is the unknown y-value. If you know the y-value, find the point on the line whose y-coordinate is that value. The corresponding x-coordinate is the unknown x-value.

You can make a calculator table. Then look for the known x- or y-value and find the corresponding y- or x-value. If you know the x-value, you can enter it as the start value; the unknown y-value will be the first y-value listed in the table. If you know the y-value, you may have to repeatedly adjust the start value and x-interval until that value (or a close approximation) appears in the table. For example, suppose the known y-value is 0.51 and the table shows that the x-value 1 corresponds to the y-value 0.3 and the x-value 2 corresponds to the y-value 0.6. This means that the unknown x-value must be between 1 and 2. Change the table settings to start at 1 and show x-values in intervals of 0.1. Then look at the table again. Continue to adjust the settings until the exact known y-value or a close approximation of it appears in the table.

3 Points

a. Answer is mostly correct but lacks detail.

b. Three correct methods are given with explanations, but one or two important details are missing, or only two correct methods are given, but the explanations are complete and detailed.

1 Point

a. The correct form of the equation is given, but the answer does not explain how to find it.

b. Two or three correct methods are given, but no details are provided, or only one correct method is given, but the explanation is complete.

4. 5 Points

Answer correctly identifies Chen's mistake and offers two clear, correct suggestions for fixing it. Possible answer: Chen's scatter plot shows the L1 values (liquid ounces) on the x-axis and the L2 values (cubic inches) on the y-axis. However, in her equation, $y = 0.56x$, x represents L2 values and y represents L1 values $\left(\frac{\text{L1}}{\text{L2}} = 0.56, \text{ so L1} = 0.56 \cdot \text{L2}\right)$. To fix her mistake, she could plot L2 on the x-axis and L1 on the y-axis. Or she could divide L2 by L1 to get 1.8 and then change her equation to $y = 1.8x$. In this equation, x represents the L1 values and y represents the L2 values $\left(\frac{\text{L2}}{\text{L1}} = 1.8, \text{ so L2} = 1.8\text{L1}\right)$.

3 Points

Chen's mistake is identified, and answer clearly describes one method for fixing Chen's mistake, or answer describes two methods, but the explanations are not completely clear.

1 Point

Chen's mistake is identified, but no suggestion is provided for correcting the mistake, or the suggestion is unclear or incorrect.

5. 5 Points

a. If the ratio of the variables is constant (or nearly constant), the relationship is a direct variation. If the product of the variables is constant (or nearly constant), the relationship is an inverse variation. If neither the ratio nor the product is constant, the relationship is neither a direct variation nor an inverse variation.

b. The equation for a direct variation is in the form $\frac{y}{x} = k$, or $y = kx$, where x and y are the variables and k is a constant. The equation for an inverse variation is in the form $xy = k$, or $y = \frac{k}{x}$, where x and y are the variables and k is a constant.

c. The graph of a direct variation is a straight line through the origin. The graph of an inverse variation is a curve that never crosses the x- or y-axis. For positive x-values, as the x-values get closer to 0, the y-values get larger. As the x-values get larger, the y-values get closer to 0.

3 Points

Answers are mostly correct and show understanding of direct and inverse variation, but are not as thorough as answers above.

1 Point

Answers make some correct points, but show little understanding of direct and inverse variation.

6. 5 Points

Problem and solution should be clear and correct and should fit the criteria. Sample problems and solutions:

Q: Peter decides to save the same amount from his allowance each week. After 2 weeks, he will have saved $4. How much will he have saved after 8 weeks?

A: The ratio of the amount saved to the number of weeks is constant. If x is the amount saved, then $\frac{4}{2} = \frac{x}{8}$. The value of x is 16, so Peter will have saved $16 after 8 weeks.

Q: The number of hours it takes to paint a house is inversely proportional to the number of painters. If it takes four painters 8 hours, how long will it take two painters?

A: The product of painters and hours is constant. Because four painters take 8 hours, the constant product is 4 · 8, or 32. Because 2 · 16 = 32, it will take two painters 16 hours to finish the job.

3 Points

Problems address the criteria given, but solutions provide little or no explanation.

1 Point

Problems meet the criteria, but no solutions are given, or only one correct problem and solution are given.

7. 5 Points

A correct expression is given for each whole number from 1 through 9. Sample answers:

$4 \div 4 + (4 - 4) = 1$

$4 \div 4 + 4 \div 4 = 2$

$(4 + 4 + 4) \div 4 = 3$

$(4 - 4) \cdot 4 + 4 = 4$

$(4 \cdot 4 + 4) \div 4 = 5$

$(4 + 4) \div 4 + 4 = 6$

$4 + 4 - 4 \div 4 = 7$

$4 + 4 - 4 + 4 = 8$

$4 + 4 + 4 \div 4 = 9$

3 Points

Only five or six correct expressions are given.

1 Point

Only two or three correct expressions are given.

1. a.

Time elapsed (mo)	Maria	Yolanda	Todd
0	$800	$1,200	$2,400
1	$825	$1,158	$2,315
2	$850	$1,116	$2,230
3	$875	$1,074	$2,145
4	$900	$1,032	$2,060
5	$925	$990	$1,975
6	$950	$948	$1,890

b. 6

c. After 5 months, there will be $925 in Maria's account, $990 in Yolanda's account, and $1,975 in Todd's account.

d. 28

2.

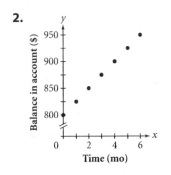

3. Jon starts 0.5 m from the 0 mark and walks away from the 0 mark at the rate of 1 m/s for the first 2 s. For the next 2 s, he walks at the rate of 0.75 m/s toward the 0 mark. For the last 2 s, he walks at 1 m/s away from the 0 mark.

4. a. ii   **b.** iii   **c.** iv

  d. The recursive routine 0.5 ENTER,
  Ans + 0.5 ENTER, ENTER, . . . generates the y-values for graph i.

1. a.

Time elapsed (mo)	Maria	Yolanda	Todd
0	$1,000	$1,200	$2,200
1	$1,045	$1,170	$2,125
2	$1,090	$1,140	$2,050
3	$1,135	$1,110	$1,975
4	$1,180	$1,080	$1,900
5	$1,225	$1,050	$1,825
6	$1,270	$1,020	$1,750

b. 3

c. After 4 months, there will be $1,180 in Maria's account, $1,080 in Yolanda's account, and $1,900 in Todd's account.

d. 23

2.

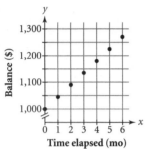

3. Jon starts 4 m from the 0 mark and walks toward the 0 mark at the rate of 1.5 m/s for the first 2 s. For the next 2 s he stands still (that is, he walks at a rate of 0 m/s). For the last 2 s, he walks at a rate of 1 m/s away from the 0 mark.

4. a. iii   **b.** iv   **c.** i

    d. The recursive routine 2 $\boxed{\text{ENTER}}$, Ans -0.25 $\boxed{\text{ENTER}}$, $\boxed{\text{ENTER}}$, ... generates the y-values for graph ii.

CHAPTER 3 · Quiz 2   Form A

1. a. $C = 5 + 1.25r$

    b. The $5 admission fee is the y-intercept. The $1.25 cost per ride affects the steepness of the graph. The graph rises 1.25 units for every 1 unit you move right. (Note: The graph of $C = 1.25r$ is added in 1e.)

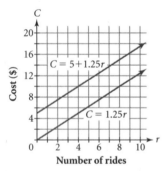

Number of rides

    c. 7

    d. $C = 1.25r$. This equation has the same coefficient of x but a different y-intercept. For this equation, the y-intercept is 0. For the equation in 1a, the y-intercept is 5.

    e. See the answer to 1b for the graph. The two graphs have the same steepness, but the graph of $C = 5 + 1.25r$ intersects the y-axis at $(0, 5)$, while the graph of $C = 1.25r$ intersects the y-axis at $(0, 0)$.

2. a. 3   **b.** -6 **c.** $y = -6 + 3x$

3. a. i. -12 **ii.** 7   **iii.** $\dfrac{8}{3}$ **iv.** -5.1

    b. i. $\dfrac{1}{12}$ **ii.** $-\dfrac{1}{7}$ **iii.** $-\dfrac{3}{8}$ **iv.** $\dfrac{1}{5.1}$, or $\dfrac{10}{51}$

4. The balancing method is shown for 4a, and undoing is shown for 4b. Students may use either method.

    a.
$$-12 - 3.75x = 6.75$$
$$-12 - 3.75x + 12 = 6.75 + 12$$
$$-3.75x = 18.75$$
$$\frac{-3.75x}{-3.75} = \frac{18.75}{-3.75}$$
$$x = -5$$

    b.
$$\frac{32 + 4(x - 8)}{3} = 10$$
$$32 + 4(x - 8) = 10 \cdot 3$$
$$32 + 4(x - 8) = 30$$
$$4(x - 8) = 30 - 32$$
$$4(x - 8) = -2$$
$$x - 8 = \frac{-2}{4}$$
$$x - 8 = -0.5$$
$$x = -0.5 + 8$$
$$x = 7.5$$

CHAPTER 3 · Quiz 2   Form B

1. a. $C = 7 + 1.50r$

    b. The $7 admission fee is the y-intercept. The $1.50 cost per ride affects the steepness of the graph. The graph rises 1.50 units for every 1 unit you move to the right. (Note: The graph of $C = 1.50r$ is added in 1e.)

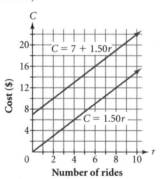

Number of rides

    c. 11

    d. $C = 1.50r$. This equation has the same coefficient of x but a different y-intercept. For this equation, the y-intercept is 0. For the equation in 1a, the y-intercept is 7.

    e. See the answer to 1b for the graph. The two graphs have the same steepness, but the graph of $C = 7 + 1.50r$ intersects the y-axis at $(0, 7)$, and the graph of $C = 1.50r$ intersects the y-axis at $(0, 0)$.

2. a. -4 **b.** 5 **c.** $y = 5 - 4x$

3. a. i. -7 **ii.** 12 **iii.** $-\dfrac{9}{2}$ **iv.** 3.8

   b. i. $\dfrac{1}{7}$ **ii.** $-\dfrac{1}{12}$ **iii.** $\dfrac{2}{9}$ **iv.** $-\dfrac{1}{3.8}$, or $-\dfrac{5}{19}$

4. The balancing method is shown for 4a, and undoing is shown for 4b. Students may use either method.

  a.
$$-3.5 - 2.25x = 5.5$$
$$-3.5 - 2.25x + 3.5 = 5.5 + 3.5$$
$$-2.25x = 9$$
$$\frac{-2.25x}{-2.25} = \frac{9}{-2.25}$$
$$x = -4$$

  b.
$$\frac{18 + 4(x + 6)}{3} = 20$$
$$18 + 4(x + 6) = 20 \cdot 3$$
$$18 + 4(x + 6) = 60$$
$$4(x + 6) = 60 - 18$$
$$4(x + 6) = 42$$
$$x + 6 = \frac{42}{4}$$
$$x + 6 = 10.5$$
$$x = 10.5 - 6$$
$$x = 4.5$$

CHAPTER 3 · Test   Form A

1. a. 120 $\boxed{\text{ENTER}}$, Ans $+ 4.75$ $\boxed{\text{ENTER}}$, $\boxed{\text{ENTER}}$, …

  b. $y = 120 + 4.75x$

  c. a is the value of the collection Leslie's sister gave her, and b is the cost of each new figurine.

  d. $y = 120 + 4.75(15) = 120 + 71.25 = 191.25$; the value is $191.25.

  e. 22

2. a.

Time elapsed (yr)	Value ($)
0	15,400
1	14,465
2	13,530
3	12,595
4	11,660

  b. $y = 15{,}400 - 935x$

  c. Possible answer:

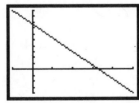

$[-5, 25, 5, -8000, 20000, 2000]$

d. The coefficient of x is -935. This is the change in the car's value each year.

e. The y-intercept is 15,400. This is the original cost of the car (that is, the car's value after 0 years have elapsed).

f. The graph crosses the x-axis at approximately $(16.47, 0)$. This means that the car has no value after approximately 16.47 years.

3. a. $\{1, -14.3\}$ $\boxed{\text{ENTER}}$, $\{\text{Ans}(1) + 1, \text{Ans}(2) + 0.8\}$ $\boxed{\text{ENTER}}$, $\boxed{\text{ENTER}}$, $\boxed{\text{ENTER}}$, …

  b. 19

4. a. $y = 4 + 1.5x$

  b. $y = -6.2 + 2.7x$

  c. $y = 7.75 - 7.25x$

5. The balancing method is shown for 5a, while undoing is shown for 5b. Students may use either method.

  a.

$-6(1 - 2x) - 12 = 0$	Original equation.
$-6(1 - 2x) - 12 + 12 = 0 + 12$	Add 12 to both sides.
$-6(1 - 2x) = 12$	Remove the 0s.
$\dfrac{-6(1 - 2x)}{-6} = \dfrac{12}{-6}$	Divide both sides by -6.
$1 - 2x = -2$	Reduce.
$1 - 2x - 1 = -2 - 1$	Subtract 1 from both sides.
$-2x = -3$	Evaluate and remove the 0.
$x = \dfrac{-3}{-2} = \dfrac{3}{2}$	Divide both sides by -2 and reduce.

  b.

$\dfrac{9 + 4x}{3} = -2$	Original equation.
$9 + 4x = -2 \cdot 3$	Multiply by 3 to undo the division.
$9 + 4x = -6$	Evaluate and reduce.
$4x = -6 - 9$	Subtract 9 to undo the addition.
$4x = -15$	Subtract.
$x = \dfrac{-15}{4} = -\dfrac{7}{2}$, or -3.5	Divide by 4 to undo the multiplication.

6. $h = \dfrac{3V}{\pi r^2}$

a. To find the rate of change, take any two points and calculate the ratio of the change in y-values to the change in x-values. The rate of change is 5. The y-intercept is the y-value when $x = 0$. This is given to be 30.

b. $y = 30 + 5x$

c. Answers will vary. Possible answer: $(-2, 20)$ and $(-4, 10)$; $20 = 30 + 5(-2)$ and $10 = 30 + 5(-4)$

CHAPTER 3 • Test   Form B

1. a. 95 ENTER, Ans + 5.25 ENTER, ENTER, ENTER, . . .

   b. $y = 95 + 5.25x$

   c. a is the value of the collection Leslie's sister gave her, and b is the cost of each new figurine.

   d. $y = 95 + 5.25(10) = 95 + 52.50 = 147.50$; the value is $147.50.

   e. 18

2. a.

Time elapsed (yr)	Value ($)
0	16,500
1	15,250
2	14,000
3	12,750
4	11,500

   b. $y = 16,500 - 1,250x$

   c. Possible answer:

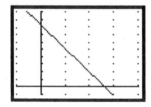

   $[-5, 20, 5, -2000, 20000, 2000]$

   d. The coefficient of x is $-1,250$. This is the change in the car's value each year.

   e. The y-intercept is 16,500. This is the original cost of the car (that is, the car's value after 0 years have elapsed).

   f. The graph crosses the x-axis at $(13.2, 0)$. This means that the car has no value after approximately 13.2 years.

3. a. $\{1, -11.2\}$ ENTER, $\{\text{Ans}(1) + 1, \text{Ans}(2) + 2.6\}$ ENTER, ENTER, ENTER, . . .

   b. 10

4. a. $y = 3.5 + 2.5x$

   b. $y = -10.8 + 1.2x$

   c. $y = 14 - 4.75x$

5. The balancing method is shown for 5a, and undoing is shown for 5b. Students may use either method.

   a.
$36 - 3(2 - 4x) = 0$	Original equation.
$36 - 3(2 - 4x) - 36 = 0 - 36$	Subtract 36 from both sides.
$-3(2 - 4x) = -36$	Evaluate and remove the 0.
$\dfrac{-3(2 - 4x)}{-3} = \dfrac{-36}{-3}$	Divide both sides by -3.
$2 - 4x = 12$	Reduce.
$2 - 4x - 2 = 12 - 2$	Subtract 2 from both sides.
$-4x = 10$	Evaluate and remove the 0.
$x = \dfrac{10}{-4} = -\dfrac{5}{2}$, or -2.5	Divide both sides by -4 and reduce.

   b.
$\dfrac{-7 + 5x}{5} = -3$	Original equation.
$-7 + 5x = -3 \cdot 5$	Multiply by 5 to undo the division.
$-7 + 5x = -15$	Multiply.
$5x = -15 + 7$	Add 7.
$5x = -8$	Evaluate.
$x = \dfrac{-8}{5} = -\dfrac{8}{5}$, or -1.6	Divide by 5 to undo the multiplication and reduce.

6. $w = \dfrac{3V}{lh}$

CHALLENGE PROBLEM

a. To find the rate of change, take any two points and calculate the ratio of the change in y-values to the change in x-values. The rate of change is 5.5. The y-intercept is the y-value when $x = 0$. This is given to be 45.

b. $y = 45 + 5.5x$

c. Answers will vary. Possible answer: $(-2, 34)$ and $(-4, 23)$; $34 = 45 + 5.5(-2)$ and $23 = 45 + 5.5(-4)$

SCORING RUBRICS

1. 5 Points

a. The situation described fits the routine, and the explanation of how the starting values and rules fit the situation is correct. Sample answer: Rachel started the school year with 213 sheets of notebook paper. Each day she used 8 sheets. The starting values {0, 213} represent the initial {*day, number of sheets*} values. This fits the situation, because on day 0 Rachel has 213 sheets. The rules {Ans(1) + 1, Ans(2) − 8} add 1 to the day and subtract 8 from the number of sheets. This fits the situation because Rachel uses 8 sheets each day.

b. Questions are clear and answers are correct. Sample questions and answers are based on the situation described in part a.

Q: How many sheets will Rachel have left after 11 days? **A:** 125

Q: When will Rachel first have fewer than ten sheets left? **A:** After 26 days

3 Points

a. The situation is correct, but the explanation is vague or incomplete. Sample answer: Tom owes his father $213. He works off $8 of debt for each hour he helps his father with the yard work. The values {0, 213} represent the starting amounts. The rules show how the debt is decreasing.

b. Questions are clear, but one or both answers are incorrect.

1 Point

a. The situation is mostly correct, but no explanation is given for how the starting values and rules fit the situation. Sample answer: Lilly has $213 and spends $8 every day.

b. Only one question and answer are given, or two questions are given without answers.

2. 5 Points

All four routines are correct.

a. {0, 3} ENTER,
{Ans(1) + 1, Ans(2) + 5} ENTER, ENTER, . . .

b. {0, −2} ENTER,
{Ans(1) + 1, Ans(2) − 6} ENTER, ENTER, . . .

c. Sample answer: {0, 19} ENTER,
{Ans(1) + 1, Ans(2) − 3} ENTER, ENTER, . . .

d. Sample answer: {0, −23} ENTER,
{Ans(1) + 1, Ans(2) + 6} ENTER, ENTER, . . .

3 Points

Three of the routines are correct.

1 Point

Only one routine is correct.

3. 5 Points

The units and scales are clearly defined. The story mentions specific times, rates, and distances, and accounts for each segment of the graph. Possible answer: The x-axis represents time in hours, with each tick mark representing 1 h. The y-axis represents distance in miles, with each tick mark representing 10 mi. Maya is training for a cross-country bike trip. She plans to ride to a park 50 mi from her house and then ride home. She begins her ride at a friend's house 10 mi from her home. For the first 2 h of her trip, she rides at 15 mi/h. After 2 h, when she is 40 mi from her home, she gets very tired and slows her pace to about 3.3 mi/h for the next 3 h. She reaches the park at the 5 h mark and stops for 1 h to rest and eat lunch. Then she starts riding toward home at a speed of 10 mi/h. After 3.5 h at this pace, she decides she is too tired to bike all the way home, so she stops at her aunt's apartment, which is 15 mi from her home.

3 Points

The units and scales are clearly defined. The story accounts for each segment of the graph, but one or two numbers are incorrect.

1 Point

The units and scales are clearly defined. The story accounts for each segment of the graph but uses few specific numbers or uses incorrect numbers. Sample story: A runner starts out going very fast and then slows down. The runner rests for a while and then runs back to where he started.

4. 5 Points

a. The lines have the same relative positions as those shown here.

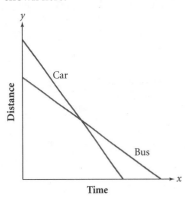

b. i. The y-intercept would be smaller, and the coefficient of x would be a larger negative number.

   ii. The y-intercept would stay the same, and the coefficient of x would be a smaller negative number.

c. Car A started farther from Chicago than car B. Both cars drove at the same speed.

3 Points

The answer to one part is incorrect or missing.

1 Point

The answers to two parts are incorrect or missing.

5. 5 Points

All the items are grouped correctly, work is shown, and a correct explanation is given. The groups are {a, d, i, k}, {b, h, l}, {c, f, j}, and {e, g}. Sample explanation: First I wrote an equation for each table, recursive routine, or graph. Then I grouped the items with matching equations.

a. $y = 1 - 2x$ **b.** $y = -1 + 2x$

c. $y = -2 + 0.5x$ **d.** $y = 1 - 2x$

e. $y = -2$ **f.** $y = -2 + 0.5x$

g. $y = -2$ **h.** $y = -1 + 2x$

i. $y = 1 - 2x$ **j.** $y = -2 + 0.5x$

k. $y = 1 - 2x$ **l.** $y = -1 + 2x$

3 Points

Two or three items are grouped incorrectly. Work is shown and an explanation is given, but the explanation is somewhat vague. Sample explanation: I looked at how *y* changed and matched things that changed the same way.

1 Point

Only a few items are grouped correctly. Some work is shown, but the explanation is unclear or missing.

6. 5 Points

Answers are correct. Explanations are thorough and demonstrate an understanding of important concepts.

a. True. Possible explanation: Find the rate of change by dividing the difference between two *profit* values by the difference between the corresponding *cups* values. You get $0.50 per cup. You can start with the profit of $1.75 for 15 cups and work backward.

Profit for 14 cups: $1.75 − $0.50 = $1.25

Profit for 13 cups: $1.25 − $0.50 = $0.75

Profit for 12 cups: $0.75 − $0.50 = $0.25

Profit for 11 cups: $0.25 − $0.50 = −$0.25

So Rob doesn't make a profit until he sells 12 cups.

b. False. Possible explanation: The rate of change between any two points is $0.50 per cup. For example, $\frac{4.75 - 1.75}{21 - 15} = \frac{3}{6} = 0.5$. So Rob earns $0.50 per cup, not $0.12 per cup.

c. True. Possible explanation: The rate of change, $0.50 per cup, can be found by dividing the difference of any two *profit* values by the difference between the corresponding *cups* values. The starting value (that is, the profit for 0 cups) can be found by starting with $1.75 and subtracting 15 · $0.50. The result is −$5.75. So the equation is $p = -5.75 + 0.5c$.

d. False. Possible explanation: If you substitute 200 for *c* in the equation, you get $94.25. Rob actually needs to sell 212 cups (you can find this by solving the equation $100 = -5.75 + 0.5c$). Some explanations might include the suggestion that $5.75 may not have bought enough cups and lemonade for 200 sales.

3 Points

At least three answers are correct. Explanations are well written, but a few minor details are missing or incorrect.

1 Point

Answers are correct, but no explanations are given. Or only one or two answers are correct, but the correct answers have clear explanations.

7. 5 Points

a.

Time (hours from noon)	Distance (miles from Flint)
1.2	140.4
2.6	213.2
4.6	317.2

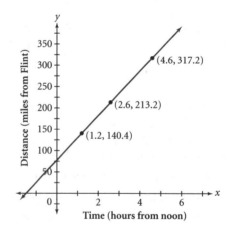

b. $d = 78 + 52t$

c. 52 mi/h. Explanations may vary. Sample explanation: In the 2 h from 2:30 to 4:30, Samantha covered 104 mi. That is 52 mi/h.

Discovering Algebra Assessment Resources / Answers
©2007 Key Curriculum Press

d. 78 mi from Flint. Explanations may vary. Sample explanation: At noon, that is, at $t = 0$, the y-intercept is 78.

e. At 10:30 A.M. Explanations may vary. Sample explanation: When she left Flint, $d = 0$. Solve the equation for t when $d = 0$:

$$0 = 78 + 52t$$

$$-78 = 52t$$

$$-\frac{78}{52} = t$$

$$t = -1.5$$

Samantha started 1.5 h before noon, or at 10:30 A.M.

This is the x-intercept of the equation.

f. At 6:30 P.M.

$$416 = 78 + 52t$$

$$338 = 52t$$

$$\frac{338}{52} = t$$

$$t = 6.5$$

That is 6.5 h after noon, or 6:30 P.M.

3 Points

a. This is done correctly.

b. The equation is correct.

c. The speed is correct, but the explanation is missing.

d. The answer is correct, but the explanation is missing.

e. The answer is correct, but the explanation is missing.

f. The answer is correct.

1 Point

a. This is done correctly.

b. The equation is close to being correct. For example, the speed is correct, but the y-intercept is read from the graph and not exactly correct.

c. The answer is consistent with the equation.

d. The answer is consistent with the equation.

e. The answer is close. If the answer is read from the graph it may not be exactly correct, but the student is looking at the x-intercept.

f. This answer is not correct.

1. a. Kerry. One state has between 50 and 54 electoral votes. That is the most populous state. Two states have between 30 and 34 electoral votes. These would be the second and third most populous states. One was won by each candidate. If Bush won the second most populous state, Kerry must have won the third.

b. 20. Add the heights of the bars: $7 + 2 + 5 + 2 + 2 + 1 + 1 = 20$.

c. This cannot be determined from the graphs. The histograms do not show the exact number of electoral votes for each state, so we cannot find the total.

d. About 32%. Find the total of the number of states won by Bush by adding the bar heights: $6 + 15 + 5 + 2 + 1 + 1 + 1 = 31$. Of these, 10 had 10 or more electoral votes; $\frac{10}{31} \approx 0.323$, so about 32% of the states won by Bush had 10 or more electoral votes.

e. This cannot be determined from the graphs. We know only that the greatest number of electoral votes was between 50 and 54.

f. About 55%. 11 states had 15 or more electoral votes. Of these, 6 were won by Kerry. $\frac{6}{11} \approx 0.545$. So about 55% of the states with 15 or more electoral votes were won by Kerry.

2. About 44; solve $\frac{22}{65} = \frac{15}{x}$.

3. Five-number summary: $\{37, 76, 147.5, 256, 440\}$

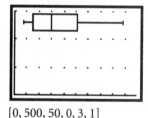

$[0, 500, 50, 0, 3, 1]$

4. a. Filler-Up

b. Filler-Up: $28.56; Lou's: $28.92

c. Filler-Up: a little more than 4.2 gal; Lou's: a little more than 4.1 gal

5. a. Inverse variation. The product of x and y is constant; $xy = 4$, or $y = \frac{4}{x}$.

b. Neither. Neither the product nor the ratio of x and y is constant.

c. Neither. Neither the product nor the ratio of x and y is constant.

d. Direct variation. The ratio of y to x is constant; $\frac{y}{x} = 5$, or $y = 5x$.

6. About 0.66 European euros

7. a. 36(0.75), ENTER; Ans + 2(0.75), ENTER, ENTER, ENTER, ENTER, ENTER, ENTER. The sequence is: 27.00, 28.50, 30.00, 31.50, 33.00, 34.50, 36.00.

Note: To show two decimal places on your calculator, press MODE and scroll to 2 in the second line.

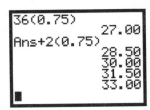

b.

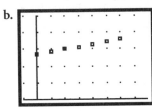

$[-1, 8, 1, 0, 50, 10]$

c. $1.50 per week

d. $V = 27 + 1.50n$

e. 16 weeks

8. a. $y = 112 - 0.85x$

b. The slope -0.85 means that 0.85 gal of water leaks out of the pool every minute. The y-intercept, 112, means that the pool contained 112 gal when it was filled.

c. In about 132 min

9. a. $a = -3$ **b.** $b = 12$ **c.** $c = 0.2$

CHAPTERS 1–3 · Exam   Form B

1. a. Bush. None of the states won by Kerry had between 25 and 29 electoral votes, but one of the states won by Bush did. So Bush must have won Florida.

b. 31. Add the heights of the bars: $6 + 15 + 5 + 2 + 1 + 1 + 1 = 31$.

c. This cannot be determined from the graphs. The histograms do not show the exact numbers of electoral votes for each state, so we cannot find the total.

d. 55%. Find the total number of states won by Kerry by adding the bar heights: $7 + 2 + 5 + 2 + 2 + 1 + 1 = 20$. Of these 20 states, 11 had 10 or more electoral votes. $\frac{11}{20} = 0.55$, so 55% of the states won by Kerry had 10 or more electoral votes.

e. This cannot be determined from the graph. We know only that the least number of electoral votes was between zero and four.

f. 70%. 30 states had fewer than 10 electoral votes. Of these, 21 were won by Bush. So $\frac{21}{30}$, or 70%, of the states with fewer than 10 electoral votes were won by Bush.

2. About 29; solve $\frac{45}{72} = \frac{18}{x}$.

3. Five-number summary: {18, 83, 133, 378, 526}

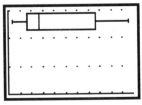

$[0, 550, 50, 0, 3, 1]$

4. a. Lou's

b. Filler-Up: $22.32; Lou's: $21.69

c. Filler-Up: a little more than 14.1 gal; Lou's: a little more than 14.5 gal

5. a. Direct variation. The ratio of y to x is constant; $\frac{y}{x} = 3$, or $y = 3x$.

b. Neither. Neither the product nor the ratio of x and y is constant.

c. Inverse variation. The product of x and y is constant; $xy = 36$, or $y = \frac{36}{x}$.

d. Neither. Neither the product nor the ratio of x and y is constant.

6. About 0.0113 European euros

7. a. 32(0.85), ENTER; Ans + 2(0.85), ENTER, ENTER, ENTER, ENTER, ENTER, ENTER; the sequence is: 27.20, 28.90, 30.60, 32.30, 34.00, 35.70, 37.40. Note: To show two decimal places on your calculator, press MODE and scroll to 2 in the second line.

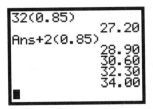

b.

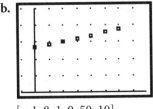

$[-1, 8, 1, 0, 50, 10]$

c. $1.70 per week

d. $V = 27.20 + 1.70n$

e. 14 weeks

8. a. $y = 124 - 0.75x$

  b. The slope, -0.75, means that 0.75 gal of water leaks out of the pool every minute. The y-intercept, 124, means that the pool contained 124 gal when it was filled.

  c. In about 165 min

9. a. $a = -4$

  b. $b = 18$

  c. $c = 11.4$

CHAPTER 4 • Quiz 1   Form A

1. a. $\frac{1}{2}; y = 1 + \frac{1}{2}x$ **b.** $-\frac{2}{3}; y = 7 - \frac{2}{3}x$

  c. $0; y = 5$

2. a. The slope is 2. Answers will vary for the other point on the line. Two possible points are $(3, 2)$ and $(4, 4)$.

  b. The slope is $-\frac{5}{3}$. Answers will vary for the other point on the line. Two possible points are $(-1, 8)$ and $(8, -7)$.

3. a. Windows will vary.

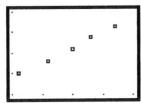

  $[60, 80, 5, 150, 190, 10]$

  b. The slope is $\frac{12}{7}$. It is the increase in height for every increase of 1 cm in the elbow-to-wrist measurement.

  c. $y = \frac{12}{7}x$

  d. Explanations may vary. Sample explanation: Because of the a value (y-intercept) I chose, the line is not within my graphing window.

e. Answers will vary. Possible answers are

  $y = 53 + \frac{12}{7}x$

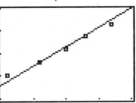

  $[60, 80, 5, 150, 190, 10]$

  $y = 52 + \frac{12}{7}x$

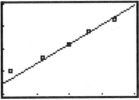

  $[60, 80, 5, 150, 190, 10]$

  $y = 54 + \frac{12}{7}x$

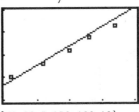

  $[60, 80, 5, 150, 190, 10]$

4. a. Line b **b.** $y = 1 + \frac{2}{3}x$

  c. They are parallel. (Students may say that they have the same slopes.)

CHAPTER 4 • Quiz 1   Form B

1. a. $-1; y = 9 - x$ **b.** $\frac{3}{4}; y = 2 + \frac{3}{4}x$

  c. Undefined; $x = 7$

2. a. The slope is $-\frac{4}{7}$. Answers will vary for the other point on the line. Two possible points are $(-9, 5)$ and $(12, -7)$.

  b. The slope is 0. Answers will vary for the other point on the line. A correct point will have a y-coordinate of -5.

3. a.
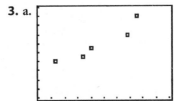

  $[10, 20, 1, 40, 60, 2]$

b. $\frac{54-49}{16.8-13.4} = \frac{5}{3.4} \approx 1.5$. The slope is the increase in distance traveled for each 1 s increase in travel time. In other words, the slope is the speed measured in feet per second. According to this slope, the cart traveled approximately 1.5 ft/s. (Note that the slope was rounded to the tenths place to match the seconds data. Students may use 1.47.)

c. Explanations may vary. The line goes through $(0, 0)$, so it is not within the graphing window.

d. Answers will vary. Possible answers are
$y = 30 + 1.5x$

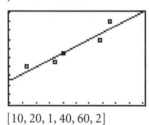

$[10, 20, 1, 40, 60, 2]$

$y = 29.5 + 1.5x$

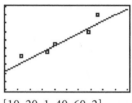

$[10, 20, 1, 40, 60, 2]$

4. a. Line a **b.** $y = 6 - \frac{2}{3}x$

c. They are parallel (or they have the same slopes).

CHAPTER 4 · Quiz 2   **Form A**

1. a. $y = 3 + 6(x + 4)$, or $6(x + 4) + 3$

b. $y = -2 - \frac{3}{7}(x - 5)$, or $y = -\frac{3}{7}(x - 5) - 2$

2. a. $y = 1 - \frac{1}{6}x$ **b.** $y = -\frac{3}{4} + \frac{5}{4}x$

c. The order of the properties may vary. Sample answer:

$-4(y - 3) + 3(x - 1) = 8$	Original equation.
$-4y + 12 + 3x - 3 = 8$	Distributive property.
$-4y + 3x + 12 - 3 = 8$	Commutative property.
$-4y + 3x + 9 = 8$	Combine like terms.
$-4y + 3x = -1$	Subtraction property.
$-4y = -1 - 3x$	Subtraction property.
$y = \frac{1}{4} + \frac{3}{4}x$	Division property.

3. $y = 8 - \frac{1}{2}(x - 10)$, or $y = 6 - \frac{1}{2}(x - 14)$

4. a. $x = \frac{4}{3}$ **b.** $x = -3.8$

CHAPTER 4 · Quiz 2   **Form B**

1. a. $y = -5 - 4(x - 2)$ **b.** $y = 7 + \frac{9}{5}(x + 2)$

2. a. $y = -\frac{3}{4} + \frac{1}{4}x$ **b.** $y = \frac{4}{5} + \frac{3}{5}x$

c. The order of the properties may vary. Sample answer:

$2(y - 3) - 5(x - 2) = 12$	Original equation.
$2y - 6 - 5x + 10 = 12$	Distributive property.
$2y - 5x - 6 + 10 = 12$	Commutative property.
$2y - 5x + 4 = 12$	Simplify left side.
$2y - 5x = 8$	Subtraction property.
$2y = 8 + 5x$	Addition property.
$y = 4 + \frac{5}{2}x$	Division property.

3. $y = 3 - \frac{1}{3}(x - 7)$, or $y = 2 - \frac{1}{3}(x - 10)$

4. a. $x = -3$ **b.** $x = 2.7$

CHAPTER 4 · Quiz 3   **Form A**

1. a.

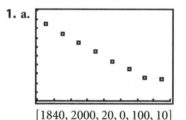

$[1840, 2000, 20, 0, 100, 10]$

b. Five-number summary for the *year* data: 1850, 1880, 1920, 1960, 1990; five-number summary for the *rural population* data: 24.8, 31.2, 49.05, 69.6, 84.7

c. The lines are: $x = 1880$, $x = 1960$, $y = 31.2$, $y = 69.6$; The Q-points are: $(1880, 69.6)$ and $(1960, 31.2)$.

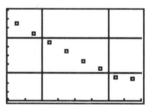

$[1840, 2000, 20, 0, 100, 10]$

d. $y = 31.2 - 0.48(x - 1960)$, or $y = 69.6 - 0.48(x - 1880)$

e. Descriptions will vary. Sample description: Every year between 1850 and 1990, the rural population percentage dropped at a rate of about 0.48% per year.

f. 1920 or 1921

g. $y = 31.2 - 0.48(x - 1960)$

$\quad y = 31.2 - 0.48(2000 - 1960)$

$\quad y = 12$

According to the equation, 12% of the population should have been rural in 2000. This is much lower than the actual percentage. The model is not very good for years after 1980. (In 1990, the model would have predicted a rural population of 16.8% instead of the actual 24.8%.) In recent years, the percentage of the population in rural areas has not been declining as quickly as the model indicates.

2. With the Q-point method, everyone will find the same linear model. With the other methods, the model depends on the points chosen or a person's ability to judge whether a line is a good fit.

CHAPTER 4 · Quiz 3   Form B

1. a.

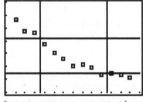

[1948, 2004, 4, 46, 60, 2]

b. Five-number summary for the *year* data: 1952, 1962, 1976, 1990, 2000; five-number summary for the *winning time* data: 48.30, 48.88, 50.40, 54.3, 57.4

c. The lines are: $x = 1962$, $x = 1990$, $y = 48.88$, $y = 54.3$; the Q-points are $(1962, 54.3)$ and $(1990, 48.88)$.

[1948, 2004, 4, 46, 60, 2]

d. $y = 54.3 - 0.19(x - 1962)$, or
$y = 48.88 - 0.19(x - 1990)$

e. Possible answer: The slope tells you that the winning time decreased at a rate of about 0.19 second per year (or 0.76 second per four years) from 1952 through 2000.

f. 1932

g. 46.32 or 46.22 (depending on the equation students use); this time is 1.85 or 1.95 s faster than the actual time.

2. With the Q-point method, everyone will find the same linear model. With the other methods, the model depends on the points chosen or a person's ability to judge whether a line is a good fit.

1. a. Line *a*: slope, -1; *y*-intercept, 2;
equation, $y = 2 - x$
Line *b*: slope, $\frac{1}{3}$; *y*-intercept, -2;
equation, $y = -2 + \frac{1}{3}x$

b. The lines intersect at $(3, -1)$.

2. a. $(3, 11)$

b. $(6, 5)$

c. $y = 5 - 2(x - 6)$

3. First use the two points to find the slope, then use the point-slope form with either point to write the equation of the line.

4. Solution methods will vary; $x = -4$.

5. a. $y = 5(x - 4)$

b. $y = 14.7x - 163.4$

c. $y = 32.6 + 6.2(x - 8)$

6. a. Commutative property of multiplication

b. Distributive property

7. a. The slope is $\frac{100 - 0}{212 - 32} = \frac{100}{180} = \frac{5}{9}$. Using the point $(32, 0)$, the equation is $C = \frac{5}{9}(F - 32)$. Using the point $(212, 100)$, the equation is $C = 100 + \frac{5}{9}(F - 212)$.

b. The slope means that for every change of 1°F, there is a change of $\frac{5}{9}$°C.

c. 20°C

d. 104°F

8. a. Possible answer:

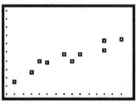

[38, 53, 1, 150, 200, 5]

b. The five-number summary for the *metacarpal I length* data is 39, 42, 45.5, 50, 52.
The five-number summary for the *height* data is 157, 169, 172, 176, 183.

c. Q-points: $(42, 169)$ and $(50, 176)$

d. The slope is $\frac{7}{8}$. This means that, generally speaking, the skeleton increases by 7 cm for every 8 mm of increase in metacarpal I length.

e. $y = 169 + \frac{7}{8}(x - 42)$ or
$y = 176 + \frac{7}{8}(x - 50)$

f.

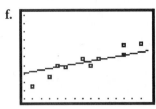

[38, 53, 1, 150, 200, 5]

The Q-line is not a particularly good model for all the data. It fits the six data points in the middle, but not the two points at either extreme. If the line were adjusted to increase the slope slightly, it would be a better fit.

CHALLENGE PROBLEM

Answers will vary. Sample answer: Using the representative points (41, 163) and (52, 183), you get the line $y = 163 + \frac{20}{11}(x - 41)$, which seems to fit the data better.

CHAPTER 4 · Test   Form B

1. a. Line a: slope, $-\frac{3}{4}$; y-intercept, 3; equation, $y = 3 - \frac{3}{4}x$

Line b: slope, $\frac{1}{4}$; y-intercept, -1; equation, $y = -1 + \frac{1}{4}x$

b. The lines intersect at $(4, 0)$.

2. a. $(2, -7)$

b. $(-4, 11)$

c. $y = 11 - 3(x + 4)$

3. Use the y-intercept and the point to find the slope of the line. Then use the slope and the y-intercept to write the equation in intercept or slope-intercept form, or use the slope and one of the points to write the equation in point-slope form.

4. Solution methods will vary; $x = 7$.

5. a. $y = -22.5x + 300.5$

b. $y = -6(x - 3)$

c. $y = 26.4 + 7.2(x - 4)$

6. a. Distributive property

b. Associative property of addition

7. a. The slope is $\frac{212 - 32}{100 - 0} = \frac{180}{100} = \frac{9}{5}$. The y-intercept is 32, so the equation in intercept form is $F = \frac{9}{5}C + 32$. (Note: Students may also use the slope and one of the points to write an equation in point-slope form.)

b. The slope means that for every change of 1°C there is a change of $\frac{9}{5}$°F.

c. 77°F

d. 15°C

8. a. Possible answer:

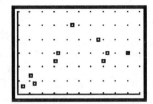

[0, 500, 50, 0, 30, 5]

b. The five-number summary for the *gestation* data is 21, 68, 195.5, 350, 450; the five-number summary for the *average longevity* data is 3, 7, 13.5, 15, 25.

c. Q-points: (68, 7) and (350, 15)

d. The slope is about 0.028. For an increase of 1 day in gestation period, the average longevity increases by 0.028 year.

e. $y = 7 + 0.028(x - 68)$, or $y = 15 + 0.028(x - 350)$

f. The line is a fairly good fit, although the points below the line are closer to the line than the points above the line. You might move the line up slightly.

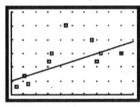

[0, 500, 50, 0, 30, 5]

CHALLENGE PROBLEM

Answers will vary. Sample answer: The line of fit is pretty good. Eyeballing, it looks like a better line would pass through (154, 12) with the same slope as the Q-point line: $y = 12 + 0.028(x - 154)$.

CHAPTER 4 · Constructive Assessment Options

SCORING RUBRICS

1. 5 Points

a. The situation is realistic and fits the given criteria. Sample answer: Ryan rode his bike to school. He lives 5 mi from school, and the trip took him 12 min.

b. The equation is $y = 5 - \frac{5}{12}x$ (or $y = 5 - 0.41\overline{6}x$), and variables are correctly identified. For the situation described in part a, x is time in minutes and y is distance from school in miles.

c. The problem is clearly stated, and the solution is correct. Sample problem and solution are based on the situation in part a.

> **Problem:** After how many minutes was Ryan 2 mi from school?
>
> **Solution:** Solve $2 = 5 - \frac{5}{12}x$.

$$2 = 5 - \frac{5}{12}x \qquad \text{Original equation.}$$

$$-3 = -\frac{5}{12}x \qquad \text{Subtract 5 from both sides.}$$

$$\frac{36}{5} = x \qquad \text{Multiply both sides by } -\frac{12}{5}.$$

$$7.2 = x \qquad \text{Divide.}$$

Ryan was 2 mi from school after 7.2 min.

3 Points

a. The situation is realistic and fits the given criteria.

b. The equation is correct but is in the wrong form, or not all variables are correctly identified.

c. The problem is clearly stated, but the solution is unclear or is missing important steps.

1 Point

a. The situation does not fit one of the criteria.

b. The equation is correct (although it may be in the wrong form), but the variables are not identified, or the equation is incorrect, but the variables are correctly identified.

c. The problem is clearly stated, but no solution is given.

2. 5 Points

Descriptions are correct and thorough, and example equations fit the criteria.

a. Sample answer: The line has a negative slope and a negative y-intercept. Example: $y = -1 - 5x$

b. Sample answer: The line passes through Quadrants I, II, and IV. The y-intercept is positive. Example: $y = -3(x - 4)$

c. Sample answer: The line is horizontal and is above the x-axis. Example: $y = 2$

d. Sample answer: The line has a negative slope and passes through Quadrants II and IV only. Example: $y = -3x$

3 Points

One of the descriptions is incorrect, and one example equation is incorrect.

1 Point

Explanations are given, but most are incorrect or inadequate. Example equations are given, but most are not correct.

3. 5 Points

Answers are correct. Explanations are thorough and demonstrate an understanding of important concepts.

a. False. Possible explanation: The line with equation $y = 7 - 2(x + 3)$ has a slope of -2. The line through $(-3, 7)$ and $(15, -2)$ has a slope of $\frac{-2 - 7}{15 - (-3)}$, or -0.5.

b. True. Possible explanation: The equation for the line though $(-3, 7)$ and $(15, -2)$ is $y = 7 - 0.5(x + 3)$. If you rewrite this in intercept form, you get $y = 5.5 - 0.5x$. This is the same equation you get when you write $y = 3 - 0.5(x - 5)$ in intercept form, so the two original equations represent the same line.

c. False. Possible explanation: The line has a positive y-intercept and a negative slope (its equation is $y = 5.5 - 0.5x$), so it passes through every quadrant but Quadrant III.

d. False. Possible explanation: I found that the equation is $y = 5.5 - 0.5x$, so the y-intercept is 5.5, not 11. (And the x-intercept is 11, not 5.5.)

3 Points

At least three answers are correct. Explanations are well written, but a few minor details are missing or incorrect.

1 Point

Answers are correct, but no explanations are given. Or only one answer is correct, but it has a good, clear explanation.

4. 5 Points

a. The situation is realistic and fits the given criteria. Sample answer: Alisha saves the same amount of money each week. After 5 wk she has $12, and after 8 wk she has $33. Alisha is in debt to start.

b. The equation is given correctly as $y = 12 + 7(x - 5)$ or $y = 33 + 7(x - 8)$, and variables are correctly identified. For the situation described in part a, x is the number of weeks and y is the amount saved.

c. The problem is clearly stated, and the solution is correct. Sample problem and solution based on the situation in part a:

Problem: When will Alisha have $100?

Solution: Solve $100 = 12 + 7(x - 5)$.

$100 = 12 + 7(x - 5)$	Original equation.
$88 = 7(x - 5)$	Subtract 12 from both sides.
$\dfrac{88}{7} = x - 5$	Divide both sides by 7.
$\dfrac{88}{7} + 5 = x$	Add 5 to both sides.
$17.6 \approx x$	Divide and add.

Alisha will have $100 after 18 wk.

3 Points

a. The situation is realistic and fits the given criteria.

b. The equation is correct but is in the wrong form, or the equation is in the correct form, but the slope is incorrect due to a calculation error. Variables are correctly identified.

c. The problem is clearly stated, but the solution is unclear or is missing important steps.

1 Point

a. The situation is realistic but does not fit one of the criteria.

b. The equation is mostly correct (it may be in the wrong form or be incorrect due to minor calculation errors), but the variables are not identified, or the equation is incorrect, but the variables are correctly identified.

c. The problem is clearly stated, but no solution is given.

5. 5 Points

The mistakes are correctly explained, and the correct solution steps are given. (Students' explanations may vary slightly from those here.)

a. She did not distribute the -3 correctly; she multiplied -3 by x but not by -6.

$$y = 4 - 3(x - 6)$$
$$y = 4 - 3x + 18$$
$$y = 22 - 3x$$

b. She did not distribute the minus sign. To remove the parentheses, she should have multiplied -1 by x and by 8.

$$y = -5 - (x + 8)$$
$$y = -5 - x - 8$$
$$y = -13 - x$$

c. She did the subtraction before the multiplication. She should have started by using the distributive property to multiply -7 by $(x + 1)$.

$$y = 3 - 7(x + 1)$$
$$y = 3 - 7x - 7$$
$$y = -4 - 7x$$

3 Points

One of the mistakes is not explained clearly, and one set of solution steps contains a minor error.

1 Point

The mistakes are identified, but corrected solutions are not given, or the mistakes are not identified, but corrected solutions are given and are mostly correct.

6. 5 Points

The answer includes clear, correct descriptions of two equation-fitting methods. Possible descriptions of the methods students used in this chapter:

- Pick two points so the line through the points shows the overall direction of the data and there are about the same number of points on both sides of the line. Use the coordinates of the points to calculate the slope. Then use the slope to write an equation of the form $y = bx$. Estimate the y-intercept value, a, and write the equation $y = a + bx$, then graph all the points and the equation on a calculator and adjust the value of a until the line fits the data.

- Pick two points so the line through the points fits the data fairly well. Calculate the slope of the line through the points. Use the slope, b, and one of the two points (x_1, y_1) to write an equation in point-slope form, $y = y_1 + b(x - x_1)$.

- Use Q-points to fit the line. Find the five-number summary for the x-values and the five-number summary for the y-values. The Q-points are $(Q1_x, Q1_y), (Q1_x, Q3_y), (Q3_x, Q1_y), (Q3_x, Q3_y)$, where $Q1_x$ and $Q3_x$ are the first and third quartiles of the x-values and $Q1_y$ and $Q3_y$ are the first and third quartiles of the y-values. Choose the two Q-points that show the direction of the data. Find the slope of the line through the chosen Q-points, and then use the slope and one of the points to write an equation in point-slope form.

3 Points

Two correct methods are described, but a few minor details are missing.

1 Point

One correct method is described, with some details missing, or two methods are described, but important details are missing.

7. 5 Points

a. The equation of the line and the data are correctly shown. The description of the method for finding the line is clear and correct. The explanation of how well the equation fits is clearly presented. Sample answer: I found the Q-line. I first found the Q-points. The quartiles of the *year* data are 1983 and 1997, and the quartiles of the *percentage* data are 39.35 and 67.05. Because the data values are increasing, the line of fit passes through the Q-points (1983, 39.35) and (1997, 67.05). The slope of the line through these points is $\frac{67.05 - 39.35}{1997 - 1983} = \frac{27.7}{14} \approx 1.98$. This slope and the point (1983, 39.35) give the equation $y = 39.35 + 1.98(x - 1983)$. I graphed the points and the equation.

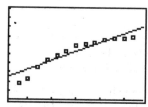

[1976, 2004, 5, 0, 100, 10]

The line is a pretty good fit for most of the data, particularly from about 1982 to 1998. It shows the general direction of the data until about 2000. There are about the same number of points above as below the line.

b. The answer is clear and convincing and is based on the data and the graph. Sample answer: The equation indicates that the average percentage increase is about 1.98% each year. However, the data show that the rate of increase in the early years (from 1978 to 1982) was greater than 1.98%, and in the later years (since the mid-'90s) has been less. So I would predict that the model will not accurately predict the percentage of households using cable over the next 10 to 15 years. Over that period of time the percentage may go up, but I predict it will be by less than 1% a year, and in some years there may be a decrease.

3 Points

a. The equation fits the data reasonably well. The description of the method and explanation of why the line is a good fit are missing minor details. Sample answer: I got the equation $y = 67.4 + 2.025(x - 1998)$ by plotting the data and finding a line through two of the points. I graphed the points and the line on my calculator and could see that the line fits very well.

b. The prediction is reasonable, but it is not strongly tied to the data or the equation. Possible answer: I think the percentage will keep increasing because many people are getting digital cable and cable modems for their computers.

1 Point

a. A reasonable equation is given, but both the description of the method and the explanation of why the line fits are missing, or the equation, description, and explanation are given, but the line is not a good fit and the explanation of why it fits is not convincing. Sample answer: I got the equation $y = 43.7 + 1.7(x - 1984)$ by plotting the data and finding a line through two of the points. The line fits because it goes in the same direction as the points and contains two of the points.

b. The prediction is unreasonable and is not tied to the data or the equation. Possible answer: I think the percentage will start going down by a lot because more people are getting satellite dishes instead of cable.

8. 5 Points

Answers are correct. Explanations are thorough and demonstrate an understanding of important concepts.

a. False. Possible explanation: The population has increased by about 160 million people every 2 years, not every year.

b. True. Possible explanation: The appropriate Q-points are (1978, 4.302) and (1996, 5.771). The slope of the line through these points is about 0.082. Using the point (1978, 4.302), we get the equation $y = 0.082(x - 1978) + 4.302$.

c. False. Possible explanation: Substituting 1999 into the model gives a population value of 6.024 billion people, so 1999, not 2000, is the first year the population was 6 billion or greater.

d. False. Possible explanation: The change from 1986 to 1988 was 172 million people, but the change from 1988 to 1990 was 175 million people.

3 Points

At least three answers are correct. Explanations are well written, but a few minor details are missing or incorrect.

1 Point

Answers are correct, but no explanations are given, or only one answer is correct, but it has a good, clear explanation.

CHAPTER 5 · Quiz 1   Form A

1. $x = 7, y = 5$

2. $x = 3, y = 1$

3. a. $s + j = 540$

   b. $1.75s + 1.10j = 730.50$

   c. 210 sandwiches and 330 juice boxes

4. a. $\begin{bmatrix} 1 & 1 & 540 \\ 1.75 & 1.10 & 730.50 \end{bmatrix}$

b. $\begin{bmatrix} 1 & 1 & 540 \\ 1.75 & 1.10 & 730.50 \end{bmatrix}$ Original matrix.

$\begin{bmatrix} 1 & 1 & 540 \\ 0 & -0.65 & -214.50 \end{bmatrix}$ Multiply row 1 by -1.75 and add result to row 2.

$\begin{bmatrix} 1 & 1 & 540 \\ 0 & 1 & 330 \end{bmatrix}$ Divide row 2 by -0.65.

$\begin{bmatrix} 1 & 0 & 210 \\ 0 & 1 & 330 \end{bmatrix}$ Multiply row 2 by -1 and add result to row 1.

CHAPTER 5 · Quiz 1   Form B

1. $x = 5, y = 9$

2. $x = 4, y = 2$

3. a. $c + b = 600$ **b.** $0.35c + 0.75b = 360$

    c. 225 cookies, 375 brownies

4. a. $\begin{bmatrix} 1 & 1 & 600 \\ 0.35 & 0.75 & 360 \end{bmatrix}$

    b. $\begin{bmatrix} 1 & 1 & 600 \\ 0.35 & 0.75 & 360 \end{bmatrix}$ Original matrix.

$\begin{bmatrix} 1 & 1 & 600 \\ 0 & 0.40 & 150 \end{bmatrix}$ Multiply row 1 by -0.35 and add to row 2.

$\begin{bmatrix} 1 & 1 & 600 \\ 0 & 1 & 375 \end{bmatrix}$ Divide row 2 by 0.4.

$\begin{bmatrix} 1 & 0 & 225 \\ 0 & 1 & 375 \end{bmatrix}$ Multiply row 2 by -1 and add to row 1.

CHAPTER 5 · Quiz 2   Form A

1. a. $y \geq 4 - \frac{4}{5}x$ **b.** $y > 4 - \frac{4}{5}x$

2. The overlap of the shaded regions is the solution of the system.

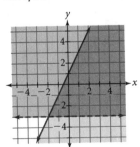

3. $-3x + 4 > 16$

     $-3x > 12$

       $x < -4$

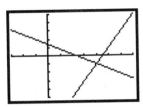

---

4. Let m be the number of months she will need to save.

    $100 + 75m \geq 600$

       $75m \geq 500$

        $m \geq 6.\overline{6}$

Sofia will need to save for at least seven months in order to have enough money for the trip.

CHAPTER 5 · Quiz 2   Form B

1. a. $y \geq \frac{2}{3}x - 3$ **b.** $y > \frac{2}{3}x - 3$

2. The overlap of the shaded regions is the solution of the system.

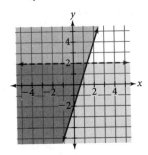

3. $-2x + 5 < 13$

     $-2x < 8$

       $x > -4$

4. Let m be the number of months he will need to save.

    $550 + 75m \geq 1200$

       $75m \geq 650$

        $m \geq 8.\overline{6}$

Jon will need to save for at least nine months in order to have enough money for the trip.

CHAPTER 5 · Test   Form A

1. a. $x = 4, y = -1$

    b. $y = -\frac{3}{5}x + \frac{7}{5}, y = 2x - 9$; the graphs intersect at $(4, -1)$.

$[-3, 7, 1, -5, 5, 1]$

Discovering Algebra Assessment Resources / Answers
©2007 Key Curriculum Press

2. Inequalities should be equivalent to those in this system:

$$\begin{cases} y \geq 4 + \dfrac{1}{11}(x - 13) \\ y \leq 3 + \dfrac{2}{3}(x - 2) \\ y \leq 7 - \dfrac{3}{5}(x - 8) \end{cases}$$

3. a.
$$700 + x \geq 130 - 59x$$
$$700 + 60x \geq 130$$
$$60x \geq -570$$
$$x \geq -9.5$$

b. You could enter $y_1 = 700 + x$ and $y_2 = 130 - 59x$, and look for the x-values for which $y_1 \geq y_2$.

4. a. Let a be the price of an adult ticket, and let c be the price of a child ticket.

$$\begin{cases} 5a + 3c = 131.25 \\ 3a + 4c = 106.25 \end{cases}$$

b. $\begin{bmatrix} 5 & 3 & 131.25 \\ 3 & 4 & 106.25 \end{bmatrix}$ Original matrix.

$\begin{bmatrix} 1 & 0.6 & 26.25 \\ 3 & 4 & 106.25 \end{bmatrix}$ Divide row 1 by 5.

$\begin{bmatrix} 1 & 0.6 & 26.25 \\ 0 & 2.2 & 27.5 \end{bmatrix}$ Subtract 3 times row 1 from row 2.

$\begin{bmatrix} 1 & 0.6 & 26.25 \\ 0 & 1 & 12.5 \end{bmatrix}$ Divide row 2 by 2.2.

$\begin{bmatrix} 1 & 0 & 18.75 \\ 0 & 1 & 12.5 \end{bmatrix}$ Subtract 0.6 times row 2 from row 1.

$a = 18.75$ and $c = 12.5$; an adult ticket costs $18.75, and a child ticket costs $12.50.

5. a. parallel

b. multiply or divide both sides by a negative number

c. are the same

CHALLENGE PROBLEM

$x = 3, y = -2, z = 1$

CHAPTER 5 · Test　　　　　　　　　　**Form B**

1. a. $x = 4, y = 2$

b. $y = \dfrac{2}{3}x - \dfrac{2}{3}, y = 3x - 10$; the graphs intersect at $(4, 2)$.

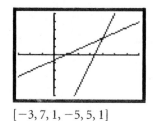

$[-3, 7, 1, -5, 5, 1]$

---

2. Inequalities should be equivalent to those in this system:

$$\begin{cases} y \geq 3 + \dfrac{2}{9}(x - 11) \\ y \leq 9 - \dfrac{3}{2}(x - 7) \\ y \leq 9 + \dfrac{8}{5}(x - 7) \end{cases}$$

3. a.
$$6 - 2x \leq 9 + 8x$$
$$6 \leq 9 + 10x$$
$$-3 \leq 10x$$
$$-0.3 \leq x$$

b. You could enter $y_1 = 6 - 2x$ and $y_2 = 9 + 8x$, and look for the x-values for which $y_1 \leq y_2$.

4. a. Let a be the price of an adult ticket, and let c be the price of a child ticket.

$$\begin{cases} 5a + 2c = 129 \\ 2a + 6c = 107.5 \end{cases}$$

b. $\begin{bmatrix} 5 & 2 & 129 \\ 2 & 6 & 107.5 \end{bmatrix}$ Original matrix.

$\begin{bmatrix} 1 & 0.4 & 25.8 \\ 2 & 6 & 107.5 \end{bmatrix}$ Divide row 1 by 5.

$\begin{bmatrix} 1 & 0.4 & 25.8 \\ 0 & 5.2 & 55.9 \end{bmatrix}$ Subtract 2 times row 1 from row 2.

$\begin{bmatrix} 1 & 0.4 & 25.8 \\ 0 & 1 & 10.75 \end{bmatrix}$ Divide row 2 by 5.2.

$\begin{bmatrix} 1 & 0 & 21.5 \\ 0 & 1 & 10.75 \end{bmatrix}$ Subtract 0.4 times row 2 from row 1.

$a = 21.5$ and $c = 10.75$; an adult ticket costs $21.50, and a child ticket costs $10.75.

5. a. one

b. multiply or divide both sides by a negative number

c. are parallel

CHALLENGE PROBLEM

$x = 2, y = -1, z = 4$

SCORING RUBRICS

1. 5 Points

a. Lines have the same relative positions as those shown here.

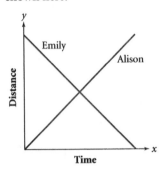

b. Lines have the same relative positions as those shown here.

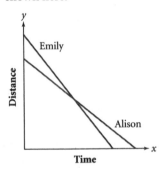

c. Lines have the same relative positions as those shown here.

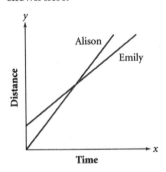

d. Lines have the same relative positions as those shown here.

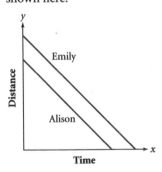

3 Points
Three graphs are correct.

1 Point
One graph is correct.

2. 5 Points
Keaton's mistakes are explained and correct solutions given. The solution steps may vary from those shown.

a. He made an error when he tried to subtract $4x$ from both sides. On the right side, he added $4x$, getting $2x + 1$ instead of $-6x + 1$. Here is the correct solution.

$$4x - 9 = -2x + 1$$
$$-9 = -6x + 1$$
$$-10 = -6x$$
$$\frac{5}{3} = x$$
$$y = 4\left(\frac{5}{3}\right) - 9$$
$$y = -\frac{7}{3}$$

The solution is $\left(\frac{5}{3}, -\frac{7}{3}\right)$.

b. His solution is correct.

c. He made a mistake when he added the equations. Because $-11 + 1 = -10$, the right side of the equation should be -10, not 12. He also forgot to substitute his answer for x into one of the original equations to find y. Here is the correct solution.

$$x - y = -11$$
$$\underline{x + y = 1}$$
$$2x = -10$$
$$x = -5$$
$$-5 + y = 1$$
$$y = 6$$

The solution is $(-5, 6)$.

3 Points
Keaton's mistakes are correctly identified, but solution steps may contain one or two errors, or correct solution steps are given, but the explanations of what Keaton did wrong are incomplete.

1 Point
The mistakes are identified, but correct solutions are not given, or the mistakes are not explained, but the correct solution is given for at least one.

Discovering Algebra Assessment Resources / Answers
©2007 Key Curriculum Press

3. 5 Points

Systems satisfy the conditions. Solutions are correct and complete.

a. Sample answer:

$$\begin{cases} y = 2x \\ y = 3x + 3 \end{cases}$$

$y = 3x + 3$	Original second equation.
$2x = 3x + 3$	Substitute $2x$ (from the first equation) for y.
$-3 = x$	Subtract $2x$ and 3 from both sides.
$y = 2(-3)$	
$y = -6$	

The solution is $(-3, -6)$, so both coordinates of the solution are negative integers.

b. Sample answer:

$$\begin{cases} y = 2x + 5 \\ y = -3x + 5 \end{cases}$$

$y = -3x + 5$	Original second equation.
$2x + 5 = -3x + 5$	Substitute $2x + 5$ (from the first equation) for y.
$0 = -5x$	Subtract 5 and $2x$ from both sides.
$0 = x$	Divide both sides by -5.
$y = 2(0) + 5$	
$y = 5$	

The solution is $(0, 5)$, so both graphs cross the y-axis at 5.

c. Sample answer:

$$\begin{cases} y = 2x + 2 \\ y = 2x + 3 \end{cases}$$

Subtract the second equation from the first to get $0 = -1$. Because $0 = -1$ is never true, the system has no solutions. This means that the lines never intersect.

d. $\begin{cases} y = x \\ y = -x \end{cases}$

Adding the equations gives $2y = 0$, so $y = 0$ and $x = 0$. The solution is $(0, 0)$.

3 Points

Three of the systems are correct. Solution steps may include minor errors.

1 Point

One of the systems and its solution are correct.

4. 5 Points

Answers are correct. Explanations are thorough and demonstrate an understanding of important concepts.

a. False. Possible explanation: If p is the number of prints and c is the cost in dollars, then the situation can be represented by this system:

$$\begin{cases} c = 5 + 0.99p \qquad \text{Quick Cam} \\ c = 3.5 + 1.05p \qquad \text{Fun Photo} \end{cases}$$

The solution of this system is $(25, 29.75)$. So, for 25 prints, both stores charge $29.75.

b. False. Possible explanation: $5 is the start-up cost (the y-intercept), and $0.99 per picture is the rate of change (the slope). So the equation is $c = 5 + 0.99p$.

c. False. Possible explanation: The solution of the system (see answer to part a) is $(25, 29.75)$, so Fun Photo is cheaper for up to 25 prints. For 25 prints, the costs are the same. For more than 25 prints, Quick Cam is cheaper.

d. True. Possible explanation: If you substitute 20 for p in the Quick Cam equation, $c = 5 + 0.99p$, you get 24.80. If you substitute 20 for p in the Fun Photo equation, $c = 3.5 + 1.05p$, you get 24.50.

3 Points

At least three answers are correct. Explanations are well written, but a few minor details are missing or incorrect.

1 Point

Answers are correct, but no explanations are given, or only one answer is correct, but it has a good, clear explanation.

5. 5 Points

The problem is clearly stated and satisfies the given conditions. A correct, clear solution is shown. Sample answer:

Problem: Chen and Roberto are running toward each other. Chen starts 25 m from the school and runs toward the school at a rate of 4 m/s. Roberto starts 4 m from the school and runs away from the school at a rate of 3 m/s. Where and when will the boys meet?

Solution: If y represents the distance from the school in meters and x represents the time in seconds, then the situation can be modeled by this system.

$$\begin{cases} y = 25 - 4x \qquad \text{Chen} \\ y = 4 + 3x \qquad \text{Roberto} \end{cases}$$

Set the right sides equal to each other and solve for x.

$25 - 4x = 4 + 3x$ Set the right sides equal.

      $21 = 7x$ Subtract 4 from both sides and add $4x$ to both sides.

         $3 = x$ Divide both sides by 7.

$y = 25 - 4(3)$

$y = 13$

The solution is (3, 13), so the boys meet after 3 s when they are 13 m from the school.

3 Points
The problem fits the conditions, but the solution is missing some steps or contains minor mistakes.

1 Point
An attempt is made to write a problem fitting the criteria, and work is shown, but the problem is incorrect.

6. 5 Points
The answer is clear and includes the following points:

- When you add a number to or subtract a number from both sides of an inequality, the direction of the inequality symbol stays the same.

- When you multiply or divide both sides of an inequality by a positive number, the direction of the inequality symbol stays the same.

- When you multiply or divide both sides of an inequality by a negative number, the direction of the inequality symbol is reversed.

- If an inequality is of the form $x < a$ or $x > a$, graph it by first making an open circle at a. For $x < a$, draw an arrow through all the values to the left of a. For $x > a$, draw an arrow through all the values to the right of a.

- If an inequality is of the form $x \leq a$ or $x \geq a$, graph it by first making a solid circle at a. For $x \leq a$, draw an arrow through all the values to the left of a. For $x \geq a$, draw an arrow through all the values to the right of a.

- For a compound inequality, such as $-2 \leq x < 4$, make open or solid circles at the numbers (depending on the signs of the inequalities) and draw a line segment through all the values in between.

3 Points
The answer mentions that the inequality symbol is reversed when both sides are multiplied or divided by a negative number. Two of the other points from the list are missing. Other minor details may also be missing.

1 Point
Four major concepts from the list are missing.

7. 5 Points
Answers are correct. Explanations in parts c and d are clear.

a. If d is the number of dimes and q is the number of quarters, then the system is

$$\begin{cases} d \geq 0 \\ q \geq 0 \\ d \leq 4 \\ q \leq 8 \\ d + q \geq 10 \end{cases}$$

Some students may not write $d \geq 0$ or $q \geq 0$. You may choose to give them full credit or to give them 4 points.

b. The solution is the shaded region of the graph.

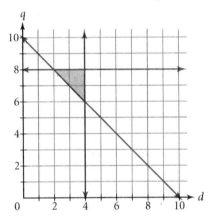

c. There are six possible combinations. Possible explanation: The points with integer coordinates in the solution region represent the possible combinations. For example, the point (2, 8) represents two dimes and eight quarters. There are six such points in the solution region.

d. Four dimes, six quarters. Possible explanation: I listed all the possible combinations and found the value of each. Only one combination, four dimes and six quarters, has a value less than $2.00.

Dimes	Quarters	Total
2	8	$2.20
3	8	$2.30
4	8	$2.40
3	7	$2.05
4	7	$2.15
4	6	$1.90

3 Points
a. The system includes the last three restraints.

b. The graph is correct.

c. The answer is correct, but the explanation is unclear, or the answer is incorrect due to minor errors (for example, the student attempts to list the

Discovering Algebra Assessment Resources / Answers
©2007 Key Curriculum Press

combinations but forgets one or lists one twice), but the explanation is clear and logical.

d. The answer is correct, but the explanation is unclear, or the answer is incorrect due to minor errors, but the explanation is clear and logical.

1 Point

The system and graph are mostly correct. Parts c and d are missing or incorrect.

8. 5 Points

Systems satisfy the conditions, and graphs and solutions are correct.

a. Sample answer:
$$\begin{cases} y \le -1 \\ y \ge -2.5 \end{cases}$$
The region of overlap is the solution.

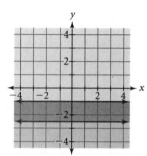

b. Sample answer:
$$\begin{cases} y \le 2x + 2 \\ y \ge 2x + 1 \end{cases}$$
The region of overlap is the solution.

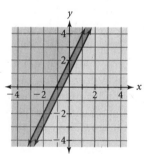

c. Sample answer:
$$\begin{cases} x > 0 \\ y > 0 \end{cases}$$
The region of overlap is the solution.

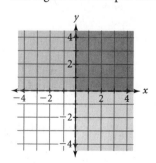

d. Sample answer:
$$\begin{cases} y \le -2x - 1 \\ y \ge -2x - 3 \end{cases}$$
The region of overlap is the solution.

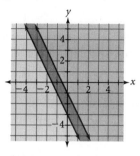

3 Points

Three answers are correct.

1 Point

Only one answer is correct.

CHAPTER 6 · Quiz 1   **Form A**

1. a.

Year	Years since 2000, x	Ticket price, y ($)
2000	0	125.00
2001	1	128.75
2002	2	132.61
2003	3	136.59
2004	4	140.69
2005	5	144.91

b. 1.03   **c.** $y = 125(1 + 0.03)^x$

d. Year 9, or 2009

2. a. $y = 4.98(1 + 0.04)^x$, where x is the number of years from now and y is the price of the cereal

b. $5.60   **c.** 11 years from now

CHAPTER 6 · Quiz 1   **Form B**

1. a.

Year	Years since 2000, x	Ticket price, y ($)
2000	0	115.00
2001	1	119.60
2002	2	124.38
2003	3	129.36
2004	4	134.53
2005	5	139.92

b. 1.04   **c.** $y = 115(1 + 0.04)^x$

d. Year 10, or 2010

2. a. $y = 4.50(1 + 0.06)^x$, where x is the number of years from now and y is the price of the cereal

b. \$5.36   **c.** Seven years from now

2. $y = 64(1 - 0.8)^x$, or $y = 64(0.2)^x$

x	-2	-1	0	1	2	3	4
y	1600	320	64	12.8	2.56	0.512	0.1024

CHAPTER 6 • Quiz 2 — Form A

1. a. $8x^{12}$ **b.** $10x^7$ **c.** $12x^5$
   d. $32x^3$ **e.** $2x^4$ **f.** $12x^2$

2. a. $-24{,}000$ **b.** 0.0000325 **c.** -0.0055

3. a. 3.714×10^7 **b.** 8.01×10^{-4}
   c. -1×10^{-5}

4. a. $\dfrac{2}{x}$ **b.** $\dfrac{1}{2x}$ **c.** 4^5 **d.** $\dfrac{y^5}{x^2}$

5. a. $2x^4$ **b.** x^2 **c.** x^{10} **d.** $3^6 2^5$
   e. $-2y$ **f.** $-45x^5y^3$ **g.** 2×10^3 **h.** y

6. a. False; $(3x^2)^3 = 27x^6$

   b. False; possible answer: $3(2x^2)^{-1} = \frac{3}{2}x^{-2}$

7. About 9567 s, or about 159 min

CHAPTER 6 • Quiz 2 — Form B

1. a. $6x^{10}$ **b.** $28x^7$ **c.** $7x^7$
   d. $75x^3$ **e.** $7x^2$ **f.** $54x^3$

2. a. -3200 **b.** 0.000489 **c.** -0.0000701

3. a. 5.814×10^6 **b.** 7.22×10^{-3}
   c. 4×10^{-5}

4. a. $\dfrac{3}{x^2}$ **b.** $\dfrac{1}{3x}$ **c.** 7^3 **d.** $\dfrac{x^2}{y^4}$

5. a. $9x^4$ **b.** x^5 **c.** x^{12} **d.** $5^5 7^7$
   e. $3y^2$ **f.** $48x^4y^5$ **g.** 6×10^4 **h.** $2y$

6. a. False; $(2x^3)^3 = 8x^9$

   b. False; possible answer: $2(3x^3)^{-1} = \frac{2}{3}x^{-3}$

7. About 4757 s, or about 79 min

CHAPTER 6 • Quiz 3 — Form A

1. a.

Years, x	Atoms remaining, y
0	200
1	164
2	134
3	110
4	90
5	74
6	61

   b. 200 represents the original number of "atoms" (i.e., counters), and 0.18 is the rate of decay.

CHAPTER 6 • Quiz 3 — Form B

1. a.

Years, x	Atoms remaining, y
0	150
1	126
2	106
3	89
4	75
5	63
6	53

   b. 150 represents the original number of "atoms" (i.e., counters), and 0.16 is the rate of decay.

2. $y = 1000(1 - 0.3)^x$, or $y = 1000(0.7)^x$

x	-2	-1	0	1	2	3	4
y	2040.8	1428.6	1000	700	490	343	240.1

CHAPTER 6 • Test — Form A

1. a. $48x^7$ **b.** $25x^6y^4$
   c. $24x^5$ **d.** $5^{x+y}3^z$
   e. 0.5×10^{-2}, or 5×10^{-3}
   f. $-36x^{11}y^4$

2. a. 170 cm

   b.

Bounce number	Height (cm)
0	200
1	170
2	144.5
3	122.8
4	104.4
5	88.7

   c. $\{0, 200\}$ ENTER, $\{\text{Ans}(1) + 1, \text{Ans}(2) \cdot (1 - 0.15)\}$ ENTER, ENTER, ... (Note: The rule $\{\text{Ans}(1) + 1, \text{Ans}(2) \cdot 0.85\}$ is also correct.)

   d. $y = 200(1 - 0.15)^x$, or $y = 200(0.85)^x$

   e. Bounce 7

3. a. $-430{,}000$ **b.** 0.000525

4. a. 3.154×10^{10} **b.** -5.02×10^{-6}

5. a. -4 **b.** -4 **c.** -3

Discovering Algebra Assessment Resources/Answers
©2007 Key Curriculum Press

6. a. $\dfrac{8^5}{8^5} = 8^{5-5} = 8^0 = 1$ **b.** $y = 10^{-x}$

7. a. $5{,}000(1 + 0.07)^{-3}$; \$4,081.49

  b. $3{,}000(1 + 0.07)^2$; \$3,434.70

  c. $2{,}000(1 + 0.07)^{40}$; \$29,948.92

8. Answers will vary. Students should indicate that using scientific notation makes very large and very small numbers easier to write and to use in calculations.

CHAPTER 6 · Test   Form B

1. a. $36x^8$ **b.** $7^3x^6y^9$, or $343x^6y^9$ **c.** $15x^4$

  d. $7^{x+z}5^y$ **e.** 0.25×10^{-4}, or 2.5×10^{-5}

  f. $-30x^7y^6$

2. a. 225 cm

  b.

Bounce number	Height (cm)
0	300
1	225
2	168.8
3	126.6
4	94.9
5	71.2

  c. $\{0, 300\}$ ENTER, $\{\text{Ans}(1) + 1, \text{Ans}(2) \cdot (1 - 0.25)\}$ ENTER, ENTER, ... (Note: The rule $\{\text{Ans}(1) + 1, \text{Ans}(2) \cdot 0.75\}$ is also correct.)

  d. $y = 300(1 - 0.25)^x$, or $y = 300(0.75)^x$

  e. Bounce 10

3. a. 28,000,000   **b.** 0.0043

4. a. 7.81×10^8 **b.** -5.33×10^{-5}

5. a. -3 **b.** -1 **c.** -4

6. a. $\dfrac{6^{-3}}{6^{-3}} = 6^{-3-(-3)} = 6^{-3+3} = 6^0 = 1$

  b. $y = \dfrac{1}{5^x}$

7. a. $200{,}000(1 + 0.08)^{-4}$; \$147,006

  b. $175{,}000(1 + 0.08)^3$; \$220,450

  c. $300{,}000(1 + 0.08)^{10}$; \$647,677

8. Answers will vary. Students should indicate that using scientific notation makes very large and very small numbers easier to write and to use in calculations.

CHAPTER 6 · Constructive Assessment Options

SCORING RUBRICS

1. 5 Points

All the items are grouped correctly, work is shown, and a correct explanation is given. The groups are {a, j}, {b}, {c, f}, {d, g, l}, {e, k}, and {h, i}. Sample

explanation: First I wrote equations for parts a–h. Then I grouped the items with matching equations.

  a. $y = 2(1 + 1)^x$ **b.** $y = 16(1 - 0.5)^x$
  c. $y = 16(1 - 0.75)^x$ **d.** $y = 2(1 - 0.5)^x$
  e. $y = 2(1 + 0.5)^x$ **f.** $y = 16(1 - 0.75)^x$
  g. $y = 2(1 - 0.5)^x$ **h.** $y = 16(1 - 0.25)^x$
  i. $y = 16(1 - 0.25)^x$ **j.** $y = 2(1 + 1)^x$
  k. $y = 2(1 + 0.5)^x$ **l.** $y = 2(1 - 0.5)^x$

3 Points

Two or three items are grouped incorrectly. Work is shown and an explanation is given, but the explanation is somewhat vague. Sample explanation: I looked at how y changed and matched things that changed the same way.

1 Point

Only a few items are matched correctly. Some work is shown, but the explanation is unclear or missing.

2. 5 Points

Situations fit the conditions. Equations are correct. Questions are clear and answers are correct.

  a. **i.** Sample situation: A baseball card is worth \$12, and each year its value appreciates by 10%.

    ii. $y = 12(1 + 0.1)^x$, or $y = 12(1.1)^x$, where y is the value of the card and x is the number of years.

    iii. Sample question and answer based on the situation in part i:

      Q: What will the card be worth in five years?
      A: \$19.33

  b. **i.** Sample situation: A car was worth \$20 thousand when it was two years old and \$18 thousand when it was three years old.

    ii. $y = 24.69(1 - 0.1)^x$, or $y = 24.69(0.9)^x$, where y is the value of the car in thousands of dollars and x is the number of years.

    iii. Sample question and answer based on the situation in part i:

      Q: How much will the car be worth ten years after it was purchased?
      A: \$8.6 thousand

3 Points

a. Answers to all three parts are correct or have very minor errors.

b. The situation meets the conditions. The decay rate in the equation is correct, but the starting value may be incorrect. The question is clear and appropriate, but the answer may be incorrect due to an incorrect equation.

1 Point

Most of the answers are attempted, with work shown, but many of the answers are incorrect.

3. 5 Points

a. $y = 80(1 + 0.034)^x$, or $y = 80(1.034)^x$

b. Questions are clear and fit the given requirements. Answers are correct, and work is shown. Sample questions and answers:

Q: How much did the ticket cost in 1995?
A: Substitute -10 for x:
$y = 80(1 + 0.034)^{-10} \approx 57.26$. The ticket cost $57.26 in 1995.

Q: How much will the ticket cost in 2030?
A: Substitute 25 for x:
$y = 80(1 + 0.034)^{25} \approx 184.55$. The ticket will cost $184.55 in 2030.

3 Points

a. The equation is correct.

b. Questions are clear and are answered correctly, but one of the requirements is not met (e.g., both questions involve positive exponents), or questions are clear and meet the requirements, but answers are incorrect or incomplete.

1 Point

a. The equation has x as an exponent but is not correct. Sample answer: $y = 80(0.34)^x$.

b. Questions are attempted, but they are not clear or do not fit the requirements. Answers are incorrect or missing.

4. 5 Points

Kristi's mistakes are explained, and correct solutions are given.

a. She added 2 to each exponent inside the parentheses. She should have multiplied each exponent by 2. The correct answer is $x^6 y^8$.

b. She added the coefficients 3 and 5. She should have multiplied them. The correct answer is $15x^9$.

c. She added all the exponents. She should first have found $(x^4)^3$, which requires multiplying the exponents to get x^{12}. Then she should have found $x^{12} \cdot x^7$, which requires adding the exponents to get x^{19}. The correct answer is x^{19}.

3 Points

Two answers are correct. The other answer is attempted but is not completely correct.

1 Point

Only one answer is correct.

5. 5 Points

The answer includes the following points:

- A statement that any number, except 0, raised to the zero power is 1 (that is, $b^0 = 1$ for $b \neq 0$)

- An example showing why the previous statement makes sense; for example,

$\frac{2^4}{2^4} = 2^{4-4} = 2^0$, and $\frac{2^4}{2^4} = \frac{\cancel{2} \cdot \cancel{2} \cdot \cancel{2} \cdot \cancel{2}}{\cancel{2} \cdot \cancel{2} \cdot \cancel{2} \cdot \cancel{2}} = 1$,

so $2^0 = 1$

- A statement that any number, except 0, raised to a negative power is equal to 1 over that number raised to the opposite power (that is, $b^{-n} = \frac{1}{b^n}$ for $b \neq 0$)

- An example showing why the previous statement makes sense; for example,

$\frac{3^2}{3^5} = 3^{2-5} = 3^{-3}$, and $\frac{3^2}{3^5} = \frac{\cancel{3} \cdot \cancel{3}}{\cancel{3} \cdot \cancel{3} \cdot 3 \cdot 3 \cdot 3} = \frac{1}{3^3}$,

so $3^{-3} = \frac{1}{3^3}$

3 Points

The answer includes the items listed, but minor details are missing or incorrect. (For example, the answer may not mention that the number raised to a zero or negative power cannot be 0.)

1 Point

The answer mentions that a number raised to the zero power is 1 and a number raised to a negative power is 1 over the number to the opposite power, but examples are missing or incorrect.

6. 5 Points

a. Equations will vary but should fit the data reasonably well. Sample equation: $y = 48.2(0.955)^x$. In this equation, 48.2 is the starting value (the value for 1950) and 0.955 was found by guessing and checking.

b. In 1960, there were 31 people per automobile.

c. Because the ratio of people to automobiles is decreasing, the number of cars is growing at a faster rate than the population.

d. Predictions will vary but should be supported by the data. Sample response: The table shows that the number of people per automobile has been leveling off. I predict that this trend will continue, with the number leveling off somewhere near 10.

3 Points

a. The equation fits the data reasonably well.

b. In 1960, there were 31 people per vehicle.

c. The answer is unclear or incomplete. Sample answer: The number of cars is increasing.

d. The prediction is reasonable, but the explanation is missing or unclear, or is not supported by the data. Sample answer: The number of people per car will not get much lower.

1 Point

Answers are attempted, but only one or two are correct. Explanations are inadequate or incorrect.

Discovering Algebra Assessment Resources/Answers
©2007 Key Curriculum Press

7. 5 Points

The equations have starting values of 100 and decay rates close to those in the equations shown here. The relative shapes and positions of the curves are the same as those shown.

a. $y = 100(1 - 0.083)^x$

b. $y = 100(1 - 0.25)^x$

c. $y = 100(1 - 0.0417)^x$

d. $y = 100(1 - 0.417)^x$

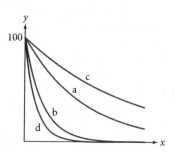

3 Points

One of the equations is incorrect. One of the graphs is incorrect.

1 Point

The equations are all exponential equations, but the graphs and equations are mostly incorrect.

8. 5 Points

Answers are correct, and explanations in parts c and d are clear.

a. 1.8 is the height from which the ball is dropped.

b. The height of the ball decreases by 23% with each bounce.

c. The starting value, 1.8, would increase, because the starting height is greater. The decay rate, 0.23, would increase because the ball would not be as bouncy and its height would decrease by a greater percentage with each bounce.

d. The starting value, 1.8, would decrease, because the starting height is less. The decay rate, 0.23, would decrease because the ball would be bouncier and its height would decrease by a smaller percentage with each bounce.

3 Points

One answer is incorrect. One explanation is inadequate or incorrect.

1 Point

Only one answer is correct. Explanations are missing or are inadequate.

1. Answers will vary. Sample answers:

a.   **b.**

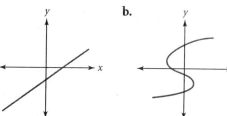

2. a. Yes; each person has a unique Social Security number.

b. No; a particular first name might be paired with many different last names; for example, Mary Smith, Mary Jones, Mary Wong, and so on.

c. No; many cities have more than one Zip code.

d. Yes; each state has only one governor.

3. a.

x	-3	-2	-1	0	1	2	3
y	6	1	-2	-3	-2	1	6

b.

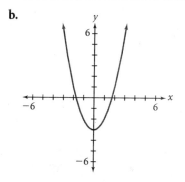

c. The relationship is a function; for each x-value, or input, there is exactly one y-value, or output.

d. The range is $-3 \le y \le 6$.

4. Check to see whether there is a vertical line that crosses the graph at more than one point. If there is, the graph does not represent a function.

5. No; in a vertical line, one x-value is paired with infinitely many y-values.

6. a. It is not a function because the input value 4 has two different output values, 1 and 0; domain: $\{-2, 0, 3, 4\}$; range: $\{-1, 0, 1, 3\}$.

b. It is a function because each input value has only one output value; domain: $\{-3, -1, 0, 1, 5\}$; range: $\{0, 2, 3, 8\}$.

1. Answers will vary. Sample answers:

a.   b.

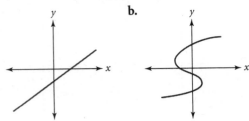

2. a. Yes; each person has one height.

   b. Yes; each person has one first name.

   c. Yes; each president corresponds to a unique country.

   d. No; there are many people who are the same age.

3. a.

x	y
-3	11
-2	6
-1	3
0	2
1	3
2	6
3	11

   b.

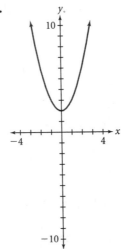

   c. The relationship is a function. For each x-value, or input, there is exactly one y-value, or output.

   d. The range is $2 < y \le 11$.

4. Check to see whether there is a vertical line that crosses the graph at more than one point. If there is, the graph does not represent a function.

5. Yes; in a horizontal line, each x-value is paired with only one y-value.

6. a. It is a function because each input value has only one output value; domain: $\{-3, -2, 0, 3, 4\}$; range: $\{-1, 0, 1, 2, 3\}$.

   b. It is not a function, because -1 has two different output values, 2 and 4; domain: $\{-3, -1, 0, 5\}$; range: $\{0, 1, 2, 3, 4\}$.

1. Stories will vary. Sample story: Sara's dog, Chico, was resting on the front lawn. He saw a cat and ran after it, speeding up rapidly to get near the cat and then chasing it around at a constant speed. The cat ran up a tree, so Chico slowed down and eventually went back to resting on the lawn. Then Sarah came by. Chico got up and walked over to greet her and then went back to resting on the lawn. The independent variable is *time*. The dependent variable is *speed*.

2. a. -3 **b.** $\frac{23}{3}$, or $7\frac{2}{3}$ **c.** $x = 10.5$

   d. -7 **e.** -5 **f.** 5

3. a. 0   **b.** 2   **c.** $1 \le x \le 3$, and $x = 5.5$

   d. $6 < x \le 7$ **e.** $0 \le y \le 6$

4. Answers will vary. Sample answers:

a.   b.

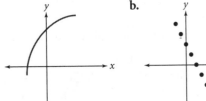

5. a. Because the cost of the call depends on the number of minutes spent talking, the independent variable is *minutes spent talking*, and the dependent variable is *cost of the call*.

   b. Because the number of cookies made depends on the amount of flour used, the independent variable is *amount of flour* and the dependent variable is *number of cookies*. (Note: Some students may argue that the amount of flour you use depends on the number of cookies you want to make, so *number of cookies* is the independent variable. Students should be given credit for this answer.)

1. Stories will vary. Sample story: Sara's dog, Chico, was resting on the front lawn. All of a sudden he saw a gopher and rapidly sped up to chase it. The gopher went into its hole, and Chico slowed down and stopped. After a short rest he thought he saw a cat and started moving toward it, slowly at first and then more quickly. He then ran at a constant speed for a while. Then Sara came by, and he slowed down and walked toward her and then went back to resting on the lawn. The independent variable is *time*. The dependent variable is *speed*.

2. a. -14 **b.** $-\dfrac{2}{3}$ **c.** $x = 3.6$

d. 9 **e.** -16 **f.** -7

3. a. 1 **b.** 1 **c.** $1 \le x \le 3$, and $x = 5.5$

d. $-1 \le x < 0$ **e.** $0 \le y \le 3$

4. Answers will vary. Sample answers:

a. 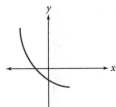 **b.**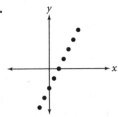

5. a. The amount of gas needed depends on how far the car has traveled since its last fill-up, so the independent variable is *number of miles driven since last fill-up* and the dependent variable is *number of gallons of gas needed*.

b. A child's height depends on his or her age, so the independent variable is *child's age* and the dependent variable is *child's height*.

CHAPTER 7 · Quiz 3   **Form A**

1. a. $|4| + |7| = |4 + 7|$

b. $\left|\dfrac{18}{-6}\right| > -\dfrac{18}{6}$

c. $|-5| \cdot |-6| = |-30|$

d. $|2^{-3}| = \left|\dfrac{1}{2^3}\right| = \dfrac{1}{8}$, and $2^{|-3|} = 2^3 = 8$, so $|2^{-3}| < 2^{|-3|}$.

2. a.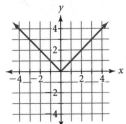

b. $y = |x|$

3. a. $x = 9$ or $x = -9$ **b.** $x = 0$

c. No solution **d.** $x = 4.5$

e. $x \ge 7$ or $x \le -7$ **f.** $x = 0.7$ or $x = -0.7$

g. $x = 6$ or $x = -6$ **h.** $x = 3$ or $x = -21$

4. Sam is incorrect. Sample explanation: A relationship is a function if each *input* has a unique *output*. Both $y = |x|$ and $y = x^2$ satisfy this condition, so they are

functions. A function can have outputs that correspond to more than one input. For example, for the relationship $y = 8$, the output 8 corresponds to *every* input, but $y = 8$ is a function.

5. a.

x	-2	-1	0	1	2	3	4	5	6	7	8	9	10
$f(x)$	36	25	16	9	4	1	0	1	4	9	16	25	36

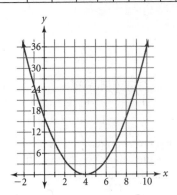

b. $0 \le f(x) \le 36$

CHAPTER 7 · Quiz 3   **Form B**

1. a. $|5| - |8| < |5 - 8|$

b. $-\left|\dfrac{18}{6}\right| < \dfrac{18}{6}$

c. $|-5| \cdot |7| = |-35|$

d. $|2^{-4}| = \left|\dfrac{1}{16}\right| = |16^{-1}|$

2. a.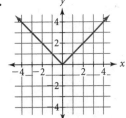

b. $y = |x|$

3. a. $x = 4$ or $x = -4$ **b.** $x = 0$

c. No solution **d.** $x = -6.2$

e. $-5 \le x \le 5$ **f.** $x = -1.1$ or $x = 1.1$

g. $x = -6$ or $x = 20$ **h.** $x = 4$ or $x = -4$

4. Sam is incorrect. Sample explanation: A relationship is a function if each *input* has a unique *output*. Both $y = -|x|$ and $y = -x^2$ satisfy this condition, so they are functions. A function can have outputs that correspond to more than one input. For example, for the relationship $y = 8$, the output 8 corresponds to *every* input, but $y = 8$ is a function.

5. a.

x	-7	-6	-5	-4	-3	-2	-1	0	1	2	3
$f(x)$	25	16	9	4	1	0	1	4	9	16	25

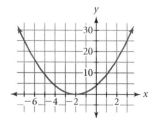

b. $0 \le f(x) \le 25$

CHAPTER 7 • Test   Form A

1. a. 2   **b.** -2 **c.** 17   **d.** 25   **e.** 6

2. Answers will vary. Possible answer: The absolute value of 0 is 0. The absolute value of a positive number is the same as the number. The absolute value of a negative number is the opposite of the number.

3. a. The table represents a function because each input value corresponds to a unique output value.

   b. The table represents a function because each input value corresponds to a unique output value.

   c. The table does not represent a function because the input value 2 corresponds to two output values, 8 and -8.

4. Answers will vary. Possible answer: Both represent functions, both are in Quadrants I and II only, both are symmetric about the y-axis, and both go through the origin. However, the graph of the absolute-value function is made up of line segments, while the graph of $y = x^2$ is a parabola.

5. Yes; it is a function if letters 22 to 26 are changed to letters 1 to 5, respectively. Each letter gets changed to exactly one new letter. If $x \le 21$, $f(x) = x + 5$. If $x > 21$, $f(x) = x + 5 - 26$, or $f(x) = x - 21$. (You might want to give extra credit for a correct rule.)

6. Answers will vary. Sample answers:

a. 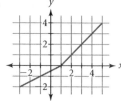   **b.**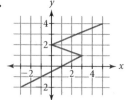

7. a. At 2:00 P.M.

   b. Between 12:00 P.M. and 2:00 P.M.

   c. At 12:00 P.M.; possible reason: He was hungry.

   d. Between 9:00 P.M. and 12:00 P.M., and after 2:00 P.M.

   e. Energy level

8. a. 800

   b. The bacteria population decreases by 9.2% each hour.

   c. Time is the independent variable.

   d. Sample graph and window:

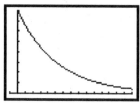

   $[-2, 30, 2, 0, 800, 100]$

   The relationship is a function; no vertical line intersects it at more than one point.

   e. About 7.2 h (Students can find this answer by using trace or the table to find the x-value corresponding to the y-value 400.)

9. a. $x = -8$ or $x = 7$

   b. No real solutions

   c. $x < 1$ or $x > 7$

   d. $x = -4.4$ or $x = 11.6$

CHAPTER 7 • Test   Form B

1. a. 3   **b.** -6 **c.** 13   **d.** 8   **e.** 8

2. Answers will vary. Possible answer: The absolute value of 0 is 0. The absolute value of a positive number is the same as the number. The absolute value of a negative number is the opposite of the number.

3. a. The table represents a function because each input value corresponds to a unique output value.

   b. The table does not represent a function because the input value -4 corresponds to several different output values.

   c. The table represents a function because each input value corresponds to a unique output value.

4. Answers will vary. Possible answer: Both represent functions, both are in Quadrants I and II only, both are symmetric about the y-axis, and both go through the origin. However, the graph of the absolute-value function is made up of line segments, and the graph of $y = x^2$ is a parabola.

5. Yes, it is a function. Each letter gets changed to exactly one new letter. If $x \ge 4$, $f(x) = x - 3$. If $x < 4$, $f(x) = x - 3 + 26$, or $f(x) = x + 23$. (You might want to give extra credit for a correct rule.)

6. Answers will vary. Sample answers:

a.
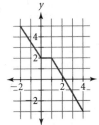

b.
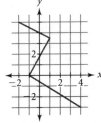

7. a. At 9:00 A.M.

  b. Between 8:00 A.M. and 9:00 A.M.

  c. At 11:00 A.M.; possible reason: He was hungry.

  d. Between 9:00 A.M. and 11:00 A.M., and after 2:00 P.M.

  e. Energy level

8. a. 650

  b. The bacteria population decreases by 8.8% each hour.

  c. Time is the independent variable.

  d. Sample graph and window:

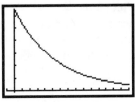

  $[-2, 30, 2, -10, 650, 100]$

  The relationship is a function; no vertical line intersects it in more than one point.

  e. About 7.5 h (Students can find this answer by making a calculator graph or table and finding the x-value corresponding to the y-value 325.)

9. a. $x = -4$ or $x = 7$

  b. No real solutions

  c. $x < -10$ or $x > -4$

  d. $x = -10.8$ or $x = 7.2$

CHAPTER 7 · Constructive Assessment Options

SCORING RUBRICS

1. 5 Points

The code is a function, and the explanation and grid are correct. Two words are coded correctly. Sample answer: Add 12 to the position number of the letter. If the result is greater than 26, subtract 26. The result is the position number of the coded letter.

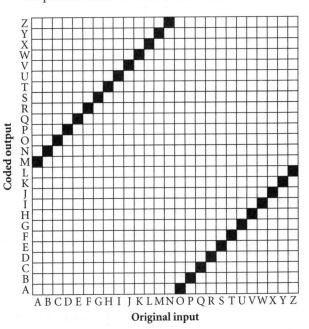

KETCHUP is coded WQFOTGB. MUSTARD is coded YGEFMDP.

3 Points

The code is a function. One of the two explanations (the grid or the written explanation) is incorrect. One word is coded correctly.

1 Point

The code is not a function, but the two words are coded correctly. Or, the code is a function and one of the two explanations is correct, but the coded words are missing.

2. 5 Points

Each graph satisfies the conditions, and the correct domain and range are given. Sample answers:

a.
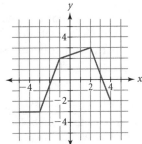

Domain: $-5 \le x \le 4$; range: $-3 \le y \le 3$

b.

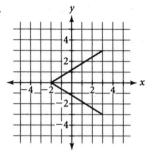

Domain: $-2 \le x \le 3$; range: $-3 \le y \le 3$

c.

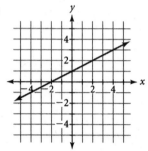

Domain: all real numbers; range: all real numbers

d.

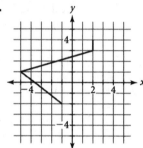

Domain: $-5 \le x \le 2$; range: $-2 \le y \le 4$

3 Points

Three of the graphs satisfy the conditions, and there are one or two minor errors in the domain and range of the other function.

1 Point

Two of the graphs satisfy the conditions, but no domain and range are given. Or, a graph, domain, and range are given for each part, but they include several significant errors.

3. 5 Points

a. All answers and explanations are correct.

   i. The relationship is not a function because most high school students have more than one teacher; the inverse relationship (*high school teacher, high school student*) is not a function because a teacher has more than one student.

   ii. The relationship is a function because each perimeter corresponds to exactly one square (specifically, the square with side length equal to one-fourth the perimeter); the inverse relationship (*square, perimeter*) is a function because each square has a unique perimeter.

   iii. The relationship is a function because each rectangle has a unique area; the inverse relationship (*area, rectangle*) is not a function because there is more than one rectangle with the same area (for example, both a 2-by-12 rectangle and a 4-by-6 rectangle have an area of 24 square units).

   iv. The relationship is not a function because many cities have more than one area code; the inverse relationship (*area code, city*) is also not a function because one area code can correspond to more than one city.

b. The example meets the conditions, and the explanation is clear and complete. Sample answer: The relationship (*vehicle, license plate number*) is a function because each vehicle has a unique license plate number; the inverse relationship (*license plate number, vehicle*) is a function because each license plate number corresponds to a unique vehicle in the state where it is issued.

c. The example meets the conditions, and the explanation is clear and complete. Sample answer: The relationship (*NBA player, NBA team*) is a function because each player is on only one team; the inverse relationship (*NBA team, NBA player*) is not a function because each team includes many players.

3 Points

a. Three of the answers are correct and have clear explanations. Or, all four answers are correct, but the explanations are somewhat vague.

b. The example is correct, but the explanation is unclear. Sample answer: (*vehicle, license plate number*) because one thing goes with one thing either way.

c. The example is correct, but the explanation is unclear. Sample answer: (*NBA player, NBA team*) because one thing goes with one, and then one thing goes with more than one.

1 Point

a. Two of the answers are correct and have fairly clear explanations, or, all four answers are correct, but no explanations are given.

b. The example and the explanation are incorrect, or, the example is correct, but no explanation is given.

c. The example and the explanation are incorrect, or, the example is correct, but no explanation is given.

4. 5 Points

The axes are labeled with variable names and scale values. The story correctly matches the labeled graph and includes several specific values. Sample answer: Lana went scuba diving. For the first 30 s, she descended from the water's surface to a depth of 50 ft at a rate of about 1.7 ft/s. She stayed at a depth of

50 ft for about 10 s and then ascended at a rate of 3 ft/s to a depth of 20 ft. She stayed at that depth for 30 s. Then she saw an interesting fish above her, and she ascended at a rate of 1 ft/s to a depth of 10 ft.

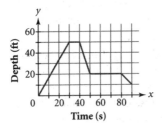

3 Points

The units and scales are clearly defined. The story accounts for each segment of the graph but mentions only a few specific values. Sample story for the graph shown: Lana went scuba diving. She descended at a steady rate to 50 ft. Then she came up at a faster rate than before to 20 ft. She stayed there for a while and then went up more at a rate of 1 ft/s.

1 Point

The axes are labeled with variable names, but the scale values may be missing or may be unreasonable for the story. The story accounts for each segment of the graph but includes few, if any, specific values or includes incorrect values. Sample story for the graph shown: Lana went scuba diving. She dove down deep and stayed there for a little while. Then she came up part way and stayed there. Then she came up a little more.

5. 5 Points

Each term is clearly and correctly explained. Possible answer:

independent variable: A variable whose values affect the values of another variable. In a graph, the horizontal axis usually represents the independent variable.

dependent variable: A variable whose values depend on the values of another variable. In a graph, the vertical axis usually represents the dependent variable.

domain: The set of input values for a relationship

range: The set of output values for a relationship

linear function: A relationship that can be represented by a straight-line graph. A linear relationship is characterized by a constant rate of change—that is, as the value of one variable changes by a constant amount, the value of the other variable also changes by a constant amount.

nonlinear function: A function whose graph is not a straight line. A nonlinear function is characterized by a nonconstant *rate of change*—that is, as the *x*-values change by a constant amount, the *y*-values change by varying amounts.

increasing function: A function for which the *y*-values increase as the *x*-values increase. The graph of an increasing function goes up as you read from left to right.

decreasing function: A function for which the *y*-values decrease as the *x*-values increase. The graph of an increasing function goes down as you read from left to right.

3 Points

Explanations include most of the key points, but minor details are incorrect or are missing, or, the explanations for five or six terms are clear and complete, but the other explanations are incorrect or missing.

1 Point

Explanations are given for at least four of the terms, but important ideas are missing.

6. 5 Points

The axes are labeled with variable names, and the graphs are reasonable. The explanation fits the graph. Sample answers:

a. My school has two lunch periods. In the early morning, no students are in the cafeteria. Then, before the first lunch period begins, students start entering the cafeteria, slowly at first and then more quickly. During the first lunch period, the number of students is fairly constant. When the first lunch period ends, students leave the cafeteria, but students are also entering for the next lunch period, so the number of students doesn't go all the way to zero. The number of students is constant during the second lunch period, and then, when lunch is over, the number of students decreases to zero.

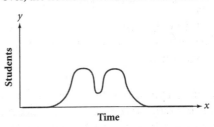

b. The number of students in the hallway increases at a fairly steady rate until the bell rings for the first class. Then the number of students in the hallway decreases quickly to almost zero. When the first class ends, the number of students in the hallway increases very quickly and then decreases quickly as the bell for the second class rings. This pattern is repeated throughout the day.

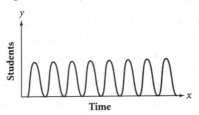

c. My school has a gym class every period except fourth period and last period. Before each gym class, the number of students in the gym increases quickly and then is constant during the class. At the end of gym class, the number of students in the gym decreases quickly to zero.

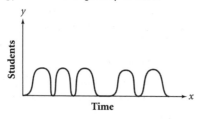

3 Points
Reasonable graphs are given, but the explanations are vague or incomplete.

1 Point
Graphs are given but are not labeled or are not reasonable. Explanations are missing or do not match the graphs.

7. 5 Points
Answers are correct, and all work is clearly shown.

a. Let $f(x) = 3x + 6$ and $g(x) = \frac{1}{3}x + 2$. Then $f(g(x)) = 3\left(\frac{1}{3}x + 2\right) + 6 = x + 6 + 6 = x + 12$. Because $f(g(x)) \neq x$, the functions are not inverses.

b. Let $f(x) = 2x - 4$ and $g(x) = \frac{1}{2}x + 2$. Then $f(g(x)) = 2\left(\frac{1}{2}x + 2\right) - 4 = x + 4 - 4 = x$, and $g(f(x)) = \frac{1}{2}(2x - 4) + 2 = x - 2 + 2 = x$. Because both $f(g(x))$ and $g(f(x))$ are equal to x, the functions are inverses.

3 Points
Answers are correct, but work shown is incomplete.

1 Point
Answers are correct, but no work is shown, or, work is shown, but mistakes are made in composing the functions, leading to incorrect answers.

CHAPTERS 4–7 · Exam   Form A

1. a. $y = -\frac{9}{2} + \frac{3}{4}x$ **b.** $y = 13 + 2x$

2. a. $\begin{cases} 11d + 14c = 573.25 \\ 22d + 9c = 790.25 \end{cases}$

b. $d = 28.25$, $c = 18.75$; it costs \$18.75 to board a cat and \$28.25 to board a dog.

3. a. $x > -\frac{8}{3}$ **b.** $x \leq 2$

4. a. $32a^{10}b^{20}$ **b.** $x^3y^3z^4$ **c.** $3^{x-y}4^y$

5. a. $\frac{d^2}{2c^4}$ **b.** $\frac{y^3}{x^7}$

c. $\frac{1}{3^3p^3}$, or $\frac{1}{(3p)^3}$, or $\frac{1}{27p^3}$

6. a. Jamesville: $20{,}000(1 + 0.05)^x$; Thomasville: $75{,}000(1 - 0.08)^x$

b. Jamesville: 25,500; Thomasville: 49,400

c. Jamesville: 12,300; Thomasville: 172,700

d. 10 years from now

7. $\begin{cases} y \leq 3 \\ y > -2 - 2.5x \\ y > -1 + x \end{cases}$

8. a. Linear; each time 1 is added to the x-value, a constant number is subtracted from the y-value.

b. Exponential; each time 1 is added to the x-value, the y-value is multiplied by a constant number.

c. Exponential; the ratio of consecutive y-values is constant.

d. Linear; the difference of consecutive y-values is constant.

9. a. Yes; possible explanation: Each x-value corresponds to a unique y-value.

b. No; possible explanation: The x-value 3 corresponds to y-values -3 and 3.

c. No; possible explanation: The input values 1 and 2 each correspond to two different output values.

d. Yes; possible explanation: Each input value corresponds to a unique output value.

e. Yes; possible explanation: The graph passes the vertical line test.

f. No; possible explanation: The vertical line $x = -2$ passes through more than one point.

10. a. Domain: $-4 \leq x \leq 4$; range: $-2 \leq y \leq 4$

b. $f(2) = 2$ **c.** $-1 \leq x \leq 0$

d. From $x = -4$ to $x = -2$, the function is nonlinear and decreasing at a slower and slower rate of change. From $x = -2$ to $x = -1$, the function is linear and therefore increasing at a constant rate of change. From $x = -1$ to $x = 0$, the function is linear and is neither increasing nor decreasing. From $x = 0$ to $x = 2$, the function is increasing at a faster and faster rate of change. From $x = 2$ to $x = 4$, the function is increasing at a slower and slower rate of change.

11. a. $x = -9$ or $x = 5$

b. $x = -8$ or $x = 14$

c. No solution

12. a. If x is the number of hits and y is the number of runs, the Q-points are $(45, 20)$ and $(137, 56.5)$, and the equation is $y = 0.397(x - 45) + 20$, or $y = 0.397(x - 137) + 56.5$.

b. For each increase of 1 hit, the number of runs increases by about 0.397; or, for every 10 hits the team gets, it scores just less than 4 runs.

c. About 50 runs

d. About 183 or 184 hits

1. a. $y = \frac{13}{2} + \frac{3}{4}x$ **b.** $y = 3 - \frac{1}{2}x$

2. a. $\begin{cases} 14d + 7c = 586.25 \\ 11d + 21c = 751.25 \end{cases}$

   b. $d = 32.5$, $c = 18.75$; it costs \$18.75 to board a cat and \$32.50 to board a dog.

3. a. $x < \frac{3}{5}$ **b.** $x > 4$

4. a. $16a^8b^{12}$ **b.** y^2z^4 **c.** $7^{3x}4^y$

5. a. $\frac{c}{2^2d^5}$, or $\frac{c}{4d^5}$ **b.** $\frac{y^4}{x^2}$

   c. $\frac{1}{2^5p^5}$, or $\frac{1}{(2p)^5}$, or $\frac{1}{32p^5}$

6. a. Jamesville: $24{,}000(1 + 0.04)^x$; Thomasville: $72{,}000(1 - 0.07)^x$

   b. Jamesville: 29,200; Thomasville: 50,100

   c. Jamesville: 16,200; Thomasville: 148,800

   d. 10 years from now

7. $\begin{cases} x \le 4 \\ y \le -1 + 1.5x \\ y > -2 + 0.5x \end{cases}$

8. a. Exponential; each time 1 is added to the x-value, the y-value is multiplied by a constant number.

   b. Linear; each time 1 is added to the x-value, a constant number is added to the y-value.

   c. Linear; the difference of consecutive y-values is constant.

   d. Exponential; the ratio of consecutive y-values is constant.

9. a. No; possible explanation: The x-value 9 corresponds to the y-values -3 and 3.

   b. Yes; possible explanation: Each x-value corresponds to a unique y-value.

   c. Yes; possible explanation: Each input value corresponds to a unique output value.

   d. No; possible explanation: The input values 4 and 8 each correspond to two different output values.

   e. Yes; possible explanation: The graph passes the vertical line test.

   f. No; possible explanation: The vertical line $x = 1.5$ passes through more than one point.

10. a. Domain: $-4 \le x \le 4$; range: $-1 \le y \le 3$

   b. $f(-2) = 3$ **c.** $x > 1$

   d. From $x = -4$ to $x = -2$, the function is nonlinear and increasing at a faster and faster rate of change. From $x = -2$ to $x = 0$, the function is linear and is neither increasing nor decreasing. From $x = 0$ to $x = 1$, the function is linear and therefore decreasing at a constant rate of change. From $x = 1$ to $x = 3$, the function is decreasing at a slower and slower rate

of change. From $x = 3$ to $x = 4$, the function is decreasing at a faster and faster rate of change.

11. a. $x = -6$ or $x = 12$

   b. No solution

   c. $x = -19$ or $x = 11$

12. a. If x is the number of hits and y is the number of runs, the Q-points are $(52, 29.5)$ and $(144.5, 84)$, and the Q-line equation is $y = 0.589(x - 52) + 29.5$, or $y = 0.589(x - 144.5) + 84$.

   b. For each increase of 1 hit, the number of runs increases by about 0.589; or, for every 10 hits the team gets, it scores almost 6 runs.

   c. About 70 runs   **d.** About 146 hits

CHAPTER 8 · Quiz 1   Form A

1. a. $(1, 1)$, $(4, 1)$, $(3, -3)$, and $(-1, -2)$

   b., c.

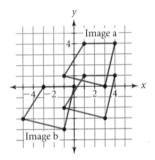

2. a. Translate it left 6 units and down 2 units; $(x - 6, y - 2)$.

   b. Translate it right 3 units and up 3 units; $(x + 3, y + 3)$.

3. a. Translation of $y = |x|$ down 3 units; $y = |x| - 3$, or $y + 3 = |x|$

   b. Translation of $y = x^2$ right 1 unit and down 2 units; $y = (x - 1)^2 - 2$, or $y + 2 = (x - 1)^2$

   c. Translation of $y = |x|$ right 5 units and up 1 unit; $y = |x - 5| + 1$, or $y - 1 = |x - 5|$

CHAPTER 8 · Quiz 1   Form B

1. a. $(2, -1)$, $(-3, -2)$, $(-3, 0)$, and $(-1, 2)$

   b., c.

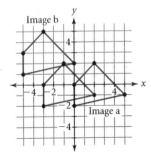

2. a. Translate it right 1 unit and down 4 units; $(x + 1, y - 4)$.

   b. Translate it left 3 units and up 3 units; $(x - 3, y + 3)$.

3. a. Translation of $y = x^2$ right 3 units; $y = (x - 3)^2$

   b. Translation of $y = |x|$ left 4 units and up 1 unit; $y = |x + 4| + 1$, or $y - 1 = |x + 4|$

   c. Translation of $y = x^2$ left 5 units and down 3 units; $y = (x + 5)^2 - 3$, or $y + 3 = (x + 5)^2$

CHAPTER 8 · Quiz 2　　　　　　　　**Form A**

1. a.

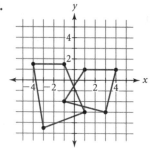

   b. $(-x, 1.5y)$

2. a. Vertical stretch by a factor of 3; $y = 3x^2$

   b. Translation left 3 units and reflection across the x-axis; $y = -(x + 3)^2$

   c. Vertical shrink by a factor of 0.5 and reflection across the x-axis; $y = -0.5x^2$

   d. Translation left 2 units, vertical stretch by a factor of 2, and translation down 2 units; $y = 2(x + 2)^2 - 2$

3. a. The graph is the image of the graph of $y = |x|$ after a translation left 2 units and down 0.5 unit.

   b. The graph is the image of the graph of $y = |x|$ after a translation right 1 unit, a vertical stretch by a factor of 2, and a reflection across the x-axis.

4. a. The graph is the image of the graph of $y = f(x)$ after a reflection across the y-axis and a vertical stretch by a factor of 3.

   b. The graph is the image of the graph of $y = f(x)$ after a reflection across the x-axis and a reflection across the y-axis.

CHAPTER 8 · Quiz 2　　　　　　　　**Form B**

1. a.

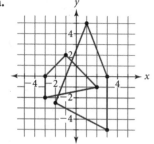

   b. $(-x, 2.5y)$

2. a. Vertical shrink by a factor of 0.5; $y = 0.5x^2$

   b. Translation right 3 units and reflection across the x-axis; $y = -(x - 3)^2$

   c. Vertical stretch by a factor of 2 and reflection across the x-axis; $y = -2x^2$

   d. Translation left 1 unit, vertical stretch by a factor of 3, and translation down 3 units; $y = 3(x + 1)^2 - 3$

3. a. The graph is the image of the graph of $y = |x|$ after a translation right 5 units and down 2 units.

   b. The graph is the image of the graph of $y = |x|$ after a vertical stretch by a factor of 2 and a translation left 3 units.

4. a. The graph is the image of the graph of $y = f(x)$ after a translation left 4 units and a reflection across the x-axis.

   b. The graph is the image of the graph of $y = f(x)$ after a reflection across the y-axis, a vertical stretch by a factor of 4, and a translation up 2 units.

CHAPTER 8 · Quiz 3　　　　　　　　**Form A**

1. a. Translate $y = \frac{1}{x}$ right 2 units; $y = \frac{1}{x - 2}$.

   b. Translate $y = \frac{1}{x}$ left 1 unit and up 3 units; $y = \frac{1}{x + 1} + 3$, or $y - 3 = \frac{1}{x + 1}$.

2. Quadrants II and IV

3. a. A vertical stretch by 2, followed by a translation left 3 units and down 5 units

   b.

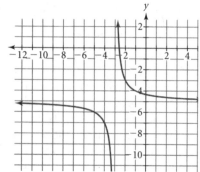

   c. $x \neq -3$

Discovering Algebra Assessment Resources/Answers
©2007 Key Curriculum Press

4. a. Rectangle

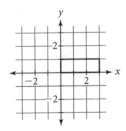

b. Vertical stretch by a factor of 2; $\begin{bmatrix} 0 & 3 & 3 & 0 \\ 0 & 0 & 2 & 2 \end{bmatrix}$

c. A reflection across one axis followed by a reflection across the other axis; $\begin{bmatrix} 0 & -3 & -3 & 0 \\ 0 & 0 & -1 & -1 \end{bmatrix}$

5. a. $\dfrac{5x}{2}$

b. $\dfrac{x-4}{2(x+1)}; x \neq -1$

c. $\dfrac{9}{x^2}; x \neq 0$

CHAPTER 8 · Quiz 3   Form B

1. a. Translate $y = \frac{1}{x}$ left 1 unit; $y = \frac{1}{x+1}$.

b. Translate $y = \frac{1}{x}$ right 3 units and up 3 units; $y = \frac{1}{x-3} + 3$, or $y - 3 = \frac{1}{x-3}$.

2. Quadrants I and III

3. a. A vertical stretch by 2, and then a translation left 1 unit and up 4 units

b.

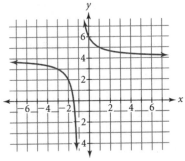

c. $x \neq -1$

4. a. Parallelogram

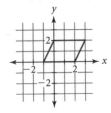

b. Vertical shrink by a factor of 0.5; $\begin{bmatrix} -1 & 0 & 3 & 2 \\ 0 & 1 & 1 & 0 \end{bmatrix}$

c. A reflection across one axis followed by a reflection across the other axis; $\begin{bmatrix} 1 & 0 & -3 & -2 \\ 0 & -2 & -2 & 0 \end{bmatrix}$

5. a. $\dfrac{7x}{2}$

b. $\dfrac{x+3}{2(x-4)}; x \neq 4$

c. $\dfrac{16}{x^2}; x \neq 0$

CHAPTER 8 · Test   Form A

1. a. $y = |x - 6|$ **b.** $y = |x| - 3$, or $y + 3 = |x|$

c. $y = -|x|$ **d.** $y = 2x^2 + 1$, or $y - 1 = 2x^2$

e. $y = -0.5(x - 3)^2$

2. a. Translates it right 1 unit and up 4 units

b. Stretches it vertically by a factor of 3 and translates it left 2 units

3. a. Translated up 3 units

b. Translated right 3 units

c. The graph is reflected across the y-axis, but because the graph of $y = x^2 + 1$ is symmetric across the y-axis, the image is identical to the original graph.

d. Stretched vertically by a factor of 2

4. Answers will vary. Possible answers:

a. $y + 2 = \dfrac{1}{x-3}$, or $y = \dfrac{1}{x-3} - 2$

b. $y = 3|x - 2| + 5$

5. a. $[B] = \begin{bmatrix} 0 & 1 & 1 & 0 \\ 1 & 1 & 0 & 0 \end{bmatrix}$ (The order of the columns may vary.)

b. A shrink by a factor of 0.5 in both directions; $(0, 0.5), (0.5, 0.5), (0.5, 0), (0, 0)$

c. A stretch by a factor of 2 in both directions and a reflection across the x-axis; $(0, -2), (2, -2), (2, 0), (0, 0)$

d. A translation left 3 units and up 2 units; $(-3, 3), (-2, 3), (-2, 2), (-3, 2)$

e. A rotation by 180°, but because this is a square, no change; $(0, 1), (1, 1), (1, 0), (0, 0)$

6. a. $\dfrac{5x^2}{6}$

b. $\dfrac{x-13}{6x}; x \neq 0$

c. $-\dfrac{y^2}{x^2}; x \neq 0$

d. $\dfrac{2(x+3)}{x-1}; x \neq 1$ and $x \neq 4$

7. a. $y = 1520.82(1 + 0.04)^x$

  b. Translate it right 5 units.

  c. $y = 1520.82(1 + 0.04)^{x-5}$

  d. $1,250

CHAPTER 8 · Test   Form B

1. a. $y = 3 - |x|$, or $y - 3 = -|x|$

  b. $y = |x + 6|$

  c. $y = |x| - 4$, or $y + 4 = |x|$

  d. $y = -0.5x^2 + 10$

  e. $y = 2(x + 5)^2$

2. a. Translates it left 2 units and down 5 units

  b. Shrinks it vertically by a factor of 0.5 and translates it right 3 units

3. a. Translated down 4 units

  b. Translated left 3 units

  c. The graph is reflected across the y-axis, but because the graph of $y = x^2 + 1$ is symmetric across the y-axis, the image is identical to the original graph.

  d. Stretched vertically by a factor of 2

4. Answers may vary. Possible answers:

  a. $y = \dfrac{1}{x + 2} + 3$, or $y - 3 = \dfrac{1}{x + 2}$

  b. $y = 0.5|x + 1| - 3$, or $y + 3 = 0.5|x + 1|$

5. a. $[B] = \begin{bmatrix} 0 & 1 & 1 & 0 \\ 1 & 1 & 0 & 0 \end{bmatrix}$ (The order of the columns may vary.)

  b. A stretch in both directions by a factor of 3; $(0, 3), (3, 3), (3, 0), (0, 0)$

  c. A stretch by a factor of 3 in both directions and a reflection across the x-axis; $(0, -3), (3, -3), (3, 0), (0, 0)$

  d. A translation right 2 units and down 1 unit; $(2, 0), (3, 0), (3, -1), (2, -1)$

  e. A rotation by 180°, but because this is a square, no change; $(0, 1), (1, 1), (1, 0), (0, 0)$

6. a. $\dfrac{7x^2}{6}$

  b. $\dfrac{3x - 7}{6x}$; $x \neq 0$

  c. $-\dfrac{4y^2}{x^2}$; $x \neq 0$ and $y \neq 0$

  d. $\dfrac{2(x - 3)}{x + 1}$; $x \neq -4$ and $x \neq -1$

7. a. $y = 1336.75(1 + 0.05)^x$

  b. Translate it right 7 units.

  c. $y = 1336.75(1 + 0.05)^{x-7}$

  d. $950

CHAPTER 8 · Constructive Assessment Options

SCORING RUBRICS

1. 5 Points

Transformations are described and carried out correctly, and at least one of the transformations is a reflection or a vertical stretch or shrink. Possible answer: I reflected my initials across the x-axis, then translated them left 5 units, and then stretched them by a factor of 1.5.

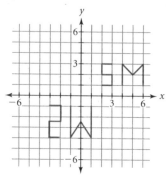

3 Points

Two or more transformations (possibly both translations) are correctly applied to the initials, but the description of the transformations includes errors or is incomplete or unclear.

1 Point

Two or more transformations are applied, possibly with minor errors, but no description is given. Or, only one transformation is applied and described.

2. 5 Points

Equations are correct, and explanations are clear.

  a. $y = -f(x + 3)$; the transformation is a reflection across the x-axis and a translation 3 units left, so in the equation $y = k + a \cdot f(x - h)$, h is -3, k is 0, and a is -1.

  b. $y = -4 + 0.5 \cdot f(x)$; the transformation is a vertical shrink by a factor of 0.5 and a translation down 4 units, so in the equation $y = k + a \cdot f(x - h)$, h is 0, k is -4, and a is 0.5.

3 Points

Both equations are correct, but the explanations are not completely clear. Or, in one part both the equation and the explanation are correct, but in the other part only one of the two transformations is correctly identified, leading to an incorrect equation.

1 Point

Equations are correct, but no explanations are given. Or, some of the work is correct, but both answers include significant errors.

3. 5 Points

The answer includes the following points:

  • k is the vertical translation; if $k > 0$, the graph moves up, and if $k < 0$, the graph moves down.

- h is the horizontal translation; if $h > 0$, the graph moves left, and if $h < 0$, the graph moves right.
- If $|a| > 1$, the graph is stretched vertically by a factor of $|a|$; if $|a| < 1$, the graph is shrunk vertically by a factor of $|a|$.
- If $a < 0$, the graph is reflected across the x-axis.

3 Points

One major point from the list is missing, and one or two other minor mistakes are made.

1 Point

Three major points from the list are missing.

4. 5 Points

a. i. Both graphs are lines with slope 1 and y-intercept 3, but the graph of the rational function has a hole where $x = 2$, which is the value that makes the denominator equal to 0.

ii. Both graphs are lines with slope 1 and y-intercept 1, but the graph of the rational function has a hole where $x = -2$, which is the value that makes the denominator equal to 0.

iii. Both graphs are lines with slope 1 and y-intercept -2, but the graph of the rational function has a hole where $x = -1$, which is the value that makes the denominator equal to 0.

b. The function has a graph that looks like $f(x) = x - 4$, but has a hole. Possible answer: $g(x) = \dfrac{x^2 - 2x - 8}{x + 2}$.

3 Points

Answers to part a are mostly correct. Part b is attempted, but the answer is incorrect.

1 Point

Answers to part a claim that the graphs in each pair are the same. Part b is attempted, but the answer is incorrect.

5. 5 Points

a. Domain: $x \neq 0$; range: $y > 0$; asymptotes: $x = 0$ and $y = 0$; increasing for $x < 0$ and decreasing for $x > 0$

b. i. The sketch has the same basic shape as the graph shown here, with asymptotes at $x = 2$ and $y = -3$.

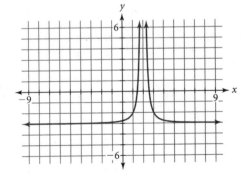

ii. The sketch has the same basic shape as the graph shown here, with asymptotes at $x = -3$ and $y = 0$.

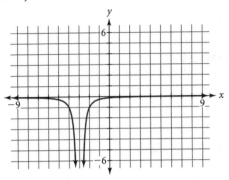

c. Answers will vary. The equation should be a transformation of $y = \dfrac{1}{x^2}$, and the description should match the equation. Sample answer: $y = 3 - \dfrac{1}{x^2}$; domain: $x \neq 0$; range: $y < 3$; decreasing for $x < 0$ and increasing for $x > 0$

3 Points

a. One part of the description is incorrect or missing.

b. One of the graphs is completely correct, or both graphs are mostly correct.

c. The equation is a transformation of $y = \dfrac{1}{x^2}$, but the description is incomplete.

1 Point

a. Only one or two parts of the description are given.

b. Both graphs are attempted, but are mostly incorrect.

c. An answer is attempted, but it includes significant errors.

6. 5 Points

a. $\begin{bmatrix} 1 & 4 & 6 \\ 2 & 5 & 3 \end{bmatrix}$ (The order of the columns may vary.)

b. i. $\begin{bmatrix} -1 & 0 \\ 0 & -1 \end{bmatrix} \cdot \begin{bmatrix} 1 & 4 & 6 \\ 2 & 5 & 3 \end{bmatrix} = \begin{bmatrix} -1 & -4 & -6 \\ -2 & -5 & -3 \end{bmatrix}$

(The order of the columns is consistent with part a.)

ii. $\begin{bmatrix} 1 & 4 & 6 \\ 2 & 5 & 3 \end{bmatrix} + \begin{bmatrix} -2 & -2 & -2 \\ -7 & -7 & -7 \end{bmatrix}$

$= \begin{bmatrix} -1 & 2 & 4 \\ -5 & -2 & -4 \end{bmatrix}$ (The order of the columns is consistent with part a.)

3 Points

Two of the three answers are correct. Or, part a is correct, but parts b and c include minor calculation errors.

1 Point

The answer to part a is correct, but other answers are incorrect or missing.

1. $x = 5$ or $x = -3$

2. $x \approx 3.24$ or $x \approx -1.24$.

3. $(1, 2.25)$; the x-intercepts are -2 and 4, so the x-coordinate of the vertex is $\frac{-2 + 4}{2}$, or 1; to find the y-coordinate of the vertex, substitute 1 for x in the equation: $y = -0.25(1)^2 + 0.5(1) + 2 = 2.25$.

4. a. $h(1) = 25.1$; after 1 s the ball will be 25.1 m above the ground.

    b. About 2.02 s after it is dropped

    c. 30 m; at $t = 0$, the ball is still at the top of the building, so $h(0)$, or 30, gives the height of the ball at the top of the building.

    d. About 2.47 s after it is dropped

5. Answers to 5a–c will vary. Sample answers are:

    a. -3 **b.** 6 or $\frac{6}{1}$ **c.** $\sqrt{2}$ **d.** Irrational

1. $x = 2 \pm \sqrt{14}$

2. $x \approx -4.19$ or $x \approx 1.19$.

3. $(-1.5, -2.45)$; the x-intercepts are -5 and 2, so the x-coordinate of the vertex is $\frac{-5 + 2}{2}$, or -1.5; to find the y-coordinate of the vertex, substitute -1.5 for x in the equation: $y = 0.2(-1.5)^2 + 0.6(-1.5) - 2 = -2.45$.

4. a. $h(1.5) = 8.975$ m; after 1.5 s the ball will be 8.975 m above the ground.

    b. About 1.56 s after it is dropped

    c. 20 m; at $t = 0$, the ball is still at the top of the building, so $h(0)$, or 20, gives the height of the ball at the top of the building.

    d. About 2.02 s after it is dropped

5. Answers to 5a–c will vary. Sample answers are:

    a. 3   **b.** 6.2   **c.** $\sqrt{2}$ **d.** Real

1. a. $x^2 - 6x + 9$ **b.** $x^2 + 4x + 3$

    c. $2x^2 + 7x - 4$

2. a. $y = x^2 - 6x + 14$ **b.** $y = 2x^2 - 4x - 0.5$

3. a.

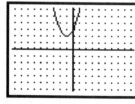

$[-9.4, 9.4, 1, -6.2, 6.2, 1]$

    b. $(-1, 2)$ **c.** $y = (x + 1)^2 + 2$

    d. $y = (x + 1)^2 + 2 = x^2 + 2x + 1 + 2$
$$= x^2 + 2x + 3$$

4. $x = 0$, $x = 4$, or $x = 5$

5. a. True

    b. False; the right side should be $(x + 4)(x - 4)$.

    c. True

    d. False; the right side should be $(x + 3)(x - 2)$.

6. Possible answers: You could graph the parabola $y = x^2 + 4$ and show that it does not intersect the x-axis, or you could rewrite the equation as $x^2 = -4$. Because the square of any real number is a nonnegative number, the equation has no real solution.

7. $y = (x + 4)(x - 7)$

8. a. $\dfrac{x + 3}{x - 4}$; $x \neq -1$ and $x \neq 4$

    b. $\dfrac{x + 2}{x - 4}$; $x \neq -4$ and $x \neq 4$

1. a. $x^2 - 10x + 25$ **b.** $x^2 + 5x + 6$

    c. $3x^2 + x - 4$

2. a. $y = x^2 + 4x + 11$ **b.** $y = 3x^2 - 12x + 10.5$

3. a.

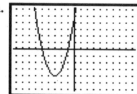

$[-9.4, 9.4, 1, -6.2, 6.2, 1]$

    b. $(-3, -4)$ **c.** $y = (x + 3)^2 - 4$

    d. $y = (x + 3)^2 - 4 = x^2 + 6x + 9 - 4$
$$= x^2 + 6x + 5$$

4. $x = 0$, $x = -2$, or $x = 8$

5. a. True

    b. False; the right side should be $(x + 5)(x - 5)$.

    c. True

    d. False; the right side should be $(x - 3)(x + 2)$.

6. Possible answer: You could graph the parabola $y = x^2 + 2x + 4$ and show that it does not intersect the x-axis.

7. $y = (x + 5)(x - 3)$

8. a. $\dfrac{x - 1}{x - 2}$; $x \neq -3$ and $x \neq 2$

    b. $\dfrac{x + 4}{x - 2}$; $x \neq -2$ and $x \neq 2$

1. $x = -2 \pm \sqrt{3}$

2. $x = 1$ or $x = -5$

3. $x = \dfrac{1 \pm \sqrt{73}}{6}$

4. $(2.5x)^3 = 6319$; $x \approx 7.40$

5. It is the image of the graph of $y = x^3$ after a vertical shrink by a factor of 0.5, and a translation right 2 units and up 4 units.

6. $x(x + 3)(x - 2)$

7. a. $l(l - 8) = 240$, or $l^2 - 8l = 240$

   b. $l = -12$ or $l = 20$

   c. 20 cm by 12 cm

1. $x = -3 \pm \sqrt{5}$

2. $x = -3$ or $x = 5$

3. $x = \dfrac{-1 \pm \sqrt{61}}{10}$

4. $(1.4x)^3 = 5284$; $x \approx 12.44$

5. It is the image of the graph of $y = x^3$ after a vertical stretch by a factor of 2, and a translation left 5 units and down 3 units.

6. $x(x + 5)(x - 1)$

7. a. $l(l - 11) = 180$, or $l^2 - 11l = 180$

   b. $l = -9$ or $l = 20$

   c. 20 cm by 9 cm

1. a. $h(3) = 155.9$ m; after 3 s, the ball is 155.9 m above the ground.

   b. After 5.89 s   c. After 6.39 s

2. a. False; the right side should be $(x - 3)(x + 8)$.

   b. True

   c. False; the right side should be $x^2 + 6x + 9$.

   d. False; the right side should be $x^2 - 3x - 10$.

3. a. x-intercepts: $-2, 6$; vertex: $(2, -16)$

   b. $y = (x - 2)^2 - 16$ c. $y = x^2 - 4x - 12$

4. $y = -(x - 2)^2 + 3$

5. a. $x = \dfrac{5}{2}$ or $x = 1$ b. No real solutions

6. $x = 0$, $x = 2$, or $x = -2$

7. $x = 2 \pm \sqrt{5}$

8. Possible answer: Yes; any equation of the form $y = a(x - r_1)(x - r_2)$ has the roots r_1 and r_2.

9. $y = -4(x + 1)^2(x + 2)$

10. $\dfrac{x + 2}{x + 1}$; $x \neq -1$ and $x \neq 2$

1. a. $h(4) = 96.6$ m; after 4 s, the ball is 96.6 m above the ground.

   b. After 4.95 s

   c. After 5.98 s

2. a. True

   b. False; the right side should be $3x^2 - 12x + 17$.

   c. False; the right side should be $x^2 - 6x + 9$.

   d. True

3. a. x-intercepts: $-3, 7$; vertex: $(2, -25)$

   b. $y = (x - 2)^2 - 25$

   c. $y = x^2 - 4x - 21$

4. $y = (x - 1)^2 - 3$

5. a. $x = \dfrac{4}{3}$ or $x = 1$ b. No real solutions

6. $x = 0$, $x = 3$, or $x = -3$

7. $x = 2 \pm \sqrt{7}$

8. Possible answer: Yes; any equation of the form $y = a(x - r_1)(x - r_2)$ has the roots r_1 and r_2.

9. $y = 4x(x - 1)^2$

10. $\dfrac{x + 1}{x + 2}$; $x \neq -2$ and $x \neq 3$

CHAPTER 9 • Constructive Assessment Options

SCORING RUBRICS

1. **5 Points**

All equations meet the given conditions.

   a. Sample answer: $y = -2x^2 - 3$ (or any equation $y = ax^2 + c$, where $a < 0$ and $c < 0$)

   b. Sample answer: $y = 4(x - 1)(x - 1)$ (or any equation $y = a(x - r)(x - r)$, where $ar^2 = 4$)

   c. Sample answer: $y = -0.25(x + 3)^2 + 4$ (or any equation $y = a(x + h)^2 + k$, where $a < 0$, $h > 0$, and $k > 0$)

3 Points

Two of the equations meet the given conditions. Or, one equation meets all the conditions, and each of the other equations meets all but one condition.

1 Point

Two of the equations partially meet the conditions.

2. **5 Points**

The answer correctly describes each form and explains how each form is related to the graph. A correct answer will include the points listed here.

(Note: Students may use specific examples rather than the general equations shown.)

- The factored form is $y = a(x - r_1)(x - r_2)$. From this form you can find the x-intercepts, r_1 and r_2.
- The vertex form is $y = a(x - h) + k$. From this form you can find the vertex, (h, k).
- The general form is $y = ax^2 + bx + c$. From this form you can find the y-intercept, c.
- In all three forms the value of a tells whether the graph opens upward or downward. If $a > 0$, the parabola opens upward. If $a < 0$, the parabola opens downward.
- In all three forms the value of a tells whether the graph is a vertical stretch or a vertical shrink of the graph of $y = x^2$. If $|a| > 1$, it is a stretch. If $|a| < 1$, it is a shrink.

3 Points
One of the major points listed is missing, and there are one or two other minor errors.

1 Point
Only one or two of the points listed are made.

3. 5 Points

a. The table is complete and correct.

Number of 10¢ increases	Price per hot dog	Number of hot dogs sold	Income
-15	$0.50	115	$57.50
-10	$1.00	90	$90.00
-5	$1.50	65	$97.50
0	$2.00	40	$80.00
2	$2.20	30	$66.00
4	$2.40	20	$48.00
6	$2.60	10	$26.00

b. The scatter plot is complete and correct.

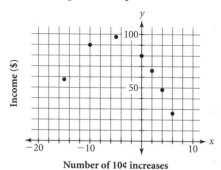

Number of 10¢ increases

c. $y = (2 + 0.1x)(40 - 5x)$, where x is the number of 10¢ increases and y is the income

d. The ski club should charge $1.40. I found this by tracing the graph to find the maximum point, which is $(-6, 98)$. This means that six 10¢ decreases would give a maximum income of $98.

After six 10¢ decreases, the price of a hot dog would be $1.40.

3 Points
The table and the scatter plot are correct. Parts c and d are attempted and some of the work is correct, but the answers are incorrect.

1 Point
All answers are attempted and some of the work is correct, but no answer is completely correct.

4. 5 Points
Questions are clear, answers are correct, and all work is shown. Possible answers:

Q: From what height is the ball dropped?
A: Substituting $x = 0$ gives the height of the ball before it is released: $y = -4.9(0)^2 + 100 = 100$, so it is dropped from 100 m.

Q: What is the height of the ball after 3 s?
A: $y = -4.9(3)^2 + 100 = 55.9$, so the height of the ball is 55.9 m after 3 s.

Q: When does the ball hit the ground?
A: Solve $-4.9x^2 + 100 = 0$.

$$-4.9x^2 + 100 = 0$$
$$-4.9x^2 = -100$$
$$x^2 \approx 20.41$$
$$x \approx \pm 4.52$$

The solutions are -4.52 and 4.52; because a negative value does not make sense in this situation, the ball hits the ground after about 4.52 s.

3 Points
Three questions are given with correct answers, but no work is shown. Or, three questions are given and work is shown, but the answers are incorrect.

1 Point
Three questions are given, but no answers are given and no work is shown. Or, only one or two questions and answers are given, and no work is shown.

5. 5 Points
Answers are correct, and explanations are thorough and demonstrate an understanding of important concepts.

a. True. Possible explanation: The general form of the equation is $y = -16x^2 + bx + c$, where y is the height of the ball and x is the time in seconds. To find the values of b and c, substitute two pairs of values from the table and solve the resulting system. Using $(1, 30)$ and $(2, 22)$ gives the system $\begin{cases} 46 = b + c \\ 86 = 2b + c \end{cases}$, which has the solution $b = 40$ and $c = 6$, so the equation is $y = -16x^2 + 40x + 6$. Substituting 0 for x gives an initial height of 6 ft.

b. False. Possible explanation: Because Camilla released the ball from a height of 6 ft, it was at a height of 4 ft only once, on the way down.

c. True. To find the number of seconds the ball was in the air, substitute 0 for y and solve for x. The solution is about 2.64, so the ball was in the air for less than 3 s.

d. True. Graphing the equation and then tracing the graph shows that the vertex is $(1.25, 31)$, so the maximum height was 31 ft.

3 Points

At least three answers are correct and explanations are well written, but a few minor details are missing or incorrect.

1 Point

Answers are correct, but no explanations are given. Or, only one answer is correct, but it has a good, clear explanation.

6. 5 Points

Work and explanations for all parts are clear and correct. Possible answers:

a.

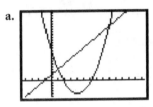

$[-4.4, 14.4, 1, -6, 25, 1]$

They intersect in two points.

b. $x^2 - 8x + 11 = 2x + 2$

$x^2 - 10x + 9 = 0$

$x = \dfrac{10 \pm \sqrt{64}}{2} = \dfrac{10 \pm 8}{2} = 9$ and 1

$y = 2(9) + 2 = 20$; one intersection point is $(9, 20)$.

$y = 2(1) + 2 = 4$; the other intersection point is $(1, 4)$.

The discriminant, $b^2 - 4ac$, shows the number of solutions, so you can tell the number of solutions (but not the values of the solutions) by checking whether the discriminant is positive, zero, or negative. Because the discriminant is positive, there are two square roots, leading to two values of x. Each value of x is the x-coordinate of a point of intersection.

c. Answers will vary. A possible answer is:

$y = 2x - 20$ is parallel to $y = 2x + 2$ and does not intersect the parabola.

$x^2 - 8x + 11 = 2x - 20$

$x^2 - 10x + 31 = 0$

$b^2 - 4ac = -24$

$x = \dfrac{10 \pm \sqrt{-24}}{2}$; no real solutions

The system has no real solutions, which means the graphs do not intersect. This can be seen when finding the discriminant, which is negative. Because there are no real numbers having negative square roots, there are no real solutions for x.

d. $y = 2x - 14$ is parallel to $y = 2x + 2$ and intersects the parabola in exactly one point. Solutions will vary. Possible solution: The discriminant should equal 0 to give only one real solution, because there is exactly one square root of 0. Because the line is parallel to $y = 2x + 2$, its equation will have the form $y = 2x + d$.

$x^2 - 8x + 11 = 2x + d$

$x^2 - 10x + (11 - d) = 0$

Set the discriminant equal to zero:

$(-10)^2 - 4(1)(11 - d) = 0$

$100 - 4(11 - d) = 0$

$-4(11 - d) = -100$

$11 - d = 25$

$-14 = d$

The equation of the line parallel to $y = 2x + 2$ that intersects the parabola $y = x^2 - 8x + 11$ exactly once is $y = 2x - 14$.

3 Points

Part a is correct. Two of the parts b, c, or d are done correctly. Or, part a is done correctly and the equations and solutions are found for b, c, and d, but no explanation is given.

1 Point

Part a is correct. One of the parts b, c, or d is done correctly.

CHAPTER 10 · Quiz 1   Form A

1. Bus: 198°; walk: 83°; car: 42°; bike: 37°

2.

Number of times	0	1	2	3	4	5	Total
Number of people	86	34	8	9	5	18	160
%		54%	21%	5%	6%	3%	11%	100%

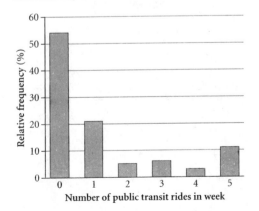

3. a. $\frac{135}{360} = 0.375$, or about 38%

  b. $\frac{30}{360} \approx 0.083$, or about 8%

  c. $\frac{75}{360} \approx 0.208$, or about 21%

  d. $\frac{285}{360} \approx 0.792$, or about 79%

4. a. $\frac{72}{330} \approx 0.218$, or about 22%

  b. $\frac{119}{330} \approx 0.361$, or about 36%

  c. $\frac{211}{330} \approx 0.639$, or about 64%

  d. $\frac{79}{330} \approx 0.239$, or about 24%

CHAPTER 10 · Quiz 1   Form B

1. Bus: 147°; walk: 100°; car: 47°; bike: 67°. Round-off error makes the total greater than 360°.

2.

Number of times	0	1	2	3	4	5	Total
Number of people	114	48	12	11	7	28	220
%		52%	22%	5%	5%	3%	13%	100%

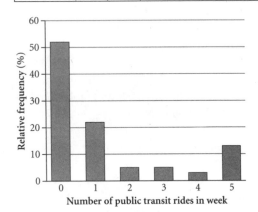

3. a. $\frac{125}{360} \approx 0.347$, or about 35%

  b. $\frac{30}{360} \approx 0.083$, or about 8%

  c. $\frac{145}{360} \approx 0.403$, or about 40%

  d. $\frac{215}{360} \approx 0.597$, or about 60%

4. a. $\frac{62}{280} \approx 0.221$, or about 22%

  b. $\frac{97}{280} \approx 0.347$, or about 35%

  c. $\frac{183}{280} \approx 0.654$, or about 65%

  d. $\frac{68}{280} \approx 0.243$, or about 24%

CHAPTER 10 · Quiz 2   Form A

1. a. Yes; Jessica cannot predict what it will do the next time. (Maybe it is not random for the worm.)

  b. $\frac{20}{105} \approx 0.190$, or about 19%

2. A permutation; $_5P_3 = 60$

3. 720 days (almost 2 years)

4. a. $\frac{7 \cdot 6 \cdot 5 \cdot 4 \cdot 3 \cdot 2 \cdot 1}{4 \cdot 3 \cdot 2 \cdot 1}$, or $7 \cdot 6 \cdot 5 = 210$

  b. $\frac{_7P_3}{3 \cdot 2 \cdot 1}$, or $\frac{7 \cdot 6 \cdot 5}{3 \cdot 2 \cdot 1} = 35$

5. a. $\frac{1}{4 \cdot 3 \cdot 2 \cdot 1} = \frac{1}{24}$

  b. $\frac{1}{12}$

6. a. $\frac{1}{_5C_3} = \frac{1}{10}$

  b. $\frac{1}{_5P_3} = \frac{1}{60}$

CHAPTER 10 · Quiz 2   Form B

1. a. Yes; Angela cannot predict what it will do the next time. (Maybe it is not random for the snail.)

  b. $\frac{46}{110} \approx 0.418$, or about 42%

2. A permutation; $_6P_3 = 120$

3. 120 days

4. a. $\frac{7 \cdot 6 \cdot 5 \cdot 4 \cdot 3 \cdot 2 \cdot 1}{3 \cdot 2 \cdot 1}$, or $7 \cdot 6 \cdot 5 \cdot 4 = 840$

  b. $\frac{_7P_4}{4 \cdot 3 \cdot 2 \cdot 1}$, or $\frac{7 \cdot 6 \cdot 5 \cdot 4}{4 \cdot 3 \cdot 2 \cdot 1} = 35$

5. a. $\frac{1}{5 \cdot 4 \cdot 3 \cdot 2 \cdot 1} = \frac{1}{120}$

  b. $\frac{1}{60}$

6. a. $\frac{1}{_5C_2} = \frac{1}{10}$

  b. $\frac{1}{_5P_2} = \frac{1}{20}$

CHAPTER 10 · Quiz 3   Form A

1. a. Marcus wins two games; Marcus wins one and loses one game; Marcus loses two games.

  b. $(0.25)(0.25) = 0.0625$, or about 6%

  c. $2(0.25)(0.75) = 0.375$, or about 38%

  d. $(0.75)(0.75) = 0.5625$, or about 56%

2. Expected value for each spin: $\frac{11}{24} \cdot 2 + \frac{1}{4} \cdot 5 + \frac{1}{6} \cdot 8 + \frac{1}{8} \cdot 20 = \$6$; expected winnings for ten spins: $60

3. a. A loss of 5 points; a loss of 50 points

  b. 0.027, or about 3%

  c. A loss of 5 points

CHAPTER 10 · Quiz 3   Form B

1. a. Danielle wins two games; Danielle wins one and loses one game; Danielle loses two games.

  b. $(0.3)(0.3) = 0.09$, or 9%

  c. $2(0.3)(0.7) = 0.42$, or 42%

  d. $(0.7)(0.7) = 0.49$, or 49%

2. Expected value for each spin: $\frac{11}{24} \cdot 3 + \frac{1}{4} \cdot 4 + \frac{1}{6} \cdot 9 + \frac{1}{8} \cdot 25 = \$7$; expected winnings for ten spins: \$70

3. a. A loss of 4 points; a loss of 40 points

   b. 0.043, or about 4%

   c. A loss of 4 points

CHAPTER 10 · Test   Form A

1.

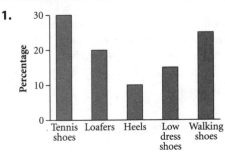

2. a. $P(\text{gray}) = \frac{99}{147} \approx 0.67$, or 67%

   b. $\frac{48}{147} \approx 0.33$, or 33%

   c. About 827

3. a. The experimental probability of blue is $\frac{3}{5}$, or 0.6. The experimental probability of red is $\frac{1}{10}$, or 0.1.

   b. $P(\text{blue}) = \frac{2}{5}$, or 0.4; $P(\text{red}) = \frac{1}{5}$, or 0.2

   c. No; the theoretical probability predicts what will happen over the long run. Tai conducted only ten trials. If he repeated the experiment many more times, then the experimental and theoretical probabilities would probably be closer.

   d. Blue: 80; yellow: 50; red: 40; orange: 30

4. $_5C_3 \cdot {}_4C_2 = 60$

5. a. $_{12}C_5 = 792$ **b.** $_9C_5 = 126$

   c. $\frac{126}{792} = 0.159$, or about 16%

6. a. She makes both shots; she makes one basket; she makes no baskets.

   b. $P(2 \text{ baskets}) = (0.4)(0.4) = 0.16$, or 16%

      $P(1 \text{ basket}) = (0.4)(0.6) + (0.6)(0.4) = 0.48$, or 48%

      $P(0 \text{ baskets}) = (0.6)(0.6) = 0.36$, or 36%

   c. Expected point value $= 6 \cdot (0.16) + 3 \cdot (0.48) + 0 \cdot (0.36) = 2.4$ points

   d. $8 \cdot 2.4 = 19.2$ points

7. Spinner of Misfortune; use the following equation to calculate the expected value of one spin (the unmarked angle is 15°):

$$2\left(\frac{90}{360}\right) - 4\left(\frac{75}{360}\right) + 5\left(\frac{40}{360}\right) - 1\left(\frac{80}{360}\right)$$
$$+ 20\left(\frac{15}{360}\right) - 10\left(\frac{60}{360}\right) = -0.83$$

The expected return on one spin is a loss of \$0.83. The more you play, the more you lose. Spinner of Misfortune is the better name.

CHAPTER 10 · Test   Form B

1.

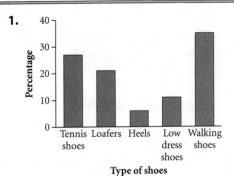

2. a. $P(\text{gray}) = \frac{83}{153} \approx 0.54$, or 54%

   b. $\frac{70}{153} \approx 0.46$, or 46%

   c. About 2814

3. a. The experimental probability of blue is $\frac{3}{10}$, or 0.3. The experimental probability of red is $\frac{2}{5}$, or 0.4.

   b. $P(\text{blue}) = \frac{8}{24} = \frac{1}{3}$, or about 0.3; $P(\text{red}) = \frac{3}{24} = \frac{1}{8}$, or about 0.13

   c. No; the theoretical probability predicts what will happen over the long run. Tai conducted only ten trials. If he repeated the experiment many more times, then the experimental and theoretical probabilities would probably be closer.

   d. Blue: 120; yellow: 45; red: 120; orange: 75

4. $_5C_2 \cdot {}_4C_3 = 40$

5. a. $_{11}C_6 = 462$

   b. $_8C_6 = 28$

   c. $\frac{28}{462} \approx 0.06$, or about 6%

6. a. She makes all three shots; she makes exactly two baskets; she makes one basket only; she makes no baskets.

   b. $P(3 \text{ baskets}) = (0.45)(0.45)(0.45) = 0.091$, or about 9%

      $P(\text{exactly 2 baskets}) = 3(0.45)(0.45)(0.55) = 0.334$, or about 33%

      $P(1 \text{ basket only}) = 3(0.45)(0.55)(0.55) = 0.408$, or about 41%

      $P(0 \text{ baskets}) = (0.55)(0.55)(0.55) = 0.166$, or about 17%

   c. Expected point value $= 9 \cdot (0.09) + 6 \cdot (0.33) + 3 \cdot (0.41) + 0 \cdot (0.17) = 4.02$, or about 4 points

   d. $5 \cdot 4 = 20$ points

7. Spinner of Misfortune; use the following equation to calculate the expected value of one spin (the unmarked angle is 10°):

$$2\left(\frac{90}{360}\right) - 4\left(\frac{80}{360}\right) + 6\left(\frac{35}{360}\right) - 1\left(\frac{85}{360}\right)$$
$$+ 25\left(\frac{10}{360}\right) - 10\left(\frac{60}{360}\right) = -1.01$$

The expected return on one spin is a loss of $1.01. The more you play, the more you lose. Spinner of Misfortune is the better name.

CHAPTER 10 · Constructive Assessment Options

SCORING RUBRICS

1. 5 Points

Answer uses the combined data to predict that there are about 31 blue tiles and 14 yellow tiles, and provides a clear, correct explanation. Possible explanation: To make my prediction, I combined the data for all the groups. There were a total of 360 trials and 249 blue tiles, so about $\frac{249}{360}$, or 69%, of the tiles are blue. Because there are 45 tiles in all, about 69% of 45, or 31, are blue, and the remaining 14 are yellow. I think this prediction is accurate because it is based on a large number of trials.

A good argument could be made for using the median result and estimating 30 blue tiles and 15 red tiles. The explanation would include the idea that the group that drew proportionally more blue tiles than the other groups used a faulty method, perhaps not mixing the tiles between draws.

3 Points

Answer is based on the combined data but is incorrect due to minor calculation errors, or answer is based on Group 6's results (which predict 33 blue and 12 yellow) or on the mean of the relative frequencies for the groups (which predicts 29 blue and 16 yellow), and explanations and calculations are correct.

1 Point

A prediction is made and work is shown, but the reasoning is unclear or is incorrect.

2. 5 Points

a. Prediction is reasonable (close to 30 blue, 40 yellow). Explanation is clear and logical and is based on the pattern in the graph. Possible answer: The y-values (the ratios of blue tiles to trials) appear to be leveling off at around 42%. Because there are 70 tiles in the bag, this indicates that about 0.42 · 70, or about 29, are blue. The remaining 41 tiles are yellow.

b. The y-values would become closer and closer to the actual percentage of blue tiles in the bag. This would cause the graph to level off, becoming almost horizontal for large values of x. This is because as more trials are conducted, the experimental

probability of drawing a blue tile becomes closer and closer to the theoretical probability.

3 Points

a. Prediction is reasonable, but explanation is unclear, or explanation is clear and logical, but prediction is unreasonable due to an error in calculation.

b. Answer is correct, but explanation is inadequate.

1 Point

a. Prediction is not reasonable, but work is shown indicating that the student understands that the graph shows experimental probabilities.

b. The incorrect answer is given with some explanation.

3. 5 Points

Answers are correct and work is clearly shown.

a. $_{10}P_3 = 720$

b. $10! = 3,628,800$

c. $\frac{1}{10}$, or 10%

d. $\frac{_9C_2}{_{10}C_3} = \frac{36}{120} = \frac{3}{10}$, or 30%

e. $\left(\frac{9}{10}\right)^5 = 0.59$, or 59%

3 Points

Four of the five parts are correct.

1 Point

Two of the five parts are correct.

4. 5 Points

a. Answers will vary. Possible tree diagram:
$P(D)$ means probability the red face is down,
$P(U)$ means probability the red face is up.

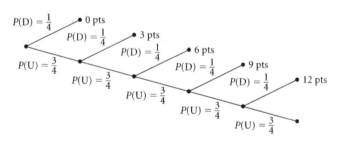

b. $P(\text{end in 1 toss}) = \frac{1}{4}$

$P(\text{end in 2 tosses}) = \frac{1}{4} \cdot \frac{3}{4} = \frac{3}{16}$

$P(\text{end in 3 tosses}) = \frac{1}{4} \cdot \left(\frac{3}{4}\right)^2 = \frac{9}{64}$

$P(\text{end in 4 tosses}) = \frac{1}{4} \cdot \left(\frac{3}{4}\right)^3 = \frac{27}{256}$

$P(\text{end in } n \text{ tosses}) = \frac{1}{4} \cdot \left(\frac{3}{4}\right)^{n-1}$

c. $0 \cdot \frac{1}{4} + 3 \cdot \frac{1}{4} \cdot \frac{3}{4} + 6 \cdot \frac{1}{4} \cdot \left(\frac{3}{4}\right)^2 + 9 \cdot \frac{1}{4} \cdot \left(\frac{3}{4}\right)^3$

Discovering Algebra Assessment Resources/Answers
©2007 Key Curriculum Press

d. $0 \cdot \frac{1}{4} + 3 \cdot \frac{1}{4} \cdot \frac{3}{4} + 6 \cdot \frac{1}{4} \cdot \left(\frac{3}{4}\right)^2 + 9 \cdot \frac{1}{4} \cdot \left(\frac{3}{4}\right)^3$
$+ \cdots + 3(n - 1) \cdot \frac{1}{4} \cdot \left(\frac{3}{4}\right)^{n-1}$

e. The recursive calculator routine is:
{1,0} {Ans(1) + 1, Ans(2) +
3Ans(1)*(1/4)*(3/4)^Ans(1)}

```
{1,0}
                {1 0}
{Ans(1)+1,Ans(2)
+3Ans(1)*(1/4)*(
3/4)^Ans(1)}
            {2 .5625}
           {3 1.40625}
```

As n gets larger, the expected value gets closer to 9. On the TI-84 Plus calculator, when $n \geq 95$, the expected value shows as 9.

```
{89 8.999999998}
{90 8.999999998}
{91 8.999999999}
{92 8.999999999}
{93 8.999999999}
{94 8.999999999}
            {95 9}
```

3 Points
Parts a to d are done correctly. The recursive routine in part e is attempted but it is not correct. Because the routine is not complete, the expected point value may not be correct.

1 Point
Parts a, b, and c are correct. Part d is attempted but the general term is not correct. Part e is not attempted or not correct.

5. **5 Points**
The specific game will vary. Sample game:

a. Angles and point values of sectors are as marked above.

b. Expected value of one spin:
$\$60 \cdot \frac{120}{360} - \$52 \cdot \frac{90}{360} + \$36 \cdot \frac{30}{360}$
$+ \$27 \cdot \frac{80}{360} - \$54 \cdot \frac{40}{360} = \$10$

3 Points
The spinner is correctly presented with sector angles that add to 360° and with dollar values in each sector, but the equation for the expected value is not correct.

1 Point
The spinner appears to be correct, but the sum of the sector angles is not 360°. The expected value equation is therefore also not correct.

CHAPTER 11 · Quiz 1   Form A

1. a. $y = 3 - \frac{3}{2}x$; the slope of line l is $-\frac{3}{2}$.
  b. Any line with a slope of $-\frac{3}{2}$ is correct. Possible answer: $y = 2 - \frac{3}{2}x$.
  c. Any line with a slope of $\frac{2}{3}$ is correct. Possible answer: $y = 1 + \frac{2}{3}x$.

2. a. Slope of $\overline{AB}$ is $\frac{1}{4}$; slope of $\overline{BC}$ is -4; slope of $\overline{CD}$ is $\frac{1}{4}$; slope of $\overline{AD}$ is -4.
  b. ABCD is a rectangle. Opposite sides have the same slope, so they are parallel. So ABCD is a parallelogram. The product of the slopes of each pair of adjacent sides is -1, so all angles are 90°, therefore ABCD is a rectangle.
  c. Yes; the slope of diagonal $\overline{AC}$ is $\frac{5}{3}$, and the slope of diagonal $\overline{BD}$ is $-\frac{3}{5}$; because the slopes are opposite reciprocals, the diagonals are perpendicular.

3. $y = x + 2$

4. $x = -3 \pm \sqrt{14}$; $x = 0.742$ and $x = -6.742$

5. Length of $\overline{AB} = 5$ units; length of $\overline{BC} = \sqrt{18}$ units; length of $\overline{AC} = \sqrt{37}$ units

6. Undefined; 0

CHAPTER 11 · Quiz 1   Form B

1. a. $y = -2 + \frac{5}{3}x$; the slope of line l is $\frac{5}{3}$.
  b. Any line with a slope of $\frac{5}{3}$ is correct. Possible answer: $y = 2 + \frac{5}{3}x$.
  c. Any line with a slope of $-\frac{3}{5}$ is correct. Possible answer: $y = 1 - \frac{3}{5}x$.

2. a. Slope of $\overline{AB}$ is 0; slope of $\overline{BC}$ is 2; slope of $\overline{CD}$ is 0; slope of $\overline{AD}$ is 2.
  b. ABCD is a parallelogram. Opposite sides have the same slope, so they are parallel, therefore ABCD is a parallelogram. There does not seem to be anything else special about the quadrilateral.
  c. The slope of diagonal $\overline{AC}$ is -2. The slope of diagonal $\overline{BD}$ is $\frac{2}{3}$. The product of the two slopes is not -1, so they are not perpendicular.

3. $y = -x + 5$

4. $x = 5 \pm \sqrt{10}$; $x = 8.162$ and $x = 1.838$

5. Length of $\overline{AB} = 13$ units; length of $\overline{BC} = \sqrt{52}$ units; length of $\overline{AC} = \sqrt{65}$ units

6. 0; undefined

1. 100 units²; $2\sqrt{5}$ units, $4\sqrt{5}$ units, and 10 units

2. 12 ft

3. a. $5\sqrt{3} - 3\sqrt{2}$ **b.** 6   **c.** $4\sqrt{6}$

4. a. $5\sqrt{3}$ **b.** $6\sqrt{2}$

5. Draw a right triangle that has legs with lengths of 2 units and 4 units; by the Pythagorean Theorem, the hypotenuse will have a length of $\sqrt{20}$ units, or draw a square with an area of 20 square units as shown here; each side will have a length of $\sqrt{20}$ units.

1. 1225 units²; 15 units, 35 units, and $\sqrt{1450} = 5\sqrt{58}$ units

2. 5 ft

3. a. $6\sqrt{3} - 3\sqrt{5}$ **b.** $2\sqrt{3}$ **c.** $3\sqrt{15}$

4. a. $6\sqrt{3}$ **b.** $7\sqrt{2}$

5. Draw a right triangle that has legs with lengths of 2 units and 3 units; by the Pythagorean Theorem, the hypotenuse will have a length of $\sqrt{13}$ units, or draw a square with an area of 13 square units as shown here; each side will have a length of $\sqrt{13}$ units.

1. a. $x = 9$ **b.** $x = 5$

2. $\sqrt{26}$ units

3. $\tan 38 = \dfrac{25}{x}$, $x \approx 32.0$ cm; $\sin 38 = \dfrac{25}{y}$, $y \approx 40.6$ cm

4. $m\angle A = \sin^{-1}\dfrac{6.4}{15.1}$; about 25°

5. a. $\sin 54 = \dfrac{h}{5.5}$

     $h = 5.5\sin 54 \approx 4.4$ cm

b. Area $= 0.5bh$

     Area $= (0.5)(7.7)(4.4) \approx 16.9$ cm²

1. a. $x = 4$ **b.** $x = 5$

2. $\sqrt{65}$ units

3. $x \approx 25.2$ cm; $y \approx 30.4$ cm

4. $B = \cos^{-1}\dfrac{6.4}{15.1}$; about 65°

5. a. $\sin 39 = \dfrac{h}{3.8}$

     $h = 3.8\sin 39 \approx 2.4$

b. Area $= 0.5bh$

     Area $= (0.5)(8.8)(2.4) \approx 10.6$ cm²

1. a. The slope of $\overline{AB}$ is 2, and the slope of $\overline{AC}$ is $-\frac{1}{2}$. Because the slopes are negative reciprocals, $\overline{AB}$ is perpendicular to $\overline{AC}$, so the triangle is a right triangle.

b. $\overline{AB} = 4\sqrt{5}$ units, $\overline{BC} = 4\sqrt{10}$ units, $\overline{AC} = 4\sqrt{5}$ units

2. 40 cm

3. a. No; if the triangle were a right triangle, then the Pythagorean Theorem would hold and $4^2 + 5^2$ would be equal to 7^2; but $4^2 + 5^2 = 41$ and $7^2 = 49$, so $4^2 + 5^2 \neq 7^2$; therefore, the triangle is not a right triangle.

b. Answers will vary. Multiplying or dividing each side length by a constant will give side lengths of a similar triangle. Possible answer: 8 cm, 10 cm, and 14 cm

4. a. $-3\sqrt{3}$ **b.** 4   **c.** $3\sqrt{2}$

d. $\sqrt{2} + \sqrt{6}$, or $\sqrt{2}(1 + \sqrt{3})$

e. 1400   **f.** 2

5. 10.6 in.

6. $\sin 70° = \dfrac{h}{150}$, $h = 150\sin 70°$, $h \approx 141$ ft

7. $\sin A = \dfrac{5\sqrt{3}}{10}$

     $A = \sin^{-1}\left(\dfrac{5\sqrt{3}}{10}\right) = 60°$

1. a. The slope of $\overline{AB}$ is $-\frac{3}{4}$, and the slope of $\overline{AC}$ is $\frac{4}{3}$; because the slopes are negative reciprocals, $\overline{AB}$ is perpendicular to $\overline{AC}$, so the triangle is a right triangle.

b. $\overline{AB} = 10$ units, $\overline{BC} = 5\sqrt{5}$ units, $\overline{AC} = 5$ units

2. $\sqrt{2856} \approx 53.44$ cm

3. a. No; if the triangle were a right triangle, then the Pythagorean Theorem would hold and $5^2 + 12^2$ would be equal to 15^2; but $5^2 + 12^2 = 169$ and $15^2 = 225$, so $5^2 + 12^2 \neq 15^2$; therefore, the triangle is not a right triangle.

b. Answers will vary. Multiplying or dividing each side length by a constant will give side lengths of a similar triangle. Possible answer: 10 cm, 24 cm, and 30 cm

Discovering Algebra Assessment Resources/Answers
©2007 Key Curriculum Press

4. a. $-2\sqrt{7}$ **b.** 6   **c.** $4\sqrt{3}$

  d. $\sqrt{3} + \sqrt{15}$, or $\sqrt{3}(1 + \sqrt{5})$ **e.** 250

  f. $2\sqrt{2}$

5. 25.5 in.

6. $\sin 65° = \dfrac{h}{120}$, $h = 120\sin 65°$, $h \approx 109$ ft

7. $\sin A = \dfrac{5}{10} = \dfrac{1}{2}$

  $A = \sin^{-1}\left(\dfrac{1}{2}\right) = 30°$

CHAPTER 11 · Constructive Assessment Options

SCORING RUBRICS

1. 5 Points

All equations meet the given conditions.

  a. Both lines must be horizontal. Sample answer: $y = 3$ and $y = 2$

  b. Sample answer: $y = -2(x + 3)$ and $y = 0.5(x + 3)$

  c. Answers will vary, but one line must be vertical and one must be horizontal. Sample answer: $y = 4$ and $x = -2$

3 Points

Two of the equations meet the given conditions, or one equation meets both conditions, and each of the other equations meets only one of the two conditions.

1 Point

Two of the equations partially meet the given conditions.

2. 5 Points

The alley is about 21.82 ft wide. Possible explanation: This sketch shows the ladder leaning against one side and then against the other side.

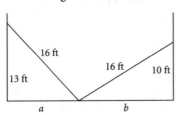

On the left side of the sketch, the ladder, the 13 ft section of the wall, and the segment labeled a form a right triangle. To find a, use the Pythagorean Theorem.

$a^2 + 13^2 = 16^2$	The Pythagorean Theorem.
$a^2 + 169 = 256$	Evaluate the exponents.
$a^2 = 87$	Subtract 169 from both sides.
$a = \sqrt{87}$	Take the square root of both sides; only the positive square root makes sense.
$a \approx 9.33$ feet	Evaluate the square root.

On the right side of the sketch, the ladder, the 10 ft section of the wall, and the segment labeled b form a right triangle. To find b, use the Pythagorean Theorem.

$10^2 + b^2 = 16^2$	The Pythagorean Theorem.
$100 + b^2 = 256$	Evaluate the exponents.
$b^2 = 156$	Subtract 100 from both sides.
$b = \sqrt{156}$	Take the square root of both sides; only the positive square root makes sense.
$b \approx 12.49$ feet	Evaluate the square root.

The width of the alley is about $9.33 + 12.49 = 21.82$ ft.

3 Points

The answer is correct, but the explanation is unclear or is incomplete, or the reasoning is correct, but the answer is incorrect due to calculation errors.

1 Point

The answer is correct, but no work is shown and no explanation is given, or the answer is incorrect, and although work is shown, it is mostly incorrect.

3. 5 Points

The problem is clearly stated, and the solution is complete and correct and uses the Pythagorean Theorem. Possible answer:

Problem: Willow Park is shaped like a rectangle, with a width of 70 yards and a length of 120 yards. Lani ran from one corner of the park to the opposite corner. How far did she run?

Solution: This drawing shows that Lani's path is the hypotenuse of a right triangle.

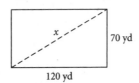

To find the distance she ran, use the Pythagorean Theorem:

$$70^2 + 120^2 = x^2$$

$$4{,}900 + 14{,}400 = x^2$$

$$19{,}300 = x^2$$

$$138.9 \approx x$$

Lani ran about 139 yards.

3 Points

The problem is clearly stated and the solution uses the Pythagorean Theorem, but the solution includes calculation errors that lead to an incorrect solution.

1 Point

The problem is clearly stated, but no solution is given, or the problem and the solution are given, but the solution involves significant errors.

4. 5 Points

Errors are identified and corrected, and explanations are clear. Explanations may vary from those given here.

a. Incorrect; it looks as if Matt forgot to add the second term, $\sqrt{2}$; the correct answer is $3\sqrt{2}$.

b. Incorrect; Matt probably thought of $\sqrt{40}$ as $\sqrt{4 \cdot 10}$, but then forgot to take the square root of 4; the correct answer is $2\sqrt{10}$.

c. Correct   d. Correct

3 Points

Errors are identified and corrected, but explanations are inadequate or incorrect.

1 Point

At least two of the problems are correctly identified as correct or incorrect, but corrected expressions and explanations are not given or are incorrect.

5. 5 Points

The explanation is clear and complete. Possible answer: To find the distance between two points (x_1, y_1) and (x_2, y_2), draw a segment joining the points, and then draw vertical and horizontal segments to form a right triangle as shown here.

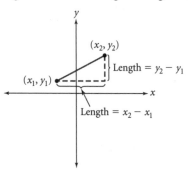

The length of the horizontal leg is $x_2 - x_1$, and the length of the vertical leg is $y_2 - y_1$. The distance between the points is the length of the hypotenuse. To find this distance, use the Pythagorean Theorem.

$$distance^2 = (length\ of\ horizontal\ leg)^2 + (length\ of\ vertical\ leg)^2$$

$$distance^2 = (x_2 - x_1)^2 + (y_2 - y_1)^2$$

$$distance = \sqrt{(x_2 - x_1)^2 + (y_2 - y_1)^2}$$

This is the distance formula.

3 Points

One major point is missing or is incorrect.

1 Point

The answer is attempted but is mostly incorrect.

6. 5 Points

a. $A(0, 0), B(p, 0), C(p, p), D(0, p)$

b. The figure has four right angles because each pair of adjacent sides are vertical and horizontal, so they are perpendicular. The length of each side is p. Consider the following:

Length of $\overline{AB} = \sqrt{(p - 0)^2 + (0 - 0)^2} = \sqrt{p^2} = p$ units

Length of $\overline{BC} = \sqrt{(p - p)^2 + (p - 0)^2} = \sqrt{p^2} = p$ units

Length of $\overline{CD} = \sqrt{(p - 0)^2 + (p - p)^2} = \sqrt{p^2} = p$ units

Length of $\overline{AD} = \sqrt{(0 - 0)^2 + (p - 0)^2} = \sqrt{p^2} = p$ units

So $ABCD$ with the coordinates given in part a is a square.

c. Midpoint of $\overline{AC} = \left(\frac{0 + p}{2}, \frac{0 + p}{2}\right) = \left(\frac{p}{2}, \frac{p}{2}\right)$; midpoint of $\overline{BD} = \left(\frac{0 + p}{2}, \frac{p + 0}{2}\right) = \left(\frac{p}{2}, \frac{p}{2}\right)$. Both diagonals have the same midpoint, so the diagonals bisect each other.

d. Slope of $\overline{AC} = \frac{p - 0}{p - 0} = 1$; slope of $\overline{BD} = \frac{0 - p}{p - 0} = -1$; $(1)(-1) = -1$; that is, the product of the slopes is -1, so the diagonals are perpendicular.

e. Length of $\overline{AC} = \sqrt{(p - 0)^2 + (p - 0)^2} = \sqrt{2p^2} = p\sqrt{2}$ units; length of $\overline{BD} = \sqrt{(0 - p)^2 + (p - 0)^2} = \sqrt{2p^2} = p\sqrt{2}$ units; both diagonals have the same length.

f. Theorem: The diagonals of a square are congruent and are perpendicular bisectors of each other.

Explanations will vary. A sample explanation follows.

In this investigation, $ABCD$ represents any square. What we show is true for all squares. We showed that the diagonal properties in the statement follow logically from the definition of a square and from what we know of the slopes of parallel and perpendicular lines and the midpoints and lengths of segments. We have therefore proven that this statement is true for any square using deductive reasoning. It is a theorem.

3 Points

Parts a, c, d, and e are done correctly. Part b is attempted and partially explained. The summary statement is given in part f, but the explanation is not given.

1 Point

Part a is done correctly. At least two of parts c, d, or e are done correctly. The summary statement is given in part f, but no satisfactory explanations are given for parts b and f.

7. 5 Points

Answers are correct, and mathematics is used to prove that each figure fits the definition.

a. Possible answer: $(5, 4), (3, 2), (5, -2), (7, 2)$; you can use the distance formula to find the length of each side.

Length of side between $(5, 4)$ and $(3, 2)$:

$$d = \sqrt{(5 - 3)^2 + (4 - 2)^2}$$
$$= \sqrt{4 + 4} = \sqrt{8} = 2\sqrt{2}$$

Length of side between $(5, 4)$ and $(7, 2)$:

$$d = \sqrt{(5 - 7)^2 + (4 - 2)^2}$$
$$= \sqrt{4 + 4} = \sqrt{8} = 2\sqrt{2}$$

Length of side between $(3, 2)$ and $(5, -2)$:

$$d = \sqrt{(3 - 5)^2 + [2 - (-2)]^2}$$
$$= \sqrt{4 + 16} = \sqrt{20} = 2\sqrt{5}$$

Length of side between $(7, 2)$ and $(5, -2)$:

$$d = \sqrt{(7 - 5)^2 + [2 - (-2)]^2}$$
$$= \sqrt{4 + 16} = \sqrt{20} = 2\sqrt{5}$$

Because two pairs of adjacent sides are the same length, the figure is a kite.

b. Possible answer: $(-5, 1), (-1, 4), (3, 1), (-1, -2)$; you can use the distance formula to find the length of each side.

Length of side between $(-5, 1)$ and $(-1, 4)$:

$$d = \sqrt{[-5 - (-1)]^2 + (1 - 4)^2}$$
$$= \sqrt{16 + 9} = \sqrt{25} = 5$$

Length of side between $(-1, 4)$ and $(3, 1)$:

$$d = \sqrt{(-1 - 3)^2 + (4 - 1)^2}$$
$$= \sqrt{16 + 9} = \sqrt{25} = 5$$

Length of side between $(3, 1)$ and $(-1, -2)$:

$$d = \sqrt{[3 - (-1)]^2 + [1 - (-2)]^2}$$
$$= \sqrt{16 + 9} = \sqrt{25} = 5$$

Length of side between $(-1, -2)$ and $(-5, 1)$:

$$d = \sqrt{[-1 - (-5)]^2 + (-2 - 1)^2}$$
$$= \sqrt{16 + 9} = \sqrt{25} = 5$$

All the sides have the same length, so the figure is a rhombus. The slope of the side between $(-5, 1)$ and $(-1, 4)$ is $\frac{4 - 1}{-1 - (-5)}$, or $\frac{3}{4}$. The slope of the side between $(-1, 4)$ and $(3, 1)$ is $\frac{1 - 4}{3 - (-1)}$, or $-\frac{3}{4}$. Because the slopes are not opposite reciprocals, the sides are not perpendicular, so the figure is not a square.

c. Possible answer: $(-3, 0), (-5, -2), (-3, -4), (-1, -2)$; you can use the distance formula to find the length of each side.

Length of side between $(-3, 0)$ and $(-5, -2)$:

$$d = \sqrt{[-3 - (-5)]^2 + [0 - (-2)]^2}$$
$$= \sqrt{4 + 4} = \sqrt{8} = 2\sqrt{2}$$

Length of side between $(-5, -2)$ and $(-3, -4)$:

$$d = \sqrt{[-5 - (-3)]^2 + [-2 - (-4)]^2}$$
$$= \sqrt{4 + 4} = \sqrt{8} = 2\sqrt{2}$$

Length of side between $(-3, -4)$ and $(-1, -2)$:

$$d = \sqrt{[-3 - (-1)]^2 + [-4 - (-2)]^2}$$
$$= \sqrt{4 + 4} = \sqrt{8} = 2\sqrt{2}$$

Length of side between $(-1, -2)$ and $(-3, 0)$:

$$d = \sqrt{[-1 - (-3)]^2 + (-2 - 0)^2}$$
$$= \sqrt{4 + 4} = \sqrt{8} = 2\sqrt{2}$$

The sides all have the same length. Now, find the slopes of the sides.

Slope of side from $(-3, 0)$ to $(-5, -2)$:

$$\frac{-2 - 0}{-5 - (-3)} = \frac{-2}{-2} = 1$$

Slope of side from $(-5, -2)$ to $(-3, -4)$:

$$\frac{-4 - (-2)}{-3 - (-5)} = \frac{-2}{2} = -1$$

Slope of side from $(-3, -4)$ to $(-1, -2)$:

$$\frac{-2 - (-4)}{-1 - (-3)} = \frac{2}{2} = 1$$

Slope of side from $(-1, -2)$ to $(-3, 0)$:

$$\frac{0 - (-2)}{-3 - (-1)} = \frac{2}{-2} = -1$$

The slopes of adjacent sides are opposite reciprocals, so adjacent sides are perpendicular. The figure is a square.

3 Points

One of the answers is incorrect, and the other two answers contain minor errors but are mostly correct.

1 Point

The coordinates in all the answers are correct, but no explanations are given and no work is shown, or all the answers are attempted and some correct work is shown, but the answers are mostly incorrect.

8. 5 Points

The minimum value for both functions is 0, and the maximum value is 1. Possible explanation: Consider these triangles.

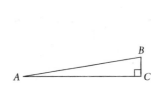

In the triangle on the left, angle A is very small. The leg opposite angle A is very small compared to the hypotenuse, so sin A, or $\frac{o}{h}$, is close to 0. As angle A gets smaller, the value of o gets even smaller, so $\frac{o}{h}$ gets closer to 0. Because it is impossible for the ratio to be less than 0 (it is the ratio of two non-negative numbers), the least possible value for the sine function must be 0.

In the triangle on the right, angle A is very large. The leg opposite angle A is close to the length of the hypotenuse, so sin A, or $\frac{o}{h}$, is close to 1. As angle A gets larger, the value of o gets even closer to h, so $\frac{o}{h}$ gets closer to 1. Because it is impossible for the ratio to be greater than 1 (the hypotenuse is always the longest side of the triangle), the greatest possible value for the sine function must be 1.

In the triangle on the left, the leg adjacent to angle A is close to the length of the hypotenuse, so cos A, or $\frac{a}{h}$, is close to 1. As angle A gets smaller, the value of a gets closer to h, so $\frac{a}{h}$ gets closer to 1. Because it is impossible for the ratio to be greater than 1, the greatest possible value for the cosine function must be 1.

In the triangle on the right, the leg adjacent to angle A is very small compared to the hypotenuse, so cos A, or $\frac{a}{h}$, is close to 0. As angle A gets larger, the value of a gets smaller, so $\frac{a}{h}$ gets closer to 0. Because it is impossible for the ratio to be less than 0, the least possible value for the cosine function must be 0.

(Note: Let students know that in trigonometry they will learn new definitions of sine, cosine, and tangent that do not involve triangles and that allow negative numbers and angles greater than 90° or less than 0°, and they will learn that the smallest value of the sine and cosine functions is actually −1.)

3 Points
Maximum and minimum values are correct, but the reasoning is unclear or incomplete, or three of the values are correct, with mostly correct reasoning, but the other value is incorrect.

1 Point
Maximum and minimum values are correct, but no explanation is given, or an answer is attempted and one or two values are correct, but the reasoning is incorrect.

CHAPTERS 8–11 · Exam   Form A

1. a. A reflection of the graph of $y = x^2$ across the x-axis, followed by a translation right 2 units and up 2 units; $y = -(x - 2)^2 + 2$

 b. A vertical stretch of the graph of $y = |x|$ by a factor of 2, followed by a translation left 3 units and down 5 units; $y = 2|x + 3| - 5$

2. a.

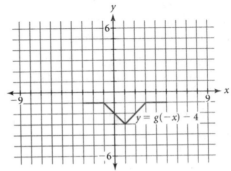

 b.

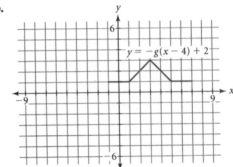

3. a. $x = -11, x = 4$ **b.** $x = 6$

 c. $x = \dfrac{-7 \pm \sqrt{65}}{2}$ **d.** $x = -1, x = \dfrac{3}{5}$

4. a. 3.5 s

 b. 49 ft; after 1.75 s

 c. After 0.7 s and after 2.8 s

5. a. 126°   **b.** 49   **c.** 27

6. a. 5040   **b.** 840

7. a. $\dfrac{3}{5}$ **b.** $\dfrac{3}{5} \cdot \dfrac{3}{5} = \dfrac{9}{25}$

 c. $\dfrac{3}{5} \cdot \dfrac{2}{4} = \dfrac{6}{20} = \dfrac{3}{10}$

8. Answers will vary. Sample answer:

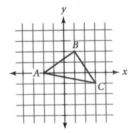

The slope of $\overline{AB}$ is $\dfrac{2 - 0}{1 - (-2)}$, or $\dfrac{2}{3}$, and the slope of $\overline{BC}$ is $\dfrac{-1 - 2}{3 - 1}$, or $-\dfrac{3}{2}$; because their slopes are opposite reciprocals, $\overline{AB}$ and $\overline{BC}$ are perpendicular, so the triangle is a right triangle. To find the length of the hypotenuse, use the distance formula.

$d = \sqrt{[3 - (-2)]^2 + (-1 - 0)^2}$
$= \sqrt{5^2 + (-1)^2} = \sqrt{26}$

9. a. $173 + 4 = 177$ ft   **b.** 60°

Discovering Algebra Assessment Resources/Answers
©2007 Key Curriculum Press

1. a. A vertical shrink of the graph of $y = x^2$ by a factor of 0.5, followed by a translation left 1 unit and down 2 units; $y = 0.5(x + 1)^2 - 2$

   b. A reflection of the graph of $y = |x|$ across the x-axis, followed by a translation right 4 units and up 2 units; $y = -|x - 4| + 2$

2. a.

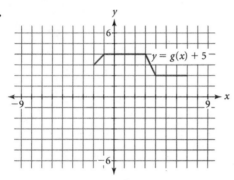

   b.

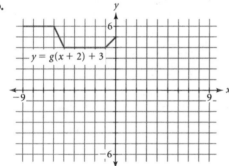

3. a. $x = -3, x = 9$ **b.** $x = -5$

   c. $x = \dfrac{5 \pm \sqrt{17}}{2}$ **d.** $x = -1, x = \dfrac{5}{3}$

4. a. 4.5 s

   b. 81 ft; after 2.25 s

   c. After 0.8 s and after 3.7 s

5. a. 72°   **b.** 35   **c.** 24

6. a. 720   **b.** 120

7. a. $\dfrac{2}{5}$

   b. $\dfrac{2}{5} \cdot \dfrac{2}{5} = \dfrac{4}{25}$

   c. $\dfrac{2}{5} \cdot \dfrac{1}{4} = \dfrac{2}{20} = \dfrac{1}{10}$

8. Answers will vary. Sample answer:

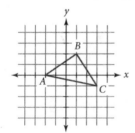

The slope of $\overline{AB}$ is $\dfrac{2 - 0}{1 - (-2)}$, or $\dfrac{2}{3}$, and the slope of $\overline{BC}$ is $\dfrac{-1 - 2}{3 - 1}$, or $-\dfrac{3}{2}$; because their slopes are opposite reciprocals, $\overline{AB}$ and $\overline{BC}$ are perpendicular, so the triangle is a right triangle. To find the length of the hypotenuse, use the distance formula.

$$d = \sqrt{[3 - (-2)]^2 + (-1 - 0)^2}$$
$$= \sqrt{5^2 + (-1)^2} = \sqrt{26}$$

9. a. $219 + 4 = 223$ ft   **b.** About 61°

Final Exam   **Form A**

1. a. First-period mean: 79.7; third-period mean: 83.4

   b. First-period five-number summary: 45, 65, 75, 98, 100; third-period five-number summary: 70, 75, 85, 89, 92

   c.

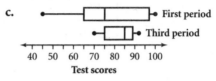

   d. Answers will vary. Possible answer: I think the third-period class did better. The first-period class had the highest scores, but it also had some very low scores. The third-period class was much more consistent. About 75% of the third-period scores were higher than the median score for the first-period class. The third-period class also had a higher mean score and a higher median score.

2. a. $4.59   **b.** 21 oz

3. a. Fixed fee: $1.60; charge per quarter-mile: $0.55

   b. $f = 1.60 + 0.55q$ **c.** $18.10

   d. 10.75 mi

4. a. $y = 828.8 + 13.3(x - 1996)$, or $y = 895.5 + 13.3(x - 2001)$

   b. Each year the number of leisure trips taken increases an average of 13.3 million trips.

   c. 962 million trips

5. $x = 3, y = -5$

6. $\begin{cases} y \le 3 \\ y \ge -0.75x \\ y > -3 + 2.5x \end{cases}$

7. a. $381   **b.** $1,378

8. a. Domain: the integers from -5 to 5; range: $\{-2, 0, 2, 4\}$

   b. $f(-2) = 4$ **c.** x-values: $-3, -1, 3, 5$

9. a. $x = \dfrac{12 \pm \sqrt{48}}{6} = \dfrac{6 \pm 2\sqrt{3}}{3}$

   b. $y = 3(x - 2)^2 - 4$

10. a.

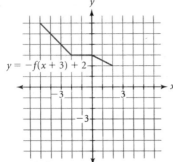

b.

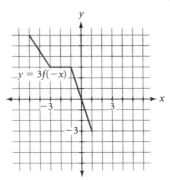

11. 122 m

12. a. $_8C_3 = 56$ **b.** $_7C_2 = 21$

  c. $\frac{_7C_2}{_8C_3} = \frac{21}{56}$, or $\frac{3}{8}$ **d.** $\frac{3}{8} \cdot \frac{2}{7} = \frac{6}{56}$, or $\frac{3}{28}$

  e. $1 \cdot \frac{1}{8} + 2 \cdot \frac{1}{8} + 3 \cdot \frac{1}{8} + 4 \cdot \frac{1}{8} + 5 \cdot \frac{1}{8} + 6 \cdot \frac{1}{8}$

    $+ 7 \cdot \frac{1}{8} + 8 \cdot \frac{1}{8} = 36 \cdot \frac{1}{8} = \frac{9}{2}$, or 4.5

Final Exam   Form B

1. a. First-period mean: 83.3; third-period mean: 79.8

  b. First-period five-number summary: 70, 75, 85, 89, 92; third-period five-number summary: 45, 65, 75, 98, 100

  c.

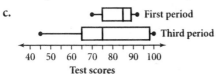

  d. Possible answer: I think the first-period class did better. The third-period class had the highest scores, but it also had some very low scores. The first-period class was much more consistent. About 75% of the first-period scores were higher than the median score for the third-period class. The first-period class also had a higher mean score and a higher median score.

2. a. $5.44   **b.** 19 oz

3. a. Fixed fee: $1.75; charge per quarter-mile: $0.65

  b. $f = 1.75 + 0.65q$ **c.** $21.25

  d. 10.75 mi

4. a. $y = 828.8 + 13.3(x - 1996)$, or $y = 895.5 + 13.3(x - 2001)$

  b. Each year the number of leisure trips taken increases an average of 13.3 million trips.

  c. 1 billion 1.7 million trips (1001.7 million trips)

5. $x = -2, y = 7$

6. $\begin{cases} x > -3 \\ y \le 1 - \frac{1}{3}x \\ y \ge \frac{4}{3}x \end{cases}$

7. a. $328   **b.** $1,686

8. a. Domain: the integers from -4 to 5; range: $\{-1, 0, 1, 2, 3\}$

  b. $f(-2) = 2$ **c.** $x = 2$ and $x = 3$

9. a. $x = \dfrac{4 \pm \sqrt{56}}{-4} = \dfrac{2 \pm \sqrt{14}}{-2}$

  b. $y = -2(x + 1)^2 + 7$

10. a.

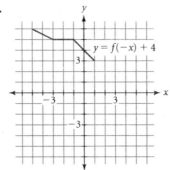

b.

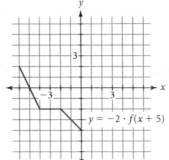

11. 36 m

12. a. $_9C_3 = 84$

  b. $_8C_2 = 28$

  c. $\frac{_8C_2}{_9C_3} = \frac{28}{84} = \frac{1}{3}$

  d. $\frac{3}{9} \cdot \frac{2}{8} = \frac{6}{72}$, or $\frac{1}{12}$

  e. $1 \cdot \frac{1}{9} + 2 \cdot \frac{1}{9} + 3 \cdot \frac{1}{9} + 4 \cdot \frac{1}{9} + 5 \cdot \frac{1}{9} + 6 \cdot \frac{1}{9}$

    $+ 7 \cdot \frac{1}{9} + 8 \cdot \frac{1}{9} + 9 \cdot \frac{1}{9} = 45 \cdot \frac{1}{9} = 5$

Key Curriculum Press
Innovators in Mathematics Education

Comment Form

Please take a moment to provide us with feedback about this book. We are eager to read any comments or suggestions you may have. Once you've filled out this form, simply fold it along the dotted lines and drop it in the mail. We'll pay the postage. Thank you!

Your Name _____

School _____

School Address _____

City/State/Zip _____

Phone _____ Email _____

Book Title _____

Please list any comments you have about this book.

_____
_____
_____
_____
_____
_____
_____
_____
_____
_____
_____

Do you have any suggestions for improving the student or teacher material?

_____
_____
_____
_____
_____
_____
_____

To request a catalog, or place an order, call us toll free at 800-995-MATH, or send a fax to 800-541-2242. For more information, visit Key's website at www.keypress.com.

Key Curriculum Press
Innovators in Mathematics Education

Comment Form

Please take a moment to provide us with feedback about this book. We are eager to read any comments or suggestions you may have. Once you've filled out this form, simply fold it along the dotted lines and drop it in the mail. We'll pay the postage. Thank you!

Your Name _____

School _____

School Address _____

City/State/Zip _____

Phone _____ Email _____

Book Title _____

Please list any comments you have about this book.

_____

_____

_____

_____

_____

_____

_____

_____

_____

Do you have any suggestions for improving the student or teacher material?

_____

_____

_____

_____

_____

_____

To request a catalog, or place an order, call us toll free at 800-995-MATH, or send a fax to 800-541-2242. For more information, visit Key's website at www.keypress.com.

NO POSTAGE
NECESSARY
IF MAILED
IN THE
UNITED STATES

BUSINESS REPLY MAIL
FIRST CLASS   PERMIT NO. 338   EMERYVILLE, CA

POSTAGE WILL BE PAID BY ADDRESSEE

Key Curriculum Press
Innovators in Mathematics Education

Attn: Editorial Department
1150 65th Street
Emeryville, CA 94608-9740

Key Curriculum Press
Innovators in Mathematics Education

Comment Form

Please take a moment to provide us with feedback about this book. We are eager to read any comments or suggestions you may have. Once you've filled out this form, simply fold it along the dotted lines and drop it in the mail. We'll pay the postage. Thank you!

Your Name _____

School _____

School Address _____

City/State/Zip _____

Phone _____ Email _____

Book Title _____

Please list any comments you have about this book.

_____

_____

_____

_____

_____

_____

_____

_____

_____

_____

Do you have any suggestions for improving the student or teacher material?

_____

_____

_____

_____

_____

_____

_____

To request a catalog, or place an order, call us toll free at 800-995-MATH, or send a fax to 800-541-2242. For more information, visit Key's website at www.keypress.com.

NO POSTAGE
NECESSARY
IF MAILED
IN THE
UNITED STATES

BUSINESS REPLY MAIL
FIRST CLASS   PERMIT NO. 338   EMERYVILLE, CA

POSTAGE WILL BE PAID BY ADDRESSEE

Key Curriculum Press
Innovators in Mathematics Education

Attn: Editorial Department
1150 65th Street
Emeryville, CA 94608-9740